Multiple-Target Tracking with Radar Applications

The Artech House Radar Library

Multiple-Target Tracking with Radar Applications

Samuel S. Blackman

Copyright © 1986
ARTECH HOUSE, INC.
685 Canton St.
Norwood, MA 02062

International Standard Book Number: 0-89006-179-3
Library of Congress Catalog Card Number: 85-073389

10   9   8   7   6   5   4

To my sons,
Jim and Ken

Acknowledgements

The author wishes to acknowledge the invaluable assistance of many of his colleagues at Hughes Aircraft Company. First, Dr. S. A. Hovanessian introduced me to the MTT problem more than twenty years ago. His initial insight into this problem and his help and encouragement during the development of this book are deeply appreciated. My understanding of MTT and related problems has benefited greatly from a long-time association with Dr. J. J. Stein, and from shorter, but equally productive, associations with Mr. T. J. Broida and Dr. P. L. Bogler. The contributions from Mr. Broida were too many to cite individually.

The author is also very grateful to those who made contributions to the book and who assisted with the review and proofreading of the manuscript. Dr. R. C. Carlson and Mr. R. T. Marloth read the entire manuscript and contributed many valuable suggestions. Others whose help and contributions are appreciated include Dr. R. R. Allen, Dr. I. P. Bottlik, Dr. P. Z. Daffer, Ms. E. Dror, Mr. N. M. Greenblatt, Mr. J. N. Hoffner, Mr. S. P. Ickovic, Mr. K. S. Jew, Dr. H. S. Nussbaum, Dr. J. B. Pearson, Dr. D. D. Rivers, Mr. R. A. Rosen, and Dr. H. D. Washburn. The artwork was done by Ms. J. K. Hiromoto.

CONTENTS

Preface

Multiple-target tracking (MTT) is an essential requirement for surveillance systems employing one or more sensors, together with computer subsystems, to interpret an environment that includes both true targets and false alarms. With the recent proliferation and the increasing sophistication of surveillance systems, designers of radar and other systems are recognizing the importance of MTT.

This text presents a survey of the existing theory and methods for MTT. It has been written at a time when there is much active research in the area of MTT, but when no comprehensive treatment of the subject is available. The emphasis is on the practical design and evaluation of operational systems. The necessary theory is presented, but the emphasis is on explaining the principles of application.

It was not possible to include detailed descriptions of all the techniques presented. Thus, in many cases the relevant features of a method are summarized. The interested reader can find more detail in the references.

The first eight chapters present the theory and evaluation methods that are basic to the design of all MTT systems. In particular, these techniques have been developed primarily for the "classical" track-while-scan (TWS) application. The methods discussed in the first eight chapters are mostly based on undergraduate-level probability theory. However, it would be helpful, but not necessary, for the reader to have some background in Kalman filtering theory.

Chapters 9-14 deal with more advanced topics and are specifically based on Bayesian methods. A graduate-level course in estimation theory would be helpful, but again not necessary, for these chapters. The required background in probability theory (including Bayesian methods) and Kalman filtering is given during discussion of applications.

The contents of the book are summarized as follows.

Chapter 1 gives the basic definitions and principles involved in MTT. Chapter 2 discusses the elements of filtering and prediction required for MTT system design. In particular, this chapter discusses Kalman and fixed-gain filtering, and gives an overview of techniques for adaptive filtering. Chapter 3 examines coordinate systems in which the filtering and prediction can be done.

Chapter 4 begins the discussion of the key issues involved in gating and data association. The discussion in this chapter is based primarily upon the use of simple nearest-neighbor correlation methods. However, the concept of branching (or track splitting) is introduced and Kalman filter covariance modification in the presence of potential miscorrelation is discussed. Chapter 5 discusses how the measurement process affects overall MTT system performance and presents methods for including the measurement process as an inherent part of the MTT logic. Chapter 6 presents techniques for track confirmation and deletion, and introduces the concept of a track score function.

Chapters 7 and 8 discuss methods for MTT system evaluation. The methods discussed in Chapter 7 are basically analytical and require relatively small simulation efforts. These methods include covariance analysis, Markov chain techniques, and the evaluation of expressions describing expected correlation performance. Chapter 8 gives the background required for development of the detailed Monte Carlo simulation, which is usually required for final system evaluation.

Chapter 9 begins the discussion of more complex methods by deriving a general mathematical expression for multiple-target data association. Chapter 10 discusses Bayesian methods — first, the multiple hypothesis tracking (MHT) method is developed and then the all-neighbors joint probabilistic data association (JPDA) method is discussed. The JPDA is a special case of the MHT approach. These methods are more advanced than the nearest-neighbor type of correlation that was emphasized in the earlier chapters and comprise the "techniques of the future." However, these methods, particularly MHT, are also computationally involved.

Chapter 11 discusses the group tracking techniques that are applicable when many closely spaced targets (such as large formations of aircraft or convoys of ground vehicles) are to be tracked. Chapters 12 and 13 discuss how MTT design can be made to utilize advanced sensor capabilities. Chapter 12 specifically addresses how the agile beam capabilities of the radar electronically scanned antenna (ESA) can be exploited. Chapter 13 discusses MTT design for multiple sensor systems. Included in Chapter 13 are methods for data association and data fusion given sensors that report different types of quantities (target attributes as well as kinematics). Chapters 12 and 13 also discuss allocation techniques.

Chapter 14 discusses four special topics. First, an algorithm is presented for solution of the assignment problem that arises in MTT data association. Second, a particular implementation of the multiple hypothesis tracking method is presented. Next, methods are discussed for efficient processing in an environment where many target returns are expected. Finally, a future system architecture that includes MTT and artificial intelligence (AI) techniques is discussed.

This book has been written so that the individual chapters are self-contained. Thus, the reader should be able to concentrate on specific design areas without extensive previous background and without the necessity of referring to other chapters.

Chapter 1

The Basics of Multiple-Target Tracking

1.1 INTRODUCTION

Multiple-target tracking (MTT) is an essential requirement for surveillance systems employing one or more sensors, together with computer subsystems, to interpret the environment. Typical sensor systems, such as radar, infrared (IR), and sonar, report measurements from diverse sources: targets of interest, background noise sources such as radar ground clutter, or internal error sources such as thermal noise. The multitarget tracking objective is to partition the sensor data into sets of observations, or tracks, produced by the same source. Once tracks are formed and confirmed (so that background and other false targets are reduced), the number of targets can be estimated and quantities, such as target velocity, future predicted position, and target classification characteristics, can be computed for each track.

The basic principles of MTT were first recognized in 1955 by Wax [1]. At that time tracks were formed in radar systems by operators who manually connected "blips" on the plan position indicator (PPI) screen. Wax saw the similarity between this radar tracking problem and the nuclear physics problem, where it is required that the path of an actual particle be identified amid a background of random noise. He then postulated that the elements of initial track formation (birth), track maintenance (life), and track deletion (death) were common to all versions of the multiple-target tracking problem. He went on to develop mathematical models for these processes, but he did not address the data association problem.

The next major breakthrough in MTT theory came in 1964 with the publication by Sittler [2] of a Bayesian formulation that provided the background for later developments. However, the pioneering work of Sittler occurred before the widespread adoption of Kalman filtering techniques [3] for recursive target state estimation. Thus, it was not until the early 1970s that MTT theory became a major topic of interest. The papers by Bar-Shalom [4,5] and Singer [6,7] began the development of modern MTT techniques that combine correlation and Kalman filtering theory.

The earliest and probably still the best known type of MTT system is the radar track-while-scan (TWS) system outlined in the book by Hovanessian [8]. The TWS system is a special case of an MTT system in which the data are received at regular intervals as the radar (or other sensor) regularly scans a predetermined search volume. For the conventional TWS system, search and track update functions are simultaneously performed. In TWS, a single sensor scanning at a constant rate illuminates new targets and targets already in track with the same time on target, detection threshold, and waveform. Also, only those target tracks that remain within the TWS search volume can be maintained.

The general MTT problem does not have the constraints of TWS. For example, data may be received at irregular intervals for a single sensor or from multiple sensors, target tracks may be maintained in a region where there is no search for new targets, and adaptive time on target and detection thresholding can be readily employed. However, the basic techniques required for TWS system development are carried over to the generally more complex MTT system. Thus, nearly all of the techniques discussed in this book are applicable to TWS system design, but the more general term multiple-target tracking (MTT) will be used.

The number of applications of multitarget tracking is increasing rapidly with expansions in computer capabilities. Some of these applications include the development of sophisticated weapon delivery systems, satellite surveillance systems, and non-military tracking systems such as air traffic control (ATC). Many different approaches to multitarget tracking have been developed recently in response to the ever-increasing importance of the subject. However, at this stage of development, no standard approaches are generally accepted for all applications. A wide variety of techniques have been proposed for many diverse applications, but the MTT system designer must choose the techniques best suited to his particular problem.

This text surveys many of the techniques available for MTT system design. Examples will be given to illustrate how design and evaluation would proceed. These examples are primarily drawn from the area of radar system design. However, the techniques described are generally applicable for sensors (such as IR) other than radar and for systems employing multiple sensors. Finally, as recognized by Wax, the general principles of MTT are even applicable to detecting the path of a particle in a bubble chamber.

The next section of this chapter will give some of the required definitions. Section 1.3 begins discussion of MTT system design by introducing the basic elements contained in most systems. The most important element of an MTT system is data association (or correlation). Thus, Section 1.3 will illustrate in some detail how the related functions of gating and correlation are used. Finally, as an introduction to the issues covered in the rest of the book, Section 1.4 gives a simplified interpretation of the most important element, data association.

1.2 BASIC PROCESSING DEFINITIONS

Observation is a collective term that will be used to refer to all the observed (or measured) quantities included in a report (or detection) output from a sensor. In general, an observation may contain measured kinematic parameters, such as position or radar Doppler (range rate), and measured attributes such as target type, identification number, length, or shape. Also, an observation should contain an estimate of the time at which the measurements were obtained.

In general, observations may be received at regular intervals of time (scans or data frames) or they may occur irregularly in time. However, because the more common occurrence is for reception at regular time intervals, we will primarily refer to observations received on scan k or with sampling interval T. The radar TWS system is an example of a system in which data are received at regular intervals as the radar scans a predetermined search volume and all observations are given as output at the end of each scan.

Older radar systems that employed a mechanically scanned antenna (MSA) were effectively constrained to use TWS for multiple-target tracking. The more recently developed electronically scanned antenna (ESA) radars can conveniently switch back and forth between the functions of searching for new targets and illuminating existing target tracks. However, blocks of data can still be indexed by a number k, but with the provision that the time interval between "scan" k and "scan" $k+1$ may not be the same for all k.

Usually, it is assumed that observations received on a single scan contain at most one observation from each target which may be within the search volume of the sensor producing the observation set. This may require some redundancy elimination logic in the measurement preprocessing so that multiple observations from the same source are combined. For example, a radar search volume may be covered using two or more bars in which the radar scans in azimuth angle while maintaining a fixed elevation angle for each bar. Thus, a redundancy elimination logic is required to ensure that detections received from the same target on multiple bars are not interpreted as being the result of multiple targets.

An important distinction when comparing MTT processing methods is between batch and recursive methods. Batch processing techniques represent the ideal situation where no information is lost due to preprocessing because all observations are processed together. As a notational convention the lower case k will be used as a running index, while the upper case K will refer to the index for the last scan of a set of observations. Then, using batch processing, at scan K the data received on that scan as well as the data received on all previous scans $k = 1, 2, \ldots, K-1$ would be processed together to form target tracks and state (positions, velocity, *et cetera*.) estimates. On the other hand, using recursive (or sequential) methods, processing is done at each scan using only data received on that scan to update the results of previous processing. For example, in the simplest recursive processing, observations received at scan K would be compared for correlation with tracks formed on the previous ($K-1$) scan, but would not affect the previous correlation decisions.

The computations associated with batch processing rapidly begin to exceed computational capacities as more and more data are received. Thus, batch methods are usually derived as the ideal (or optimal) solution, and simplifications are made so that a computationally feasible form of recursive processing is obtained for implementation. The next section introduces the elements of MTT by considering a simple recursive processing system.

1.3   ELEMENTS OF A BASIC MTT SYSTEM

Figure 1-1 gives a representation of the functional elements of a simple recursive MTT system. There is considerable overlap of the functions of these elements, but this representation provides a convenient partitioning which will be used to introduce the typical functions required for an MTT system. The purpose of the discussion below is to give an overview of the MTT problem and to show how the elements interrelate. Later chapters will be devoted to more detailed descriptions of these elements and their design and analysis.

Let us assume recursive processing so that tracks have been formed on the previous scan. Now, input data are received from the sensor, and the processing loop described in Fig. 1-1 is to be performed. Incoming observations are first considered for the update of existing tracks. Gating tests determine which possible observation-to-track pairings are "reasonable," and a more refined correlation algorithm is used to determine final pairings. Observations not assigned to existing tracks can initiate new tentative tracks. A tentative track becomes confirmed when the number and quality of the observations included in the track satisfy confirmation criteria. Similarly, low quality tracks, as usually determined by the update history, are deleted. Finally, after inclusion of the new observations, tracks are predicted ahead to the arrival time for the next set of observations. Gates are placed around these predicted positions and the processing cycle repeats. Next, we shall discuss these elements in more detail.

1.3.1   Measurement Data Processing

For MTT the sensor will typically spend a limited amount of time on a single target because scanning is necessary in order to provide updated information on existing multiple target tracks and to search for new targets. One important sensor design consideration is the determination of a decision

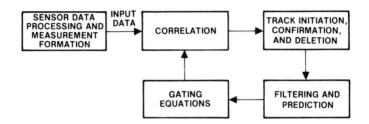

FIGURE 1-1. BASIC ELEMENTS OF A SIMPLE RECURSIVE MTT SYSTEM

rule on the return, which is received during the time on target, so as to discriminate between returns from targets of interest and returns from extraneous sources, such as potential false alarms produced by noise and radar clutter.

The simplest approach to the decision process is to compare the incoming signal power to a threshold which is set so that the probability of false alarm (P_{FA}) remains constant. For a given threshold setting, the probability of detection (P_D) generally will be a complicated function of the sensor capabilities, the target size and distance from the sensor, and the environment (atmospheric attenuation, *et cetera*). Detection issues are discussed in detail elsewhere (such as in References [8] and [9]) and thus will not receive much attention here. However, it should be noted that the threshold setting (and resulting P_D and P_{FA}) should be chosen with consideration for the effect on overall MTT system performance. As discussed in Chapter 5, it may be desirable to choose the threshold setting adaptively.

The design of other MTT elements is greatly simplified if it can be assumed that the sensor does not produce multiple simultaneous observations from the same source. For example, a radar or an IR sensor may achieve a required elevation angle coverage by scanning two or more bars at different elevation angles. Then, for a typical TWS radar system, observations received on different bars from the same target are combined, and the composite observation is input to the rest of the MTT loop. Thus, for all types of sensors, preprocessing redundancy-elimination logic will be required to combine multiple observations received from the same source.

In addition to combining multiple observations from a single target, it is also desirable to recognize when a single observation was produced by multiple targets. For example, radar measurement techniques might not be able to resolve several closely spaced targets that are within the radar's beamwidth. However, radar data processing techniques have been developed to determine when there are multiple targets within the radar's beamwidth, even if distinct measurements from all targets cannot be obtained.

Several other functions may be performed during the process of measurement formation. First, the measured kinematic quantities may be transformed to a coordinate system which is more convenient for performing the other MTT functions. Second, further processing may be performed to improve the observation quality. For example, certain known characteristics of the radar signal return may be used to remove the undesired components caused by jet engine modulation (JEM).

1.3.2 Gating

Gating is the first part of the correlation algorithm used to decide if an observation belongs to a previously established target track or to a new target. Gating is a coarse test that classifies an observation into one of two categories.

1. *Candidate for Track Update.* The observation may satisfy the gates of one or more existing tracks. In this case the observation becomes a candidate for association with that track. Note that more than one observation may satisfy the gate of a single track. Also, note that an observation ultimately might not be used to update the track, even if the gate is satisfied. Thus, it may be used to initiate a new track.

2. *Initial Observation for New Tentative Track.* The observation might not satisfy the gate of any existing track. In this case the observation becomes an immediate candidate for the initiation of a new target track.

Figure 1-2 illustrates gating for two closely spaced targets and four observations. Note that the gates may overlap for closely spaced targets. Gates are established, and gating is performed in the following general manner.

1. Estimates are made of what the measured quantity should be at the time of the next observation. This usually means kinematic quantities, such as position as estimated by tracking filters, but the definition can be expanded to included attributes such as target type. This process is called prediction, and statistics describing the accuracy of these estimates are required. Also, an estimate of measurement accuracy is required.

2. The difference between each measurement and its corresponding estimate is formed. It is often useful to form a total distance* d_{ij}^2 from track i to observation j. Thus, a normalization process is required whereby the differences in each of the component measurements are squared, divided by the variances of the expected differences, and

---

*The quantity d_{ij}^2 is actually a squared distance, but, for convenience, it will be referred to simply as a *distance*.

summed to form a total normalized (or statistical) distance. For example, if range (R) and angle (θ) are measured, the normalized distance is

$$d^2 = \frac{(R_p - R_o)^2}{\sigma_R^2} + \frac{(\theta_p - \theta_o)^2}{\sigma_\theta^2}$$

where (R_p, θ_p) is the predicted position, (R_o, θ_o) is the measured position, σ_R^2 is the variance of $R_p - R_o$, and σ_θ^2 is the variance of $\theta_p - \theta_o$.

3. A maximum error between estimate and measurement is formed for all measured quantities by using the estimate and measurement accuracy statistics. The computed differences are compared to the computed maximum allowable error. Normally, these allowable errors are set to at least the three-standard-deviation level for assumed-zero-mean Gaussian statistics. If the differences do not exceed the corresponding maximum allowable errors, the observation satisfies the gate. Alternatively, the gating may be carried out by using the normalized distance, but computations can usually be saved if the measurement components are first examined individually.

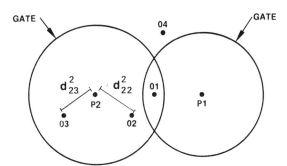

01,02,03,04 = OBSERVATION POSITIONS
P1, P2 = PREDICTED TARGET POSITIONS
d_{22}^2 = DISTANCE FROM P2 TO 02

FIGURE 1-2. EXAMPLE OF GATING AND CORRELATION
FOR TWO CLOSELY SPACED TRACKS

Example of Gating

The gating process can be illustrated by a simple example. Assume a two-dimensional observation with observed quantities:

$$x_o = 100, y_o = 200$$

and common observation standard deviation:

$\sigma_o = 4$

Further assume the predictions and the common prediction-error standard deviation to be

$x_p = 85, y_p = 217, \sigma_p = 2\sqrt{5}$

The difference between the prediction and the measurement is defined as the residual (or innovation). For our example, the residual standard deviation for both the x and y components is

$\sigma_r = \sqrt{\sigma_o^2 + \sigma_p^2} = 6$

If the gating logic first tests the measurements at the three-standard-deviation level, both tests will be satisfied because

$|x_o - x_p| = 15 = 2.5\,\sigma_r$

and

$|y_o - y_p| = 17 = 2.83\,\sigma_r$

Both error components are less than three standard deviations of the expected error so that this portion of the gating test is satisfied.

If the normalized distance is formed, then we have

$d^2 = (2.5)^2 + (2.83)^2 = 14.26$

The theoretical normalized distance function for this case is the sum of squares of two zero-mean, unit standard-deviation Gaussians, and thus has the chi-square distribution with two degrees of freedom. (χ_2^2). In order to use the computed value of d^2 to test the hypothesis that the observation-to-track pairing is correct, we consider the likelihood that a χ_2^2 distributed

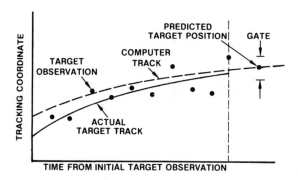

FIGURE 1-3. ILLUSTRATION OF PREDICTION AND GATING

variable will be as large as 14.26. Using the chi-square table contained in any standard statistical reference book, we find that the probability of a χ_2^2 distributed variable exceeding 13.815 is only 0.001. Based upon this, a value for d^2 as large as 14.26 is very unlikely for a correct observation-to-track pairing, so this gating test is not satisfied and the hypothesized pairing is rejected. Thus, use of d^2 has provided a more powerful gating test than the examination of the individual components.

The gating process is repeated for each track-observation pair. Figure 1-3, reproduced from [8], gives another illustration of the gating process.

1.3.3 Correlation

The correlation function takes the output of the gating function and makes final observation-to-track assignments. In the case where a single observation is within the gate of a single track, the assignment can be immediately made. However, for closely spaced targets, it is more likely that conflict situations, such as those shown in Fig. 1-2, will arise.

Correlation conflict situations arise when multiple observations fall within the same gate (or gates) and when observations fall within the gates of more than one track. There are two basic approaches to this problem. The first approach, called "nearest-neighbor," looks for a unique pairing so that at most one observation can be used to update a given track. Using this approach, the optimal solution is obtained by assigning observations to tracks in order to minimize the total summed distance from all observations to the tracks to which they are assigned. This is a version of the well-known assignment problem for which optimal, as well as computationally efficient suboptimal, solutions have been developed.

At least two commonly used suboptimal assignment algorithms have been proposed for use in implementing the nearest-neighbor correlation method. Unfortunately, as will be illustrated in Chapter 4, these solutions often differ from each other as well as from the optimal solution. Thus, as computational capabilities improve, utilization of these suboptimal solutions will be reduced.

To illustrate one suboptimal solution, the example shown in Figure 1-2 is solved using the following rules:

1. $O1$ is assigned to $T1$ because $O1$ is the only observation within the gates of $T1$ while $T2$ has other observations ($O2$, $O3$) within its gates.
2. $O3$ is assigned to $T2$ because $O3$ is closer than $O2$ ($d_{23}^2 < d_{22}^2$).
3. $O4$ can, without question, be used to initiate a new track, but new track initiation using $O2$ may be restricted. This restriction is based upon the practical consideration that multiple observations within the gate of a single established track are often the result of a failure in the

observation redundancy-elimination logic. Thus, this restriction serves to prevent initiation of extraneous tracks.

The alternative to nearest-neighbor correlation is the "all-neighbor" approach, which incorporates all observations within the neighborhood, as defined by the gate around the predicted target position. The position update is then based on a weighted sum of all observations, with the weighting calculated using probability theory [5]. For the example shown in Fig. 1-2, this means that $O1$, $O2$, and $O3$ would all be used to update the position estimate of $T2$, but the weighting for $O1$ would be much smaller than the weightings for $O2$ and $O3$, since $O1$ is also within the gate of $T1$.

1.3.4 Track Initiation, Confirmation, and Deletion

Observations not assigned to existing tracks are used to form new tentative tracks. Restrictions are sometimes used so that observations within gates of existing tracks may not be used to initiate new tentative tracks, even if, using nearest-neighbor correlation, the observations are not assigned to an existing track. The problem of tentative track initiation becomes still more difficult using the all-neighbor approach. The author's experience with airborne radar systems using the nearest-neighbor approach indicates that in order to maintain accurate tracking it is best to initiate new tracks whenever initiation may be questionable, but then to make confirmation requirements more stringent.

Once a tentative track is formed, a confirmation logic is usually required because the probability of a single observation being from an extraneous source is too high for immediate confirmation. Thus, it is usually required that at least one other observation be assigned to a tentative track before the track is considered to be confirmed. The gate size and the length of time allowed for that confirming observation can be chosen as functions of the confidence in the validity of the original observation. A typical simple rule for track confirmation is that M correlating observations should be received within N scans. Typical confirmation criteria are three out of four or three out of five [10]. However, for a radar system in which Doppler (range rate) information is available, two observations may suffice so that two-out-of-three or two-out-of-four criteria may be used. If the required confirming observations are not received, the previous observations are dismissed as false alarms.

A track that is not updated becomes degraded, and therefore must be deleted. If a sufficiently long time elapses without detection, the target probably will no longer be within the scan volume. Also, even if the lack of detections is consistent with an assumed low probability of detection, it might be best to delete a track just because of its low quality. A typical simple rule is to delete a track after N_D consecutive scans have produced no correlating observation. Alternatively, a test based upon the total elapsed time since track update may also be used.

1.3.5 Filtering and Prediction

The filtering step incorporates the correlating observations into the updated track parameter estimates. For those tracks that did not receive a correlating observation, the previous predicted estimates become the filtered estimates. Then, predictions are made to the time when the next data scan is to be received. Thus, prediction quantities are of great importance because they define the center of the gated region discussed above. The size of the gate is also directly affected by the prediction uncertainty, which can be determined by the filter if Kalman filtering is used.

Typically, the choice of filtering and prediction algorithm involves deciding between Kalman and fixed-coefficient methods. A major advantage of Kalman filtering is the associated covariance matrix which can be used for gating. Using Kalman filtering also provides a convenient way to determine the filter gains as a function of the assumed measurement model, the assumed target maneuver model, and the detection sequence. However, this flexibility is obtained at the cost of additional computation and computer storage requirements.

Figure 1-3 illustrates the prediction and gating processes. Note that as more observations are received, the predicted target position should approach the true target position unless the target performs a random maneuver. Also, as more data are received, the track gate sizes should decrease while remaining large enough to enclose a maneuvering target.

1.4 OVERVIEW OF DATA ASSOCIATION ISSUES

This section introduces the observation-to-track correlation (or data association) problem, which is the key element of MTT. Also, the methods to be presented in this book are discussed with respect to their effect upon correlation. To begin, Fig. 1-4 gives a simplified, but instructive, interpretation of MTT data correlation. Under this interpretation there are basically three regions. These comprise a region of unambiguous correlation for widely spaced targets, an unstable region where highly inaccurate tracking may occur, and a region for closely spaced targets where miscorrelation occurs but tracking remains stable.

First, for sufficiently large target spacings unambiguous correlation occurs. This region of unambiguous correlation can be expanded by improving correlation techniques and detection performance (as measured by the probability of detection P_D). Also, for most cases, this region can be expanded by sampling at a faster rate (decreased sampling interval, T).

Next, an unstable region has been identified. Miscorrelation frequently occurs in this region. The result is erratic track performance and frequent premature track deletion, leading to a very inaccurate assessment of the target environment. Assuming typical aircraft maneuvers and that targets are not resolvable in range or range rate, results show that this region may occur for target angular separations of about two to five times the angular measurement-error standard deviation. Reference [11], examining targets separated in range and using a 1 Hz update rate, shows that unambiguous tracking of two targets occurs for target separations of about five times the measurement-error standard deviation.

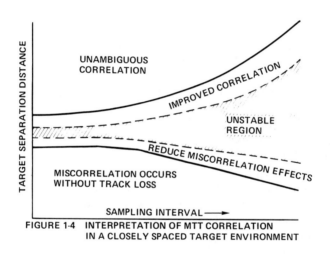

FIGURE 1-4 INTERPRETATION OF MTT CORRELATION
IN A CLOSELY SPACED TARGET ENVIRONMENT

The extent of the unstable region is also a function of the sampling rate and the probability of detection. Faster sampling decreases the size of the unstable region. However, as will be discussed later, results have indicated that instability may remain even when the sampling interval is decreased as long as simple correlation techniques are used.

Figure 1-5 gives an example of the type of tracking that may occur in the unstable region. For this example, there were four targets at an approximately constant (as seen by the radar) azimuth angle separation of about three times the angular measurement-error standard deviation. Figure 1-5 shows the true targets' and the tracks' predicted azimuth angles as functions of time. Also, selected observations are denoted by dots, and the symbol D refers to the points of track deletion. This example shows how miscorrelation leads to large prediction errors with the result that tracks become "starved" for observations and are thus deleted. Clearly, a major goal of MTT system design must be to decrease (or eliminate) the unstable tracking region.

Finally, consider the lower region in Fig. 1-4. For very closely spaced targets miscorrelation will occur without an associated large number of tracks being degraded and lost. In this region, tracks may be erratic and there are typically fewer tracks than targets, but track loss is infrequent. Figure 1-6 illustrates what happens in this region of very closely spaced targets. For this example there were four targets with angular separation of about 1.5 times the measurement-error standard deviation. We see that there are fewer tracks (three) than targets (four). The tracks tend to wander back and forth and to cross, but none are lost.

1.4.1 Techniques for Reducing Unstable Tracking

Miscorrelation leading to unstable tracking can be decreased by increasing the probability of detection (P_D), by decreasing the sampling interval, or by using improved correlation methods. Chapter 5 will discuss techniques for choosing the radar threshold adaptively and thus potentially increasing P_D. Use of the electronically scanned antenna (ESA) discussed in Chapter 12 readily leads to adaptive sampling (decreased T) and increased P_D. Chapters 4, 9, and 10 are primarily devoted to discussing techniques for improving correlation. Finally, the appropriate choice of filtering techniques and tracking coordinate system, as discussed in Chapters 2 and 3, can lead to better prediction and as a result improved correlation.

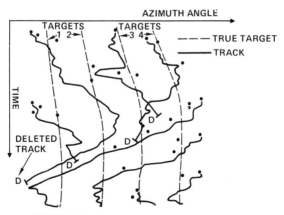

FIGURE 1-5   EXAMPLE OF DEGRADED TRACKING
IN UNSTABLE REGION

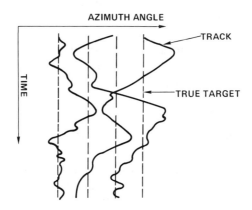

FIGURE 1-6   TYPICAL TRACKING RESULTS FOR
              CLOSELY SPACED TARGETS

Techniques which expand the lower region of Fig. 1-4, and thus decrease the unstable region, use an all-neighbors approach so that a single miscorrelation is less likely to degrade a track. An example of this approach is the joint probabilistic data association (JPDA) method discussed in Chapter 10. The extreme in this direction is the group tracking approach discussed in Chapter 11. Generally, in using the group tracking approach, there will be no attempt to maintain individual tracks on closely spaced targets such as shown in Fig. 1-6. Another approach for decreasing the unstable region in the presence of unavoidable miscorrelations is to increase the Kalman filter covariance matrix in order to reflect the uncertain correlation history. Several approaches for doing this are given in Chapter 4.

To illustrate the concepts discussed in this section, Table 1-1 summarizes the results of an MTT study for an agile beam radar such as the ESA discussed in Chapter 12. The agile beam radar system can use adaptive sampling (either 2.5s or 1.25s sampling interval) and enhance detection performance. The enhanced detection performance was modeled by assuming two independent "looks" at the target. Two essentially independent looks at a target can be achieved by appropriate choice of the radar waveform so that the effects of scintillation and eclipsing (discussed in Chapters 8 and 12) are uncorrelated between the two looks. A relatively simple, sequential nearest-neighbor correlation technique was used. Results were derived using a Monte Carlo simulation, which was designed in the manner discussed in Chapter 8.

TABLE 1-1

NUMBER OF CONFIRMED TRACK DELETIONS FOR VARIOUS SPACINGS AND SYSTEM CONFIGURATIONS

Case	Normalized Separation [2]	Total Number of Targets	Nominal P_D (P_{D1})		Enhanced [1] P_D (P_{D2})	
			Fixed Sampling	Adaptive Sampling	Fixed Sampling [3]	Adaptive Sampling [3]
1	4.2	180	25	5	NE	NE
2	3.1	200	45	37	11	13
3	1.4	200	9	23	4	1

Note 1: $P_{D2} = 1 - (1-P_{D1})^2$

Note 2: The target separation divided by the measurement-error standard deviation

Note 3: NE = not examined

The results shown in Table 1-1 give the number of confirmed tracks that were deleted for various system configurations and target spacings. The second column gives the target spacing (taken to be constant throughout a Monte Carlo run) as normalized with respect to the angular measurement-error standard deviation. The third column gives the total number of targets that were considered (using all Monte Carlo runs). The fixed sampling method always used the longer sampling interval (2.5s), while the adaptive sampling method chose between the two sampling intervals. The adaptive sampling method used the shorter sampling interval (1.25s) when the existence of closely spaced targets was recognized.

Referring to Table 1-1, the adaptive sampling option effectively reduces the number of deleted tracks for the largest separation. Unfortunately, as illustrated in Figure 1-4 and by the results for cases 2 and 3 of Table 1-1, instability (as measured by track deletions) can remain for certain target separations, even if the sampling interval is decreased. However, with an agile beam radar another convenient option is to use enhanced probability of detection in order to decrease the unstable region. Results from the last, closely spaced, target case demonstrate the advantages of enhanced detection while noting the futility of increasing the sampling rate for certain conditions.

1.5 SUGGESTED FURTHER BACKGROUND READING

This chapter provides an introduction to both the MTT problem and the remainder of the book. Reference [8] also presents an introductory discussion of a TWS system. References [10, 12, 13] give more detailed general discussions of MTT and would also serve as excellent introductions to the remainder of this book. References [14, 15] present very comprehensive bibliographies and summary discussions that include work done on MTT through the late 1970s. Finally, [16] gives a survey discussion of the methodologies of various approaches to MTT.

REFERENCES

1. Wax, N., "Signal-to-Noise Improvement and the Statistics of Tracking Populations," *Journal of Applied Physics,* Vol. 26, May 1955, pp. 586–595.
2. Sittler, R.W., "An Optimal Data Association Problem in Surveillance Theory," *IEEE Transactions on Military Electronics,* MIL-8, April 1964, pp. 125–139.
3. Kalman, R.E., "A New Approach to Linear Filtering and Prediction Problems," *Journal of Basic Engineering,* March 1960, pp. 35–46.
4. Jaffer, A.J., and Y. Bar-Shalom, "On Optimal Tracking in Multiple Target Environments," *Proceedings of the Third Symposium on*

Non-Linear Estimation Theory and Its Applications, San Diègo, CA, Sept. 11–13, 1972, pp. 112–117.

5. Bar-Shalom, Y., and E. Tse, "Tracking in a Cluttered Environment with Probabilistic Data Association," *Automatica,* Vol. 11, Sept. 1975, pp. 451–460.

6. Singer, R.A., and J.J. Stein, "An Optimal Tracking Filter for Processing Sensor Data of Imprecisely Determined Origin in Surveillance Systems," *Proceedings of the 1971 IEEE Conference on Decision and Control,* Miami Beach, FL, Dec. 1971, pp. 171–175.

7. Singer, R.A., R.G. Sea, and K.B. Housewright, "Derivation and Evaluation of Improved Tracking Filters for Use in Dense Multi-Target Environments," *IEEE Transactions on Information Theory,* IT-20, July 1974, pp. 423–432.

8. Hovanessian, S.A., *Radar System Design and Analysis,* Dedham, MA: Artech House, 1984.

9. Wolfe, W.L., and G.J. Zissis, "The Infrared Handbook," Washington, DC, Office of Naval Research, 1978.

10. Trunk, G.V., "Survey of Radar ADT," *Microwave Journal,* Vol. 26, No. 7, July 1983, pp. 77–88.

11. Browne, B.H., L. Ekchian, and L.J. Lawdermilt, "Adaptive Features and Measurement Requirements for Advanced Surveillance Radars," *Proceedings of EASCON '80,* Arlington, VA, Sept. 29–Oct. 1, 1980, pp. 190–194.

12. Bridgewater, A.W., "Automatic Tracking Techniques for Surveillance Radars," CRC Report 1357, Communication Research Center, Department of Communications, Ottawa, Canada, July 1982.

13. Farina, A., and S. Pardini, "Survey of Radar Data-Processing Techniques in Air-Traffic-Control and Surveillance Systems," *IEE Proceedings,* Vol. 127, Part F, No. 3, June 1980, pp. 190–204.

14. Wiener, H.L., *et al.,* "Naval Ocean-Surveillance Correlation Handbook, 1978," NRL Report 8340, Naval Research Laboratory, Washington, DC, Oct. 31, 1979.

15. Goodman, I.R., H.L. Wiener, and W.W. Willman, "Naval Ocean-Surveillance Correlation Handbook, 1979," NRL Report 8402, Naval Research Laboratory, Washington, DC, Sept. 17, 1980.

16. Bar-Shalom, Y., "Tracking Methods in a Multitarget Environment," *IEEE Transactions on Automatic Control,* AC-24, Aug. 1978, pp. 618–626.

2.1 INTRODUCTION

This chapter discusses filtering and prediction, which are the fundamental elements of any tracking system. An understanding of these elements is required in the discussion of other functions of a multiple-target tracking (MTT) system.

Filtering and prediction methods are used to estimate present and future target kinematic quantities such as position, velocity, and acceleration. The introductory techniques presented in this chapter are most applicable when considering widely separated targets in a sparse false-alarm background so that the errors introduced by uncertain observation-to-track correlation can be ignored. Later chapters discuss modifications which may be required in the presence of miscorrelation.

This chapter initially discusses two commonly used approaches to filtering and prediction for multitarget tracking. The first is to use fixed tracking coefficients, and the second, Kalman filtering, generates time-variable tracking coefficients that are determined by *a priori* models for the statistics of measurement noise and target dynamics. The first approach has computational advantages for systems with large numbers of targets. However, with expanding computer capabilities, the high-accuracy tracking associated with Kalman filtering is becoming increasingly more appealing to the system designer.

Both of these types of filters are of the fading memory type, which can be implemented recursively. Data received in the past are included in the present estimates, and therefore all data are utilized but forgotten at an exponential rate. The estimate at scan time k given data through scan k ($\hat{x}(k|k)$) will be denoted the smoothed estimate x_s when considering fixed-coefficient filtering. The term "smoothed," as used in the literature of fixed-coefficient filtering, is synonymous with the term "filtered," which is used in Kalman terminology. We will also be concerned with the one-step prediction denoted $x_p = \hat{x}(k+1|k)$, which is the estimate at scan time $k+1$ given data through scan time k.

After discussing fixed-coefficient and Kalman filters, we will discuss several techniques for approximating the Kalman filter in an attempt to reduce computational requirements without a significant sacrifice in performance. Next, several approaches to maneuver detection and adaptive filtering will be outlined. Using adaptive filtering, the incoming data are used to refine the target maneuver and the measurement noise models.

This chapter will primarily consider tracking in one dimension (x) of a simple Cartesian coordinate system. Thus, the states (quantities being tracked) will be position (x), velocity (v_x), and, possibly, acceleration (a_x). The next chapter will discuss other coordinate systems. However, the choice of basic tracking methods and the design issues discussed in this chapter are relatively insensitive to the choice of coordinate systems.

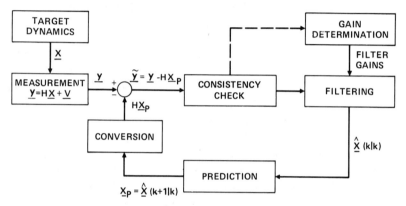

FIGURE 2-1   FILTERING AND PREDICTION FLOW DIAGRAM

Figure 2-1 gives a flow diagram of the filtering and prediction processes, valid for both fixed-gain and Kalman filtering. The target is characterized by a state vector x which will include such quantities as position, velocity and acceleration. The observation (y) is assumed to be a linear combination (Hx) of the states corrupted by additive measurement noise (v). The gains are used to provide filtered state estimates, which are then used to obtain estimates predicted to the next scan time. These gains, as discussed below, may have fixed, predetermined values or may be computed dynamically, such as through use of the Kalman filter.

The residual (or innovation) process $\tilde{y}$ is the difference between the actual (y) and the expected measurement (Hx_p). In addition to being used for updating the filtered estimates, the residual may be checked for consistency. This consistency check can be used to adjust the filter gains if the residual time history is determined to be mathematically inconsistent with a predetermined model. An example of this kind of check is maneuver detection, which is discussed later, whereby large residuals are interpreted as indicating increased target dynamics, thus implying the necessity for larger (more responsive) gains.

2.2 FIXED-COEFFICIENT FILTERING

2.2.1 The α-β Tracker

Fixed-coefficient filters have the advantage of simple implementation using fixed parameters for the filter gains. Probably the most extensively applied fixed-coefficient filter is the α-β tracker. This filter is used when only position measurement is available, and is defined by the following equations:

$$x_s(k) = \hat{x}(k|k) = x_p(k) + \alpha[x_o(k) - x_p(k)] \qquad (2.1a)$$

$$v_s(k) = \hat{\dot{x}}(k|k) = v_s(k-1) + \frac{\beta}{qT}[x_o(k) - x_p(k)] \qquad (2.1b)$$

$$x_p(k+1) = \hat{x}(k+1|k) = x_s(k) + Tv_s(k) \qquad (2.1c)$$

$$x_o(k) \triangleq \text{observation received at } k$$

$$T \triangleq \text{sampling interval}$$

$$\alpha, \beta = \text{fixed-coefficient filter parameters}$$

The quantity q is normally defined to be unity, but in the case where missing observations occur its value may be taken as the number of scans since the last measurement. Finally, the usual initialization process is defined by

$$x_s(1) = x_p(2) = x_o(1)$$

$$v_s(1) = 0$$

$$v_s(2) = \frac{[x_o(2) - x_o(1)]}{T}$$

Equation (2.1) is used directly when an observation is received on scan k. However, in the case where the probability of detection (P_D) is less than unity, there may be scans for which no observation is received. Then, the smoothed position is set equal to the prediction, $x_s(k) = x_p(k)$, and $v_s(k)$ is unaltered. This effectively amounts to setting $x_o(k) = x_p(k)$. The prediction, $x_p(k+1)$, to the next scan is computed as before.

Several criteria are used to quantify performance for fixed-coefficient filters. The first is the variance reduction ratio which is defined for the case when the input to the filter is only measurement noise. Then, the variance reduction ratio (K_x) is the steady-state ratio of the output variance of the smoothed position estimate ($\sigma^2_{x_s}$) to the input measurement variance (σ^2_o). The steady-state condition is defined to occur after initial errors have damped out. A similar quantity (K_v) is defined for the output velocity estimation variance given only noise input. For the case of unity probability of detection, these quantities are [1]:

$$K_x = \frac{2\alpha^2 + \beta(2 - 3\alpha)}{\alpha[4 - \beta - 2\alpha]} \tag{2.2}$$

$$K_v = \frac{1}{T^2} \frac{2\beta^2}{\alpha[4 - \beta - 2\alpha]}$$

Turning from noise to dynamic inputs, note that the α-β tracker will follow an input ramp (constant velocity target) with no steady-state mean error. However, a steady-state mean error will develop for a constant input acceleration ($\ddot{x}$). For unity probability of detection, this steady-state error is

$$\lim_{k \to \infty} [x(k) - x_s(k)] = \frac{(1 - \alpha)T^2 \ddot{x}}{\beta} \triangleq \frac{\ddot{x}}{k_a} \tag{2.3}$$

In analogy to the description normally applied to servomechanisms, using (2.2) it is possible to relate the noise bandwidth (B_n) of the α-β tracker to the acceleration error constant (k_a) given in (2.3). As shown in Appendix 2A, this relationship is

$$\frac{B_n}{\sqrt{k_a}} = \frac{(6-5\alpha)\sqrt{(2-\alpha)(1-\alpha)}}{\alpha^2 - 8\alpha + 8}$$

2.2.2 The α-β-γ Tracker

The logical extension of the α-β tracker is the α-β-γ tracker, which includes an estimate of acceleration. The equations for the α-β-γ tracker are defined as:

$$x_s(k) = x_p(k) + \alpha[x_o(k) - x_p(k)] \tag{2.4a}$$

$$v_s(k) = v_s(k-1) + T a_s(k-1) + \frac{\beta}{qT}[x_o(k) - x_p(k)] \tag{2.4b}$$

$$a_s(k) = a_s(k-1) + \frac{\gamma}{(qT)^2}[x_o(k) - x_p(k)] \tag{2.4c}$$

$$x_p(k+1) = x_s(k) + T v_s(k) + \frac{T^2}{2} a_s(k) \tag{2.4d}$$

where the usual initialization is

$$x_s(1) = x_p(2) = x_o(1)$$

$$v_s(1) = a_s(1) = a_s(2) = 0$$

$$v_s(2) = \frac{[x_o(2) - x_o(1)]}{T}$$

$$a_s(3) = \frac{[x_o(3) + x_o(1) - 2\,x_o(2)]}{T^2}$$

For the case of unity P_D, the variance reduction ratios for the α-β-γ tracker are [2]:

$$K_x = \frac{\sigma_{x_s}^2}{\sigma_0^2} = \frac{2\beta\,(2\alpha^2 + 2\beta - 3\alpha\beta) - \alpha\gamma\,(4 - 2\alpha - \beta)}{Q} \qquad (2.5a)$$

$$K_v = \frac{4\beta^3 - 4\beta^2\,\gamma + 2\gamma^2\,(2-\alpha)}{T^2\,Q} \qquad (2.5b)$$

$$K_a = \frac{4\beta\gamma^2}{T^4\,Q} \qquad (2.5c)$$

where

$$Q = (4 - 2\alpha - \beta)\,[2\alpha\beta + \alpha\gamma - 2\gamma]$$

The α-β-γ tracker hypothesizes constant acceleration. Thus, it will follow a ramp plus acceleration input with no steady-state error. As a measure of dynamic tracking error, the response of the α-β-γ tracker to a constant third derivative ($\dddot{x}$) input is

$$\lim_{k \to \infty}\,[x(k) - x_s(k)] = \frac{(1-\alpha)\,T^3\,\dddot{x}}{2\gamma} \qquad (2.6)$$

2.2.3 Choice of Fixed-Coefficient Gains

Equations (2.1) and (2.4) give examples of commonly used constant-coefficient filters. We next discuss how to determine the coefficient values. Decreasing coefficient values will lead to less responsive filters and as a result improved measures of performance (as given in (2.2) and (2.5)) for random noise input, while increasing coefficients leads to better performance *versus* dynamic inputs (as measured, for example, by (2.3) and (2.6)).

Relationships between the coefficients for the α-β and α-β-γ trackers are derived in [1, 2, 3]. The relationships define gains which give a compromise between noise reduction and maneuver-following capability in the steady state. Considering a steady-state Kalman filter, Kalata [3] shows the relationships to be

$$\beta = 2\,(2-\alpha) - 4\,\sqrt{1-\alpha} \qquad (2.7)$$

$$\gamma = \beta^2/2\alpha \qquad (2.8)$$

Equation (2.7) is valid for both filters, while (2.8) provides the additional relationship required for the α-β-γ tracker. The relationship given in (2.8) differs (by a factor of $1/2$) from that of [3] because of a different definition of the α-β-γ tracker.

Alternative derivations [1, 2] consider the weighted sum of the variance reduction ratio and the sum square transient error (due to ramp input for the α-β tracker and parabola input for the α-β-γ tracker). Using this criterion the relationships for the α-β-γ tracker, which closely agree with those of (2.7) and (2.8) for $\alpha \gtrsim 0.6$, are

$$2\beta - \alpha \left(\alpha + \beta + \frac{\gamma}{2} \right) = 0$$

while for the case of $\gamma = 0$ (the α-β tracker), we have

$$\beta = \frac{\alpha^2}{2-\alpha}$$

It is important to note that steady-state relationships are generally not valid prior to steady-state, nor in the case of missing observations. In fact, initial performance can be very poor if steady-state gains are used [3].

Even if steady-state performance is of primary concern, such that the relationships given by (2.7) and (2.8) can be used, at least one free coefficient must be specified. This can be done by examining the steady-state gains of the corresponding Kalman filter. Also, closed-form expressions for the steady-state Kalman filter gains can be computed for certain conditions [3,4].

The choice of gains for a constant-coefficient filter must reflect an overall compromise between noise and dynamic (maneuver) performance. One commonly proposed solution to this problem is to choose filter gains based on target behavior as determined by a maneuver detector. For example, for the α-β tracker, the coefficients would be chosen using (2.2) and (2.5) to ensure desired steady-state noise performance when assuming the target to be basically on a straight-line trajectory. Theoretically, a maneuver detector could be used to determine when the target departs from the straight-line trajectory. Then, upon maneuver detection, the tracking coefficients are increased so as to follow the target maneuver. Lefferts [5] describes a procedure for adaptive tracking parameter choice with an α-β tracker, and we will outline other techniques later in conjunction with a discussion of adaptive Kalman filtering.

A final problem associated with the use of constant-coefficient filters occurs when P_D is less than one. For nonunity P_D, in order to improve tracking performance, the coefficients should be adjusted according to the input data detection sequence [6]. Thus, although the simplicity of constant-coefficient filters is appealing, their inadequacy in many areas makes the choice of a variable gain sequence through Kalman filtering preferable when high accuracy is required. Kalman filtering techniques are presented next, and then methods for approximating the Kalman gains are discussed.

2.3 KALMAN FILTERING

The Kalman filter is the general solution to the recursive, minimized mean-square estimation problem within the class of linear estimators. Use of the Kalman filter will minimize the mean-squared error as long as the target dynamics and the measurement noise are accurately modeled. In addition to minimizing the mean-squared error, the Kalman filter has a number of other advantages for application to MTT. These advantages include the following properties:

1. The gain sequence is chosen automatically, based on the assumed target maneuver and measurement noise models. This means that the same filter can be used for varying target and measurement environments by changing a few key parameters. For example, as a target closes in range, its intensity increases, so angular measurement accuracy usually improves. On the other hand, as range decreases, the target angular dynamics tend to increase. The optimal response to this complex changing environment is readily obtained from the Kalman filter by using simple range-dependent target dynamic and measurement noise models.

2. The Kalman gain sequence automatically adapts to changing detection histories. This includes a varying sampling interval as well as missed detections.

3. The Kalman filter provides a convenient measure of the estimation accuracy through the covariance matrix. This measure is required to perform the gating and correlation functions accurately, and, as discussed in Chapters 5 and 13, it can also be used for determining the threshold setting of a single sensor, or the allocation of multiple sensors. Finally, having a measure of the expected prediction error variance is useful for maneuver detection, and upon maneuver detection the Kalman filter model provides a convenient way to adjust for varying target dynamics.

4. Through use of the Kalman filter it is possible to at least partially compensate for the effects of miscorrelation in the dense MTT environment. As discussed in Chapter 4, one convenient technique is to increase the Kalman covariance matrix elements to reflect the expected error associated with uncertain correlation.

2.3.1 Kalman Filter Definition

Many good derivations of the Kalman filter are presented in the literature (*see*, for example, Gelb [7]), so only the resulting equations are given here after we introduce the notation and the formulas. First, assume that the target dynamic process can be modeled in the discrete Markov form:

$$x(k+1) = \Phi \, x(k) + q(k) + f(k+1|k) \tag{2.9}$$

where x is the n-dimensional target state vector that includes the quantities to be estimated. Also, Φ is the assumed known transition matrix; $q(k)$ is the zero-mean, white, Gaussian process noise with assumed known covariance Q; and $f(k+1|k)$ is a known deterministic input, such as the relative position change associated with own-ship motion.

Equation (2.9) is a difference equation that describes the target dynamics in terms of a Markov process represented by the state vector. For our application, the discrete-time Markov process can be defined as a process in which the statistical representation of the process in the future (scan $k+1$) is completely determined by the present state (scan k). Dynamic relationships are usually derived in terms of continuous-time state equations and then converted to the discrete representation of (2.9). Techniques for placing a process in this form are discussed in the next chapter and by Gelb [7]. The state equation is driven by the deterministic dynamics $f(k+1|\mathbf{k})$, as well as by the random driving (or plant) noise $q(k)$, which represents the randomness entering the system, such as random target acceleration.

Measurements are in the form of linear combinations of the system state variables, corrupted by uncorrelated noise. Thus, the M-dimensional measurement vector is modeled as

$$y(k) = H \, x(k) + v(k) \tag{2.10}$$

where H is the $M \times n$ measurement matrix, and $v(k)$ is zero-mean, white, Gaussian measurement noise with covariance R_c. Note that in general Q and H may also vary with time, and thus could be indexed by k, but for notational convenience Q and H will not be indexed.

Given the target dynamics and measurement models from (2.9) and (2.10), the Kalman filter equations become

$$\hat{x}(k|k) = \hat{x}(k|k-1) + K(k)\,[y(k) - H\,\hat{x}(k|k-1)] \tag{2.11a}$$

$$K(k) = P(k|k-1)\,H^T\,[H\,P(k|k-1)\,H^T + R_c]^{-1} \tag{2.11b}$$

$$P(k|k) = [I - K(k)\,H]\,P(k|k-1) \tag{2.11c}$$

$$\hat{x}(k+1|k) = \Phi\,\hat{x}(k|k) \tag{2.11d}$$

$$P(k+1|k) = \Phi\,P(k|k)\,\Phi^T + Q \tag{2.11e}$$

The covariance matrix is defined in terms of the zero-mean Gaussian estimation error vector:

$$P(k) = E\{[x(k) - \hat{x}(k)][x(k) - \hat{x}(k)]^T\}$$

The vector difference between measured and predicted quantities, $\tilde{y}(k) = y(k) - H\hat{x}(k|k-1)$, is defined to be the residual vector with residual covariance matrix, $S = HPH^T + R_c$. Finally, note that a version of the Kalman filter may also be defined in which the filtered quantities are bypassed and only one-step prediction quantities are used. This is convenient because the real-time operation of MTT systems often dictates that only the predicted quantities are of practical importance. For this formulation, we derive

$$\hat{x}(k+1|k) = \Phi \hat{x}(k|k-1) + K_p(k)[y(k) - H\hat{x}(k|k-1)]$$

$$K_p(k) = \Phi P(k|k-1) H^T [H P(k|k-1) H^T + R_c]^{-1} \qquad (2\text{-}11')$$

$$P(k+1|k) = [\Phi - K_p(k) H] P(k|k-1) \Phi^T + Q$$

2.3.2   Correspondence Between Kalman and α-β-γ Filters

Next, we will show how the parameters of the α-β-γ tracker are related to the Kalman gains. An illustration is the case where

$$\Phi = \begin{bmatrix} 1 & T & \dfrac{T^2}{2} \\ 0 & 1 & T \\ 0 & 0 & 1 \end{bmatrix}, \quad H = [1\ 0\ 0], \quad x = \begin{bmatrix} x \\ v \\ a \end{bmatrix} \qquad (2.12)$$

Then, (2.11) becomes

$$\begin{bmatrix} \hat{x}(k|k) \\ \hat{v}(k|k) \\ \hat{a}(k|k) \end{bmatrix} = \begin{bmatrix} \hat{x}(k|k-1) \\ \hat{v}(k|k-1) \\ \hat{a}(k|k-1) \end{bmatrix} + \begin{bmatrix} K_1(k) \\ K_2(k) \\ K_3(k) \end{bmatrix} [x_o(k) - \hat{x}(k|k-1)]$$

$$(2.13)$$

with

$$\hat{x}(k|k-1) = \hat{x}(k-1) + T\hat{v}(k-1|k-1) + \dfrac{T^2}{2}\hat{a}(k-1|k-1)$$

$$\hat{v}(k|k-1) = \hat{v}(k-1|k-1) + T\hat{a}(k-1|k-1)$$

$$\hat{a}(k|k-1) = \hat{a}(k-1|k-1)$$

Comparing (2.4) and (2.13), the correspondences are

$$\alpha = K_1, \quad \frac{\beta}{T} = K_2, \quad \frac{\gamma}{T^2} = K_3$$

Continuing with this example, denote the elements of the (symmetric) covariance matrix to be p_{ij} so that

$$P = \begin{bmatrix} p_{11} & p_{12} & p_{13} \\ p_{12} & p_{22} & p_{23} \\ p_{13} & p_{23} & p_{33} \end{bmatrix}$$

Also, note that the measurement noise covariance matrix R_c becomes the scalar measurement noise variance σ_o^2. Then, the Kalman gain equation gives

$$K_1 = \frac{p_{11}}{p_{11} + \sigma_o^2}, \quad K_2 = \frac{p_{12}}{p_{11} + \sigma_o^2}, \quad K_3 = \frac{p_{13}}{p_{11} + \sigma_o^2}$$

Thus, the first state gain (K_1) depends on the ratio of the estimation error variance to the total residual (including measurement noise and estimation error) variance. The other two gains (K_2, K_3) are computed through the covariances between the second and third states and the first state that is observed.

2.3.3 Example of a Two-State Kalman Filter

Next, we illustrate the concepts of Kalman filtering using a simple example. The target states will be x and v_x. The target random motion will be described by a model in which a random acceleration enters the system every T sec. This random acceleration is assumed to be of negligible duration and is reflected in a random change in velocity (δv). It is assumed that δv has Gaussian distribution with zero mean and variance $\sigma_{\delta v}^2$. The matrix Q in (2.11e) represents the random motion entering the system between sampling intervals. Thus, for this example,

$$Q = \begin{bmatrix} 0 & 0 \\ 0 & \sigma_{\delta v}^2 \end{bmatrix}$$

Initial estimates of x and v_x are assumed to be zero. The uncertainty of these estimates is reflected in the initial value for the covariance matrix:

$$P(0) = \begin{bmatrix} \sigma_{xo}^2 & 0 \\ 0 & \sigma_{v_{xo}}^2 \end{bmatrix}$$

Finally, a one-dimensional measurement is assumed so that $H = [1 \ 0]$, and the measurement noise covariance matrix R_c becomes the scalar measurement noise variance σ_o^2.

Figure 2-2 shows the behavior of the Kalman gains, for the filtering version given in (2.11), as a function of time (sample number) for the above example with parameter values:

$$\sigma_{\delta v} = 1 \text{ m}/\text{s}, \ \sigma_{xo} = 10 \text{ m}, \ \sigma_{v_{xo}} = 5 \text{ m}/\text{s}$$
$$\sigma_o = 5 \text{ m}, \ T = 1 \text{ s}$$

Also, a random detection sequence was generated by assuming that an observation was received each time with probability of detection (P_D) equal to 0.5.

Referring to Fig. 2-2, note that the position gain begins high (0.997) and thereafter oscillates from about 0.5 to 0.9. The second gain starts at zero and then goes to about 0.3 for the next two observations. Thereafter K_2 remains at about 0.15. As an aside, Fig. 2-2 also illustrates the manner in which strings of missed detections can occur, even though there is assumed to be no correlation between detection attempts on successive frames. Chapter 8 discusses the generation of uniform random numbers (which are used in determining detection histories) and other aspects of Monte Carlo simulation.

Using Fig. 2-2, a set of constant gains $K_1 = 0.7$ and $K_2 = 0.15$ was chosen to approximate the Kalman filter. Then, the one-step position prediction error was compared for the Kalman and the constant-gain approximation filters. Results indicated that the use of this set of constant gains only increased the prediction error standard deviation by about five percent for this particular case. However, for other cases with larger values assumed for $\sigma_{\delta v}$ increases of at least ten percent in prediction error standard deviation were noted for all constant gain choices. Also, for the above example, choosing K_2 through either the "classical" relationship $\beta = \alpha^2/(2-\alpha)$ of Benedict and Bordner [1] or use of (2.7) led to severely degraded response. This example illustrates the dynamic manner in which the Kalman gains adapt to missing data and the care that must be taken when choosing constant-gain approximations.

2.3.4 System Driving Noise and Maneuver Model

Next, we consider the random input as represented by the term $q(k)$ in (2.9). Several types of random process can be modeled by (2.9). Often, a correlated (or *colored*) measurement noise process is present. This correlated noise varies from the usually assumed *white* measurement noise insofar as its values are not independent from one scan to the next. A radar process of this type is angular scintillation noise. Theoretically, it becomes possible to estimate the correlated noise, and thereby improve tracking performance for the target dynamic states. This improved tracking performance for the

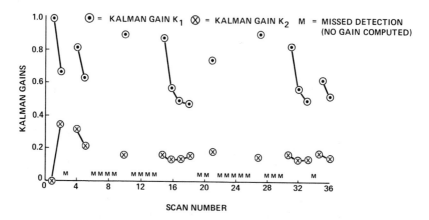

FIGURE 2-2   EXAMPLE OF KALMAN GAIN BEHAVIOR

target dynamic states results because a portion of the measurement noise can be removed due to the scan-to-scan correlation of the noise values.

A correlated noise process is typically represented in the first-order Markov form:

$$v\,(k{+}1) = \rho_c\, v\,(k) + \sqrt{1 - \rho_c^2}\ \sigma_v\ r\,(k) \tag{2.14}$$

where the correlation coefficient ρ_c is defined in terms of the sampling interval T and correlation time constant τ_c

$$\rho_c = e^{-\frac{T}{\tau_c}}$$

Also, σ_v is the standard deviation of the correlated measurement noise, and $r\,(k)$ is a zero-mean, Gaussian variable with unit standard deviation. Equation (2.14) results from the discrete-time solution of the continuous-time model of the form [7]:

$$\frac{dv}{dt} = -\beta_c\, v + w$$

where $\tau_c = 1/\beta_c$ and w is white noise input.

Equation (2.14) represents a scalar version of the vector Markov process given in (2.9). This state equation for the correlated noise process can be conveniently appended to the target state model. However, the measurement matrix (H) must reflect the fact that the measurement contains the additional state. For example, if the colored measurement noise process is added to the process defined in (2.12), the measurement matrix becomes $H = [1\ 0\ 0\ 1]$.

The most common model for random target motion uses the target acceleration. The standard target acceleration (or maneuver) model developed by Singer [8] is a first-order Markov process, which can be written

$$a(k+1) = \rho_m \, a(k) + \sqrt{1 - \rho_m^2} \; \sigma_m \, r(k) \tag{2.15}$$

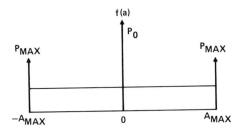

FIGURE 2-3. SINGER'S TARGET ACCELERATION MODEL

The maneuver correlation coefficient ρ_m is defined in terms of the maneuver time constant τ_m

$$\rho_m = e^{-\frac{T}{\tau_m}}$$

and σ_m is the maneuver standard deviation.

The maneuver standard deviation (σ_m) can be chosen in several ways. Probably, the most common is to assume a maximum value (A_{max}) and to divide this value by three. For example, an aircraft with assumed maximum acceleration capability of 6g would be modeled by using a value of 2g for σ_m. Singer proposed a model (shown in Fig. 2-3) whereby the target accelerates at the maximum rates $(A_{max}$ and $-A_{max})$, each with probability P_{max}, and has no acceleration with probability P_0. The probability distribution of other values for acceleration is taken to be uniform in the interval $(A_{max}, -A_{max})$. The height of the uniform distribution is $(1-2P_{max}-P_0)/(2A_{max})$. For the Singer model the target acceleration variance σ_m^2 is

$$\sigma_m^2 = \frac{A_{max}^2}{3}[1 + 4 \, P_{max} - P_0]$$

Continuing with the Singer model and defining β to be the inverse of the maneuver time constant $(\beta = 1/\tau_m)$, the transition matrix is

$$\Phi = \begin{bmatrix} 1 & T & \dfrac{1}{\beta^2}(-1 + \beta T + \rho_m) \\[2ex] 0 & 1 & \dfrac{1}{\beta}(1 - \rho_m) \\[2ex] 0 & 0 & \rho_m \end{bmatrix} \tag{2.16}$$

Typically, the sampling interval is less than the maneuver time constant $(T < \tau_m)$ so that a second-order approximation frequently used is

$$\Phi = \begin{bmatrix} 1 & T & \dfrac{T^2}{2} \\[2ex] 0 & 1 & T\left(1 - \dfrac{T}{2\tau_m}\right) \\[2ex] 0 & 0 & \rho_m \end{bmatrix}$$

The exact solution for the process (or maneuver) excitation covariance matrix is [8]:

$$Q = \frac{2\sigma_m^2}{\tau_m} \begin{bmatrix} q_{11} & q_{12} & q_{13} \\ q_{12} & q_{22} & q_{23} \\ q_{13} & q_{23} & q_{33} \end{bmatrix} \tag{2.17}$$

where

$$q_{11} = \frac{1}{2\beta^5}\left[1 - e^{-2\beta T} + 2\beta T + \frac{2\beta^3 T^3}{3} - 2\beta^2 T^2 - 4\beta T e^{-\beta T}\right]$$

$$q_{12} = \frac{1}{2\beta^4}\left[e^{-2\beta T} + 1 - 2e^{-\beta T} + 2\beta T e^{-\beta T} - 2\beta T + \beta^2 T^2\right]$$

$$q_{13} = \frac{1}{2\beta^3}\left[1 - e^{-2\beta T} - 2\beta T e^{-\beta T}\right]$$

$$q_{22} = \frac{1}{2\beta^3}\left[4e^{-\beta T} - 3 - e^{-2\beta T} + 2\beta T\right]$$

$$q_{23} = \frac{1}{2\beta^2}\left[e^{-2\beta T} + 1 - 2e^{-\beta T}\right]$$

$$q_{33} = \frac{1}{2\beta}\left[1 - e^{-2\beta T}\right]$$

There are several limiting cases of interest. First, for short sampling intervals $(T \ll \tau_m)$, (2.17) becomes

$$\lim_{\beta T \to 0} Q = \frac{2\sigma_m^2}{\tau_m} \begin{bmatrix} \dfrac{T^5}{20} & \dfrac{T^4}{8} & \dfrac{T^3}{6} \\[2mm] \dfrac{T^4}{8} & \dfrac{T^3}{3} & \dfrac{T^2}{2} \\[2mm] \dfrac{T^3}{6} & \dfrac{T^2}{2} & T \end{bmatrix}$$

Similarly, in this case the transition matrix of (2.16) reduces to the Newtonian matrix:

$$\lim_{\beta T \to 0} \Phi = \begin{bmatrix} 1 & T & \dfrac{T^2}{2} \\[2mm] 0 & 1 & T \\[2mm] 0 & 0 & 1 \end{bmatrix}$$

Simplified expressions for Φ and Q can also be derived for the limiting case where the sampling interval is much longer than the maneuver correlation time $(T \gg \tau_m)$. This represents the case in which the acceleration is essentially seen as a white noise process. The results are found by letting βT in (2.16) and (2.17) become large, whence we write

$$\lim_{\beta T \to \infty} Q = \sigma_m^2 \begin{bmatrix} \dfrac{2T^3 \tau_m}{3} & T^2 \tau_m & \tau_m^2 \\[2mm] T^2 \tau_m & 2T \tau_m & \tau_m \\[2mm] \tau_m^2 & \tau_m & 1 \end{bmatrix}$$

and

$$\lim_{\beta T \to \infty} \Phi = \begin{bmatrix} 1 & T & T \tau_m \\[2mm] 0 & 1 & \tau_m \\[2mm] 0 & 0 & 0 \end{bmatrix}$$

For the limiting case when $T \gg \tau_m$ the cross-correlation terms q_{13} and q_{23} become relatively small as τ_m decreases relative to T. This will be reflected by decreasing gains associated with the acceleration estimate. Thus, the computationally convenient reduction to a two-state filter becomes valid because an estimate of acceleration is no longer obtained. The two states are x and v_x, and the random excitation covariance and transition matrices become

$$Q = 2\sigma_m^2 \tau_m \begin{bmatrix} \dfrac{T^3}{3} & \dfrac{T^2}{2} \\ \dfrac{T^2}{2} & T \end{bmatrix}, \quad \Phi = \begin{bmatrix} 1 & T \\ 0 & 1 \end{bmatrix} \tag{2.18}$$

Chapter 7 will show an example where a two-state Kalman filter using the form given in (2.18) produces essentially the same performance as does the corresponding three-state Kalman filter. This represents one technique for Kalman filter simplification. Others will be discussed later.

2.3.5 Nonlinear Filtering

The discussion in this section so far has been limited to the linear Kalman filter, which strictly speaking is only applicable for linear systems with joint Gaussian process and measurement noise of known statistics. In practical problems it is often necessary to use nonlinear filtering because the process is described by a nonlinear state equation, or because the measurement is a nonlinear function of the system state variables. As discussed by Gelb [7], a number of nonlinear filtering techniques have been developed which are applicable to MTT. For example, the extended Kalman filter (EKF) uses the Kalman filter in a system that is linearized around the latest state estimate. The EKF provides the same form of predictions and covariance matrix as does the linear Kalman filter. For most practical purposes, the overall MTT system design problems are the same, regardless of whether a linear or nonlinear filter is used. Thus, subsequent discussions will assume use of either the linear Kalman filter or a linear constant-coefficient filter.

Finally, the covariance matrix of the standard Kalman filter (linear or EKF) does not take into account the potential error source associated with miscorrelation. Thus, in a dense multiple-target environment the standard Kalman filter can become overconfident, thus causing divergence. This problem and proposed solutions will be discussed in Chapter 4.

2.4 APPROXIMATIONS AND SIMPLIFICATIONS OF KALMAN FILTERING

The computational requirements of the Kalman filter are sometimes considered to be beyond system capability. Each Kalman filter requires matrix multiplications of order $n \times n$, where n is the order of the state vector. Also, matrix inversions of order M, where M is the measurement dimension, are required. These computations are usually required for at least three dimensions (such as the three Cartesian components x, y, z). However, the adaptivity and accuracy of the Kalman filter make it highly preferable from the performance viewpoint. Thus, considerable effort has been made to develop approximations and simplifications of the Kalman filter in an attempt to reduce computational requirements and loading without unacceptable degradation of overall tracking performance. This section discusses several of the more prominent schemes for approximating and simplifying the Kalman filter.

2.4.1 Constant Gain Filtering

Probably the simplest approximation of the Kalman filter is to use the constant gains that are obtained as the Kalman filter is allowed to reach a steady state. This approach is referred to as Weiner filtering, and, of course, it assumes that there is a steady state. This steady-state assumption may not be valid for many practical cases, such as angle tracking with changing range, or when data are missing. As an alternative to running the Kalman filter to steady state, it may be possible to find the steady-state Kalman gain and covariance from analytical expressions [3, 4, 9, 10]. Another approach is to use the Kalman filter to determine a gain table that is computed *a priori*, stored and appropriately called upon. However, we take care that use of the table does not require more computational effort and storage than the Kalman filter computations which it replaces.

2.4.2 Simplified Generation of Kalman Gains

One major objection to the use of steady-state gains is (as illustrated in [3]) the large errors which may develop for the initial tracking phases. Kalata [3] has developed a computationally convenient means of circumventing this problem.

First, Kalata solves for the steady-state gains using the tracking index as defined by

$$\Lambda = T^2 \; \frac{\sigma_w}{\sigma_o} \tag{2.19}$$

where σ_o and σ_w are the measurement noise and the system acceleration standard deviations, respectively. For example, for the α–β–γ tracker corresponding to the three-state Kalman filter, the steady-state gains are defined by (2.7) and (2.8) and the relationship (again noting the factor of $1/2$ that arises due to different definitions of the α–β–γ tracker):

$$\Lambda^2 = \frac{\gamma^2}{1-\alpha}$$

The gains for use prior to steady state are computed recursively using an exponential decay relationship.

The major problem with Kalata's method arises in the case of missing data (or a varying sampling interval). If an observation is missed (or the extrapolation period is extended), the Kalman gains will increase rather than exponentially decay to steady-state values. This is illustrated in Fig. 2-2, where it may be noted that the gain K_1 always increases after missing data.

Bridgewater [4] presents a general algorithm for recursively computing Kalman gains. With this method, changes in sampling interval, measurement noise variance, and assumed target-maneuver variance are readily incorporated into the gain calculations. This technique is applied to the $\alpha-\beta$ and $\alpha-\beta-\gamma$ trackers for random velocity and acceleration models. Steady-state expressions for $\alpha-\beta$ and $\alpha-\beta-\gamma$ trackers, which are applicable for various assumed target dynamic models, are also presented by Bridgewater [4].

The Kalata and Bridgewater methods both model the random input process noise as white, which differs from the more general correlated acceleration model of Singer. Thus, in general, a response similar to that found for a Kalman filter using Singer's model cannot be ensured. A convenient way to compare responses for various filters is through the use of covariance analysis as described in Chapter 7.

Use of Kalman filtering provides the covariance matrix whose terms are used for gating. Replacing the Kalman filter with a filter in which the gains are either constant or calculated recursively eliminates the necessity for the covariance matrix. However, a prediction variance (p_{11}) consistent with the gain can be simply computed by noting the relationships involved in the Kalman gain computation. For example, the position prediction variance consistent with the Kalman gain K_1 is found through the relationship

$$K_1 = \frac{p_{11}}{p_{11} + \sigma_o^2}$$

so that

$$p_{11} = \frac{K_1 \sigma_o^2}{1 - K_1}$$

2.4.3 Kalman Filter State Reduction

Another standard technique for simplification is to reduce the number of states (or order) of the Kalman filter. In particular, the reduction from three-state to two-state Kalman filters can lead to very significant reductions in required storage and processing time. This typically implies elimination of the acceleration state. The elimination of acceleration as a state is generally valid if only the position is measured (no derivative measurement, such as range rate, is available), and if the sampling interval is a significant fraction of the maneuver time constant. One practical way to determine the utility of the acceleration state is to compare (through simulation) acceleration estimates in the presence of a typical target maneuver with the corresponding estimates that occur due to input noise alone for a non-maneuvering target.

If random acceleration, or any other state, is eliminated as an estimated state, its effects must still be introduced into the system model. The usual technique for doing this is by introducing "state noise" in the Q matrix. Hutchinson [11] develops a technique for determining the state noise which should be used in order to minimize the estimation error variance for reduced-order filters. Chapter 7 will show how the performance of a three-state angle filter is essentially replicated by a two-state filter with the form for Q given in (2.18).

2.5 MANEUVER DETECTION AND ADAPTIVE FILTERING

The Kalman filter is determined by the assumed target kinematic model as described by (2.9). Also, the choice of parameters for any approximate or simplified filter must inherently depend upon an assumed target maneuver model or capability. When the actual target kinematics differ from the model used for filter design, mean tracking errors will develop. The Kalman filter models the target dynamics through the use of continuous random variables, statistically described by known parameters. This is exemplified by the previously discussed Singer model in which a time-correlated acceleration is used to describe the target's dynamics. The Kalman filter will provide optimum estimates of target position and velocity only if this underlying target model is correct.

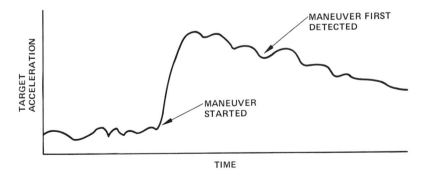

FIGURE 2-4. TYPICAL TARGET MANEUVER TIME HISTORY

Unfortunately, if the target initiates and sustains a sudden maneuver (such as a pilot-induced evasive aircraft maneuver), then this underlying statistical target model is not correct. As shown in Fig. 2-4, at the moment when the target maneuver begins, there may be a step discontinuity in acceleration. The target acceleration can be well modeled as a continuous random variable, both before and after the maneuver event, but the step acceleration input is not efficiently handled by the continuous model. Unless this type of acceleration is accounted for, the resulting time lag between the initiation and the detection of the acceleration can lead to track loss.

We will outline techniques representative of three general approaches to maneuver adaptive filtering. The first, and probably simplest, approach is to maintain the same filter form after maneuver detection, but to modify the filter parameters. With this approach, the successful development of adaptive filtering techniques would result in a filter capable of monitoring its own performance and making appropriate parameter adjustments when performance deteriorates. The second approach is to augment the filter state model upon maneuver detection. The third approach is to use multiple Kalman filters, each with a differing maneuver model, thereby the filter with the "best" output can be chosen. Alternatively, the filters' outputs may be linearly combined with coefficients given by the calculated *a posteriori* probabilities of each maneuver model being the correct model. Finally, this section closes with a brief discussion of a method for adaptive noise estimation, but first we will discuss the additional problems posed for adaptive filtering by a dense multiple-target environment.

Several practical problems, not usually mentioned in the filtering literature, arise in the application of maneuver detection and adaptive filtering techniques to the dense multiple-target environment. These problems may lead to premature track loss. The first of these problems is that an incorrect correlation with an observation which is not from the target in track can trigger the maneuver detector. Then, the tracking filter typically will be implemented so that it responds quickly to the incorrect observation. A similar situation can occur due to a false observation from noise or from a corrupting source such as jet engine modulation (JEM) found in the aircraft tracking problem [12].

A second problem associated with using maneuver detection in the presence of potential miscorrelation is that a detected maneuver typically is used to increase the covariances for a Kalman filtering system. Then, because gating is usually carried out by using covariance terms, the probability of a false observation falling within the association gates increases on scans subsequent to the detected maneuver. Again, miscorrelation and rapid response to a false observation can lead to further miscorrelation and eventual track loss.

The best solution to these problems is to maintain two tracks with parallel filters after target maneuver detection. Then, the ambiguity can be resolved when more data are received. This solution is termed track splitting (or branching), which is discussed in Chapter 4. The methods discussed below in which filter modifications are made can be applied to one branch of a split (or bifurcated) track. Finally, maneuver detection should probably only be attempted under conditions that are relatively free from miscorrelation. Techniques for obtaining estimates of the probability of miscorrelation, which can be used to determine the feasibility of maneuver detection, are presented in Chapter 7.

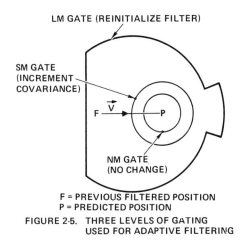

F = PREVIOUS FILTERED POSITION
P = PREDICTED POSITION
FIGURE 2-5.   THREE LEVELS OF GATING
USED FOR ADAPTIVE FILTERING

2.5.1   Maneuver Detection and Parameter Adjustment

Probably the simplest form of maneuver adaptive filtering is by the use of two or more correlation regions. The filtering parameters are then determined (or adjusted) by the region (or gate) that the correlating observation falls within. For example, a ship tracking system, developed by Hughes Aircraft Company and implemented as part of a Navy-sponsored research and development effort, defined three levels of gating and filter adjustment. The technique demonstrated successful performance in spite of rather long (one- to two-hour) sampling intervals. For this system, observation-to-track pairings that indicated little or no maneuver (NM) led to no Kalman filter adjustment. Small-maneuver (SM) pairings led to increases in the elements of the Kalman covariance matrix but no modification of the state variable estimates. A large-maneuver (LM) gate was defined based on a single-turn assumption and constraints on target dynamics. Then, when the LM gate, but not the NM or SM gates, was satisfied, the filter was reinitiated using the last two data points. This is the simplest method for decreasing the effects of the time lag between the initiation and the detection of target maneuver. Figure 2-5 illustrates the form of the three gates. The manner in which the LM gate was formed will be discussed in Chapter 4.

Another method for maneuver detection is to examine the time history of the residual. With the use of Kalman filtering a generalized form of the distance function d^2, discussed in Chapter 1, can be formed from the residual vector $\tilde{y}(k)$, and the residual covariance matrix S,

$$d^2(k) = \tilde{y}^T(k) \, S^{-1} \, \tilde{y}(k)$$

where

$$\tilde{y}(k) = y(k) - H\,\hat{x}(k|k-1)$$
$$S = S(k|k-1) = HP(k|k-1)\,H^T + R_c$$

$P(k|k-1)$ = one step prediction covariance matrix

R_c = measurement noise covariance matrix

The quantity $d^2(k)$ has a chi-square (χ_M^2) probability distribution with M degrees of freedom, where M is the measurement dimension. Thus, $d^2(k)$ can be monitored in comparison to a threshold determined by the χ_M^2 distribution. This technique will be discussed in more detail in Chapter 6.

For airborne radar tracking systems that have accurate Doppler (range rate) measurement capability, changes in target range rate may be used for maneuver detection. However, as discussed by Nelson [12], care must be taken in the presence of JEM.

Reference [13] outlines a simple maneuver detection technique based upon the range rate residual and using the suboptimum maneuver detection method given in [14]. Once maneuver is detected, the sampling (or update) interval can be reduced for an electronically scanned antenna [13]. Also, the elements of the covariance matrix are increased and a filter model assuming larger target acceleration capability is used. When the detectors indicate that the target has ceased to maneuver, the nominal target acceleration model is restored. Simulation results have shown the technique to successfully track targets that performed maneuvers with acceleration up to $6g$.

The problem associated with the maneuver adaptive filtering approach discussed above is that, as illustrated in Fig. 2-4, there may be a significant lag between the time when the maneuver begins and when it is detected. Then, the adaptation to the maneuver through the choice of more responsive filter parameters may not occur until large tracking errors have already developed. Thus, other approaches have been proposed in which, in addition to adapting filter parameters, there is a correction of the past effects of the acceleration.

Chan [15] defines a method for estimating the target input acceleration and updating the filter using the effects of the estimated acceleration. Thus, using this approach there may be a lag in detection, but, once detection occurs, an estimate of the cumulative effect of the acceleration is applied to the filter state estimates. Other techniques that effectively apply filter correction as well as adaptation are discussed below.

2.5.2 Maneuver Detection and State Augmentation

Bar-Shalom and Birmiwal [16] have developed an algorithm in which a different state model is used by the filter upon maneuver detection. Before maneuver detection, an essentially constant velocity target model is assumed. After maneuver detection, tracking is performed with an augmented state model that uses an acceleration state. This method requires the storage of previous measurements, which are used for filter reinitialization after maneuver detection. The augmented state model is used until the magnitude of the acceleration estimate is determined to be insignificant, when use of the initial state model is resumed. In addition to a full development of this method and comparative performance results, Bar-Shalom and Birmiwal also discuss other techniques and present an extensive list of references.

By storing past measurements, this method anticipates the effects of a delay between the time when a maneuver begins and when it is detected. Then, if a maneuver is detected at scan k the filter is reinitiated (using the past stored data) at scan $k-\Delta-1$, where Δ is the effective lag time associated with the detector.

2.5.3 Use of Several Parallel Filters

Starting with Magill [17], a number of methods (including those in [18], [19], and [20]) have been proposed based on the use of several target state models. The measurement data are used to decide upon the appropriate model or to obtain a "best" composite estimate based upon a statistical weighting. This approach typically requires the maintenance of several Kalman filters operating in parallel and the maintenance of concurrent *a posteriori* estimates of the relative validity of these filter models. These probability calculations are usually based upon application of Bayes' rule.

Figure 2-6 illustrates the method by showing a bank of N parallel Kalman filters. Each filter utilizes a different process model, and each filter operates simultaneously on the measurement sequence. Thus, there are effectively N hypothesized target state estimation vectors.

One implementation of parallel filters uses a different assumed maneuver model for each filter. For example, the simplest approach is to have just two filters in which one filter assumes essentially straight-line motion, while the other is matched to a worst case maneuver condition [18]. The non-maneuver case is assumed until a detector is triggered and the switch is made to the filter with maneuver following ability. For an ESA system the sampling rate can also be increased at the same time that the more responsive filter is used. Thus, using this approach, upon maneuver detection, adaptation and correction are effectively applied together by switching to a more responsive filter whose output will be more representative of the true target state.

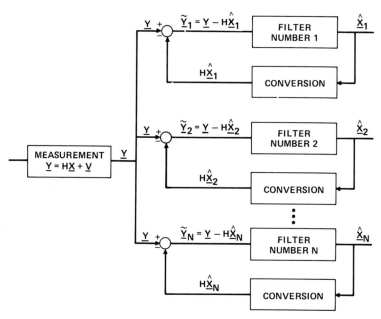

FIGURE 2-6. BANK OF N PARALLEL FILTERS

An alternative bank of N filters might be implemented to model an acceleration that could have been initiated at any one of N discrete times in the past. In this case, the maneuver characteristics are governed by the starting time of the maneuver and the N hypotheses refers to the times of maneuver initiation. McAulay and Denlinger [14] present a version of this method that operates on the Kalman filter residual sequence to determine the time at which the maneuver was initiated.

2.5.4 Adaptive Measurement Noise Estimation

A convenient method for adaptive estimation of the measurement noise variance has been developed [21]. The technique involves the use of recursive equations that can be computed in conjunction with the Kalman filtering equations. With this method, an updated estimate of the observation variance is obtained at each measurement $\hat{\sigma}_o^2 = \hat{\nu}\ \sigma_{oN}^2$ where σ_{oN}^2 is the initial (nominal) estimate. Initially, $\hat{\nu}$ is chosen to be unity, and a new estimate of $\hat{\nu}$ is obtained at each measurement through the relationship (assuming one-dimensional observation y) derived in [21]:

$$\hat{\nu}(k+1) = \frac{\hat{\nu}(k)}{\nu+1} \left\{ \nu + \frac{[y(k) - H\ \hat{x}\ (k|k-1)]^2}{H\ P\ (k|k-1)\ H^T + \hat{\nu}\ (k)\ \sigma_{oN}^2} \right\}$$

The parameter ν is set to some initial value ν_o and incremented by one each time another observation is used. Suggested values for ν_o range from 10 for a good initial estimate of noise variance to 2 for a poor initial estimate.

Finally, as with maneuver detection, it is to be expected that adaptive noise estimation will suffer in the presence of miscorrelation. Also, problems would be expected in the presence of mismatch between true and assumed target maneuver models.

2.6 SUMMARY AND CONCLUSIONS

The choice of methods for filtering and prediction is usually the first task facing the designer of an MTT system, and an overwhelming variety of approaches exist. Experience with airborne radar systems has shown the versatility of Kalman filters to be almost indispensable when dealing with the problems presented by missing data, variable measurement noise statistics, and maneuvering targets with variable dynamic capabilities. If possible, reduced-state Kalman filters should be used. For example, before a designer proposes a three-state Kalman filter, including an acceleration state, he should ascertain that the data rate is high enough to allow an accurate estimate of acceleration.

Fixed-coefficient filters may be required as a result of computational limitations if the sampling interval is short or if many targets must be handled. Problems associated with transient response and missing data must be expected unless some adaptive gain calculations are performed. However, the closed-form expressions for tracking performance with $\alpha-\beta$ and $\alpha-\beta-\gamma$ trackers, given above, are often useful in preliminary design and performance prediction, even if Kalman filters are eventually used.

Much analysis has been performed to develop techniques for adaptive filtering in the presence of variable target maneuver capability and measurement noise. An outline of some of these methods has been given, but the applicability of maneuver detection and adaptive filtering is very questionable in the presence of miscorrelation. Incorrect correlation can result from other target returns in a dense environment or from extraneous observations such as produced by aircraft JEM. These incorrect correlations can then "trigger" the maneuver detector, which leads to more weight being assigned to incorrect data.

Tracking performance with even the best designed filter may become very degraded in the presence of miscorrelation. The effects of miscorrelation can completely invalidate the Kalman filter covariance and lead to divergence [22]. Thus, for tracking in a dense multiple-target environment, the emphasis should be on developing correlation logic. The filtering techniques should be kept as simple as possible in order to accommodate the computational requirements of data association.

REFERENCES

1. Benedict, T., and G. Bordner, "Synthesis of an Optimal Set of Radar Track-While-Scan Smoothing Equations," *IRE Transactions on Automatic Control*, AC-7, July 1962, pp. 27–32.

2. Simpson, H.R., "Performance Measures and Optimization Conditions for a Third-Order Sampled Data Tracker," *IEEE Transactions on Automatic Control*, AC-8, April 1983, pp. 182–183.

3. Kalata, P.R., "The Tracking Index: A Generalized Parameter for α–β and α–β–γ Target Trackers," *IEEE Transactions on Aerospace and Electronic Systems*, AES-20, March 1984, pp. 174–182.

4. Bridgewater, A.W., "Analysis of Second and Third Order Steady-State Tracking Filters," *AGARD Conference Proceedings No. 252, Strategies for Automatic Track Initiation*, Monterey, CA, Oct. 1978, pp. 9–1 to 9–11.

5. Lefferts, R.E., "Adaptive Correlation Regions for Alpha-Beta Tracking Filters," *IEEE Transactions on Aerospace and Electronic Systems*, AES-17, Nov. 1981, pp. 738–747.

6. Kanyuck, A.J., "Transient Response of Tracking Filters with Randomly Interrupted Data," *IEEE Transactions on Aerospace and Electronic Systems*, AES-6, May 1970, pp. 313–323.

7. Gelb, A., *Applied Optimal Estimation*, Cambridge, MA: MIT Press, 1974.

8. Singer, R.A., "Estimating Optimal Tracking Filter Performance for Manned Maneuvering Targets," *IEEE Transactions on Aerospace and Electronic Systems*, AES-5, July 1970, pp. 473–483.

9. Fitzgerald, R.J., "Simple Tracking Filters: Closed-Form Solutions," *IEEE Transactions on Aerospace and Electronic Systems*, AES-17, Nov. 1981, pp. 781–784.

10. Ramachandra, K.V., "Analytical Results for a Kalman Tracker Using Position and Rate Measurements," *IEEE Transactions on Aerospace and Electronic Systems*," AES-19, Sept. 1983, pp. 776–778.

11. Hutchinson, C.E., J.A. D'Appolito, and K.J. Roy, "Applications of Minimum-Variance Reduced-State Estimators," *IEEE Transactions on Aerospace and Electronic Systems*, AES-11, Sept. 1975, pp. 785–794.

12. Nelson, N., "Aircraft Tracking Problems from Range Rate Turbine Modulation," *NAECON '77 Proceedings of the National Aerospace and Electronics Conference*, Dayton, OH, May 17–19, 1977, pp. 679–682.

13. Blackman, S.S., T.J. Broida, and M.F. Cartier, "Applications of a Phased Array Antenna in a Multiple Maneuvering Target Environment," *Proceedings of the 1981 IEEE Conference on Decision and Control*, San Diego, CA, Dec. 16–18, 1981, pp. 1413–1418.

14. McAulay, R., and E. Denlinger, "A Decision-Directed Adaptive Tracker," *IEEE Transactions on Aerospace and Electronic Systems*, AES-9, March 1973, pp. 229–236.

15. Chan, Y.T., A.G.C. Hu, and J.B. Plant, "A Kalman Filter Based Tracking Scheme with Input Estimation," *IEEE Transactions on Aerospace and Electronic Systems*, AES-15, March 1979, pp. 237–244.

16. Bar-Shalom, Y., and K. Birmiwal, "Variable-Dimension Filter for Maneuvering Target Tracking," *IEEE Transactions on Aerospace and Electronic Systems*, AES-18, Sept. 1982, pp. 621–629.

17. Magill, D.T., "Optimal Adaptive Estimation of Sampled Stochastic Processes," *IEEE Transactions on Automatic Control*, AC-10, Oct. 1965, pp. 434–439.

18. Van Keuk, G., "Adaptive Computer Controlled Target Tracking with a Phased Array Radar," *Proceedings of the 1975 IEEE International Radar Conference*, Arlington, VA, April 21–23, 1975, pp. 429–434.

19. Thorp, J.S., "Optimal Tracking of Maneuvering Targets," *IEEE Transactions on Aerospace and Electronic Systems*, AES-9, July 1973, pp. 512–519.

20. Gholson, N.M., and E.L. Moose, "Maneuvering Target Tracking Using Adaptive-State Estimation," *IEEE Transactions on Aerospace and Electronic Systems*, AES-13, May 1977, pp. 310–317.

21. Smith, G.L., "Sequential Estimation of Observation Error Variances in a Trajectory Estimation Problem," *AIAA Journal*, Vol. 5, Nov. 1967, pp. 1964–1970.

22. Singer, R.A., and J.J. Stein, "An Optimal Tracking Filter for Processing Sensor Data of Imprecisely Determined Origin in Surveillance Systems," *Proceedings of the 1971 IEEE Conference on Decision and Control*, Miami Beach, FL, Dec. 1971, pp. 171–175.

Appendix 2A*

Relationship Between Equivalent Noise Bandwidth
and Acceleration Error Constant

This appendix shows how the dynamic response for the α–β tracker can be related to noise bandwidth performance as measured by an equivalent noise bandwidth. First, the input noise variance is represented

$$\sigma_o^2 = \frac{N_o}{T}$$

where N_o is the spectral density for the input noise. Similarly, the output noise variance ($\sigma_{x_s}^2$) is represented in terms of an equivalent noise bandwidth B_n as

$$\sigma_{x_s}^2 = B_n \, N_o$$

so that the variance reduction ratio defined in the text becomes

$$K_x = \frac{\sigma_{x_s}^2}{\sigma_o^2} = B_n \, T \tag{2A.1}$$

Thus, solving (2A.1) and (2.2) for B_n gives

$$B_n = \frac{K_x}{T} = \frac{1}{T} \frac{[2\alpha^2 + \beta \, (2 - 3\alpha)]}{\alpha \, [4 - \beta - 2\alpha]}$$

Finally, using the relationship of Benedict and Bordner:

$$\beta = \alpha^2 / (2 - \alpha) \tag{2A.2}$$

gives

$$B_n = \frac{1}{T} \left[\frac{\alpha \, (6 - 5\alpha)}{\alpha^2 - 8\alpha + 8} \right] \tag{2A.3}$$

Next, define an acceleration error constant k_a in terms of the steady-state error, given by (2.3), of the α–β tracker in response to an acceleration input:

$$\lim_{k \to \infty} [x \, (k) - x_s \, (k)] = \frac{\ddot{x}}{k_a} = \frac{(1 - \alpha) \, T^2 \, \ddot{x}}{\beta} \tag{2A.4}$$

Combining (2A.3) and (2A.4) and using (2A.2) gives a relationship between the equivalent noise bandwidth and the acceleration error constant:

$$B_n = \sqrt{k_a} f(a)$$

where

$$f(\alpha) = \frac{(6 - 5\alpha) \sqrt{(2 - \alpha)(1 - \alpha)}}{\alpha^2 - 8\alpha + 8}$$

Typical values for $f(\alpha)$ range from 0.998 for $\alpha = 0.1$ to 0.22 for $\alpha = 0.95$. A representative intermediate value is 0.63 for $\alpha = 0.6$.

*This appendix contributed by Dr. H.D. Washburn.

Chapter 3

Choice of Tracking Coordinate System and Filtering State Variables

3.1 INTRODUCTION

In this chapter, a discrete formulation of the continuous state equations is presented and the considerations involved in choosing tracking coordinates are discussed. Several coordinate systems and sets of state variables that have been implemented for multiple-target tracking (MTT) are presented.

Section 3.2 considers the discrete formulation of the continuous linear state equation. For moving platforms, and in particular for airborne radar, the solution should contain terms to compensate for own-ship* motion.

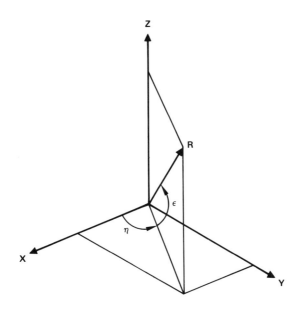

FIGURE 3-1. SPHERICAL POLAR AND CARTESIAN
COORDINATE SYSTEMS

---

*The term "own-ship" refers to "our own airplane."

A number of coordinate systems have been utilized for MTT. Two commonly used systems, spherical polar and Cartesian coordinates, are illustrated in Fig. 3-1. The spherical coordinate system is defined by the range and two angles (azimuth (η) and elevation (ϵ)) with respect to the Cartesian (x, y, z) axes so that

$$x = R\cos\epsilon\cos\eta, \quad y = R\cos\epsilon\sin\eta, \quad z = R\sin\epsilon$$

An alternative type of polar coordinate system, discussed in Section 3.5, defines the range vector with respect to the Cartesian coordinates by using the three direction cosines.

It is preferable to use a non-rotating (or inertial) coordinate system so that the multiple target tracks can be processed with respect to the same fixed reference. Thus, Section 3.3 discusses the transformation to the North-East-Down (NED) coordinate system that is convenient for airborne radar MTT systems. For airborne radar MTT applications the NED coordinate system can practically be considered inertial.

Section 3.4 discusses tracking in Cartesian coordinates. The use of Cartesian coordinates is convenient for target extrapolation, but coupling between filters is introduced by the form of the radar measurement. Section 3.5 discusses several types of polar coordinates that have been considered and Section 3.6 presents results from a study comparing angle tracking performance derived using three polar coordinate angle tracking methods. Finally, Section 3.7 gives a brief overview discussion of systems that have been proposed for tracking when range and range rate measurements are unavailable.

Because of computational constraints, many MTT systems require relatively simple filtering schemes. This is particularly true for airborne radar systems, but such may not be the case for some other applications, such as sonar [1], where more time and more computational capabilities may be available. A requirement for simple filters implies the desirability of uncoupled filtering in which independent tracking is performed in each coordinate. For example, a particularly desirable simple filtering system for use with Cartesian coordinates would employ independent two-state (position and velocity) filters in each of the three components (x, y, z).

Less accurate filtering may result if independent, uncoupled filters are used when the dynamics or the measurement noise are not independent in each tracking coordinate. For example, radar measurements — usually consisting of range, azimuth, and elevation angles — when transformed to x, y, and z components, are not independent in a Cartesian coordinate system. This implies that it would be preferable to use one six-state (x, v_x, y, v_y, z, v_z) filter rather than three two-state filters. However, the computational requirements for a six-state filter are generally much greater than the requirements for three two-state filters. Thus, a trade-off between potential performance loss and computational requirements exists.

When considering the choice of a tracking system, note that experience with filtering and prediction in MTT systems indicates the primary source of error to be miscorrelation. This motivates allocation of most computing resources to the improvement of correlation performance. Thus, the discussion in this chapter will emphasize tracking coordinates for use with linear, uncoupled filters, which minimize computational requirements for the filtering and prediction functions of MTT.

3.2 SOLUTION OF CONTINUOUS LINEAR STATE EQUATION

The first step in defining a Kalman filter is to represent the system dynamics by a continuous linear state equation. The usual desired form is

$$\dot{x}(t) = A(t)\,x(t) + G(t)\,w(t) + L(t)\,u(t) \tag{3.1}$$

where $x(t)$ is the system state vector, $w(t)$ is the random forcing function, $u(t)$ is a deterministic input (typically due to own-ship motion), and $A(t)$, $G(t)$, and $L(t)$ are known matrices arising in the formulation. Section 3.5.2 shows in detail how the form of (3.1) is derived for a specific example. Here, we briefly outline techniques for solution of (3.1). References [2, 3] present more complete discussions.

We wish to put the continuous Equation (3.1) into the discrete form,

$$x(k + 1) = \Phi x(k) + \psi w(k) + f(k + 1|k) \tag{3.2}$$

where $w(k)$ and $f(k + 1|k)$ are the contributions from the random forcing function and the deterministic input, respectively, and Φ is the transition matrix. The general solution of (3.1) for $x(t)$ given the value $x(t_o)$ at initial time t_o is

$$x(t) = \Phi(t,t_o)\,x(t_o) + \int_{t_o}^{t} \Phi(t,\tau)\,[G(\tau)w(\tau) + L(\tau)u(\tau)]\,d\tau$$

Defining T to be the sampling interval, choose $t = (k + 1)T$, $t_o = kT$ and assume stationarity, so that [2]:

$$\Phi(t,t_o) = \Phi(t - t_o) = \Phi(T)$$

Also, assuming stationarity, the limits of integration can be set to 0 and T, so that, as a first step in the discrete formulation of (3.1), we have

$$x(k + 1) = \Phi(T)x(k) + \int_{0}^{T} \Phi(T - \tau)\,[G(\tau)w(\tau) + L(\tau)u(\tau)]\,d\tau$$

Again under the assumption of stationarity, the transition matrix can be expressed in terms of the matrix exponential. Then, an expansion can be performed to give an approximate solution:

$$\Phi(T) = e^{AT} \cong I + AT + \frac{A^2 T^2}{2} + \ldots \tag{3.3}$$

The expansion given by (3.3) will be used in this book. However, two other methods, outlined below, can sometimes provide convenient closed form expressions without requiring the assumption of stationarity. First, following [3], upon taking the Laplace transformation of $A(t)$ to obtain $A(s)$, $\Phi(T)$ may be obtained by taking the inverse Laplace transform ($\mathscr{L}^{-1}$) of the following expression:

$$\Phi(T) = \mathscr{L}^{-1} [sI - A(s)]^{-1} \Big|_{t = T}$$

Second, a convenient solution for the elements of the transition matrix can sometimes also be obtained by solving the equation:

$$\frac{d\Phi(t, t_o)}{dt} = A(t)\, \Phi(t, t_o) \tag{3.4}$$

The solution of (3.4) is obtained by setting the arbitrary reference time (t_o) to zero and using the condition that $\Phi(t, t) = I$. Finally, upon solution of (3.4), the sampling interval T is used for t.

Solution for the deterministic input is given by

$$f(k + 1|k) = \int_0^T \Phi(T - \tau)\, L(\tau)\, u(\tau)\, d\tau$$

The vector $f(k + 1|k)$ is typically due to compensation for own-ship acceleration, which is assumed constant over the sampling interval, or a shorter time period may be defined for updating f. Thus, taking L to be a constant matrix, assuming constant input ($u(\tau) \cong u(k)$) and expanding $\Phi(t - \tau)$ gives

$$f(k + 1|k) \cong \left[\int_0^T [I + A(T - \tau)]d\tau \right] Lu(k) = \left[IT + \frac{AT^2}{2} \right] Lu(k) \tag{3.5}$$

A similar approach may also be taken in order to obtain the solution ($\psi w(k)$) for the random input. (For notational convenience, we use $q(k) \overset{\triangle}{=} \psi w(k)$ in the rest of this book.) However, Markov processes are typically assumed so that the exact solution can be obtained directly, as discussed in Chapter 2, and as will be done for the examples in this chapter.

3.3   NORTH-EAST-DOWN (NED) COORDINATE SYSTEM

The NED coordinate system, shown in Fig. 3-2, is particularly useful for airborne systems, but it is also applicable for surface (ground or ship based) tracking systems. As shown in Fig. 3-2, the origin of an aircraft tracking system is the own-ship position. Then, the axes are determined by the north direction and the down direction pointing to the center of the earth. The east direction is the direction perpendicular to the north and down axes.

Note that the NED system is not strictly an inertial system for a moving platform because the platform axes are slowly changing their orientation in space as the vehicle moves over the earth's surface. However, except near the North Pole, the effects of the rotations are negligible, and the NED system is essentially inertial for aircraft platforms.

Radar measurements typically give the target range and angles with respect to the antenna boresight axes. However, the antenna boresight axes will be rotating as a result of changes in aircraft orientation. A convenient way of representing the angular measurements is to convert to direction cosines (Λ_N, Λ_E, Λ_D) with respect to the NED system. In order to perform this conversion to direction cosines, it is necessary to transform through five angles representing aircraft and antenna orientation. These angles are aircraft heading (ψ), aircraft pitch (θ), aircraft roll (ϕ), antenna azimuth (η_a), and antenna elevation (ϵ_a). The resulting transformation from the antenna coordinate system where the target is located along the range axis to the NED system is

$$
\begin{pmatrix} \Lambda_N \\ \Lambda_E \\ \Lambda_D \end{pmatrix} = T_1\, T_2\, T_3\, T_4\, T_5 \begin{pmatrix} 1 \\ 0 \\ 0 \end{pmatrix}
$$

where

$$
T_1 = \begin{pmatrix} \cos\psi & -\sin\psi & 0 \\ \sin\psi & \cos\psi & 0 \\ 0 & 0 & 1 \end{pmatrix}, \quad
T_2 = \begin{pmatrix} \cos\theta & 0 & \sin\theta \\ 0 & 1 & 0 \\ -\sin\theta & 0 & \cos\theta \end{pmatrix},
$$

$$
T_3 = \begin{pmatrix} 1 & 0 & 0 \\ 0 & \cos\phi & -\sin\phi \\ 0 & \sin\phi & \cos\phi \end{pmatrix}, \quad
T_4 = \begin{pmatrix} \cos\eta_a & -\sin\eta_a & 0 \\ \sin\eta_a & \cos\eta_a & 0 \\ 0 & 0 & 1 \end{pmatrix},
$$

$$
T_5 = \begin{pmatrix} \cos\epsilon_a & 0 & \sin\epsilon_a \\ 0 & 1 & 0 \\ -\sin\epsilon_a & 0 & \cos\epsilon_a \end{pmatrix}
$$

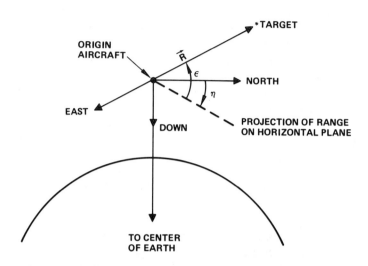

FIGURE 3-2. AIRCRAFT CENTERED INERTIAL (NED) COORDINATE SYSTEM

Target angular position with respect to the NED coordinate system can also be conveniently specified by the stabilized azimuth (η) and elevation (ϵ) angles shown in Fig. 3-2. These angles can be computed from the direction cosines using the relationships:

$$\epsilon = -\sin^{-1} \Lambda_D, \quad \eta = \tan^{-1} (\Lambda_E / \Lambda_N) \tag{3.6}$$

Given that tracking is to be performed with reference to the NED coordinate frame, there are at least three sets of tracking states which can be used. The first coordinate system for consideration is the Cartesian in which position components (R_N, R_E, R_D) along the NED axes are used as states. Conversion from the radar measurement parameters to these components is carried out through the relationships:

$$R_N = R\Lambda_N, \quad R_E = R\Lambda_E, \quad R_D = R\Lambda_D$$

Also, two forms of polar coordinate systems have been used. Both forms use one tracking filter with states for range, range rate, and possibly range acceleration. Then, additional filters are used to track either the three direction cosines or the two stabilized angles (ϵ, η). The latter method eliminates the redundancy associated with the use of four tracking filters (radial and three directional cosines), but may require computation of the inverse trigonometric functions given by (3.6). The next three sections (Sec. 3.4 to 3.6) discuss these filters in more detail.

3.4 TRACKING IN CARTESIAN COORDINATES

Tracking in Cartesian coordinates has the advantage of allowing the use of linear target dynamic models for extrapolation. For example, given estimates of target velocity and acceleration, the Cartesian target x position prediction can be computed from the simple linear equation:

$$x(k + 1) = x(k) + T\, v_x(k) + \frac{T^2}{2}\, a_x(k)$$

As will be discussed in the next section, the use of polar coordinates may lead to more complicated extrapolation.

The use of Cartesian coordinates has two major disadvantages. The first is that measured (or estimated) range must be available in order to transform the measurements to the Cartesian coordinates. However, measured range is not always available, as for the case of infrared (IR) sensors. This can present a problem for multiple-sensor systems using Cartesian coordinates. Also, the use of electronic countermeasures (ECM) may deny the radar range measurement.

A second disadvantage with Cartesian coordinates is that measurement errors are coupled. Consider, for example, a two-dimensional radar system that measures range (R_o) and azimuth angle (η_o), and tracks in the x, y Cartesian coordinate system. The measurements are formed through the equations:

$$x_o = R_o \cos\eta_o, \quad y_o = R_o \sin\eta_o$$

Then, the measurement covariance matrix is

$$R_c = \begin{bmatrix} \sigma_{x_o}^2 & \sigma_{x_o y_o}^2 \\ \sigma_{x_o y_o}^2 & \sigma_{y_o}^2 \end{bmatrix} \tag{3.7}$$

where, using a first order expansion,

$$\sigma_{x_o}^2 = \sigma_{R_o}^2 \cos^2\eta + R^2 \sin^2\eta\, \sigma_{\eta_o}^2$$

$$\sigma_{y_o}^2 = \sigma_{R_o}^2 \sin^2\eta + R^2 \cos^2\eta\, \sigma_{\eta_o}^2$$

$$\sigma_{x_o y_o}^2 = \frac{1}{2} \sin 2\eta \left[\sigma_{R_o}^2 - R^2 \sigma_{\eta_o}^2 \right]$$

$\sigma_{R_o}^2, \sigma_{\eta_o}^2$ = range and azimuth angle measurement variances, respectively.

As shown in (3.7) the radar measurements expressed in the Cartesian coordinates (x, y) are not independent. The non-zero value for $\sigma^2_{x_o y_o}$ that occurs for η other than zero (or any multiple of $\pi/2$) implies a coupling in the measurement, which preferably would require coupled filtering, and may involve use of the extended Kalman filter. In other words, the use of independent filters in the x and y coordinates may lead to less accurate filtering than would occur if a coupled four-state (x, v_x, y, v_y) or six-state filter were used.

Reference [4] discusses the coupled four-state filter and shows that gains and covariance values can be computed by using the appropriate transformations of quantities derived from the uncoupled filters. The gains are computed in an uncoupled system (in which $\eta = 0$) and are transformed to the coupled system. However, the computations are fairly involved and require an estimate of the azimuth angle.

References [5, 6] discuss the extension to three dimensions with measured target range, and azimuth and elevation angles. Again, the approach is to determine the Kalman gains in a system where there is no coupling. Using this approach, the gains are computed using three separate (i.e., decoupled) three-state trackers. Then, the gains and the covariance matrices from the decoupled system are transformed for use in the coupled system. Baheti [6] presents results in which performance using this approximate method is found to be very close to the performance from a system employing an extended Kalman filter that includes the full coupling. Finally, Fitzgerald [7] gives a concise summary of the techniques involved, and the required matrix transformation equations for two and three dimensions.

A further discussion of the use of Cartesian coordinate system filtering is presented by Brammer [8]. First, the author states that the use of two-state Kalman filters has been justified by the practical results obtained. Also, results are presented which indicate that the effects of ignoring the coupling are negligible. Thus, a strong argument can be made that uncoupled two-state filters may be adequate for most systems. Then, if simple filtering systems are used, the primary allocation of computational resources can be made for the data association aspects of MTT.

3.5 POLAR COORDINATE SYSTEMS*

Using polar coordinates allows tracking to be performed in the same system from which the radar measurements are obtained. Also, if the measured range rate is available, it can be used directly in the range filter. There will be a range filter and, if azimuth and elevation angles are used,

---

*Techniques discussed in this section have been developed jointly by Dr. J.J. Stein, Dr. J.B. Pearson, Mr. D.M. Peller, and the author.

there will also be two angle filters. If direction cosines are used, there will be three angle filters. The range filter is defined in a straightforward manner, but the choice of angle filters is more difficult.

The most direct choice of polar coordinate angle filtering states would be angle, angle rate, and possibly angle acceleration. This set of states could be used for azimuth and elevation angles or for direction cosines. However, nonlinearities arise in the sense that a constant velocity target may not produce a constant angle rate (or even acceleration). Thus, in order for the filter to match the system dynamics, higher order derivatives are required in the system model, even for non-maneuvering targets. The introduction of these "pseudo-accelerations" makes accurate extrapolation difficult because estimates of these higher order derivatives are required.

An angle tracking filter using angle, angle rate, and angle acceleration can be derived by an adaptation of the Singer model, discussed in Chapter 2, to the angular states. The adaptation is that the magnitude of the angular acceleration is range dependent. Unfortunately, results presented in the next section show that accuracy is degraded by the higher order derivatives which arise in this system.

To alleviate the problems associated with the system angular dynamics, two other sets of angular tracking states have been developed and will be discussed below. The resulting angle tracking filters require the use of range and range rate estimates, which are taken from the range tracker and which are effectively assumed to be known constants, in the transition matrices. An alternative is to convert to Cartesian coordinates for extrapolation [9]. The following discussion begins with range filtering, and then two angle tracking filters are presented.

3.5.1 Range, Range Rate Filtering

The range direction filter will use range, range rate, and usually range acceleration as states. The Singer model can be used for range acceleration. The derivation, presented in Appendix 3A, leads to the Kalman filter defined by the state vector and transition matrix:

$$
x_R = \begin{bmatrix} R \\ v_R \\ a_R \end{bmatrix}, \quad
\Phi_R = \begin{bmatrix}
1 + \dfrac{\omega_p^2 T^2}{2} & T & \dfrac{T^2}{2} \\[2ex]
\omega_p^2 T & 1 + \dfrac{\omega_p^2 T^2}{2} & T\left(1 - \dfrac{\beta_R T}{2}\right) \\[2ex]
0 & 0 & \rho_{aR}
\end{bmatrix}
$$

where the symbols v_R and a_R have replaced $\dot{R}$ and $\ddot{R}$. The correlation coefficient is defined by $\rho_{aR} = e^{-\beta_R T}$ where $\beta_R = 1/\tau_R$ is the inverse of the maneuver time constant. Also, ω_p^2 is the square of the angular rate perpendicular to the line-of-sight vector to the target. As discussed below, it is defined in terms of quantities that are taken from the angle filters.

The random driving matrix Q is as given in (2.17) for the Singer model, while the measurement matrix is

$$H = \begin{cases} \begin{bmatrix} 1 & 0 & 0 \end{bmatrix} & \text{, range rate observation not available} \\[2ex] \begin{bmatrix} 1 & 0 & 0 \\ 0 & 1 & 0 \end{bmatrix} & \text{, range rate observation available} \end{cases}$$

Finally, the deterministic driving vector (f_R) expresses the contribution due to own-ship acceleration in the radial direction (a_{IR}):

$$f_R = \begin{bmatrix} \dfrac{-T^2}{2} a_{IR} \\[2ex] -T \, a_{IR} \\[2ex] 0 \end{bmatrix}$$

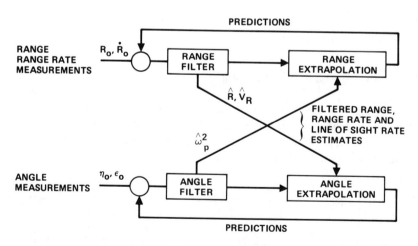

FIGURE 3-3. PROCESSING FLOW CHART FOR COUPLED RANGE AND ANGLE FILTERS

The polar coordinate systems discussed in this section eliminate the requirement for higher order derivatives in the prediction at the cost of introducing a coupling between range and angle that arises during the extrapolation. This coupling is shown by the term ω_p^2 in the range filter transition matrix, and it also arises in terms involving range and range rate, which will be shown to appear in the angle filter transition matrices. Figure 3-3 illustrates the manner in which the filtered quantities are exchanged and used for extrapolation. Next, we present the form of two angle filters that are useful for radar MTT systems.

3.5.2 The Direction Cosine, Velocity, Acceleration (ΛVA) Filter

The direction cosine (Λ) is defined in terms of a component of target position (d) in the north, east, or down direction, and the range (R):

$$\Lambda = d/R \tag{3.8}$$

In order to derive the state equation form given in (3.1), we differentiate (3.8) and define $v \triangleq \dot{d}$, so that

$$\dot{\Lambda} = \dot{d}/R - \dot{R}d/R^2 = v/R - \dot{R}\Lambda/R \tag{3.9}$$

The relative velocity v is composed of two components:

$$v = v_T - v_I$$

where v_T is the target velocity and v_I is the own-ship velocity. Then, assuming the acceleration also to be composed of target (a_T) and own-ship (a_I) components

$$\dot{v} = a_T - a_I \tag{3.10}$$

Finally, following the Singer model discussed in Chapter 2, assume a first-order Markov target acceleration model,

$$\dot{a}_T = -\beta\, a_T + w \tag{3.11}$$

Choose for the state estimation vector x:

$$x = \begin{bmatrix} \Lambda \\ v \\ a_T \end{bmatrix}$$

Using (3.9) through (3.11) and defining $v_R \triangleq \dot{R}$, the state equation for this application becomes

$$\begin{bmatrix} \dot{\Lambda} \\ \dot{v} \\ \dot{a}_T \end{bmatrix} = \begin{bmatrix} -\dfrac{v_R}{R} & \dfrac{1}{R} & 0 \\ 0 & 0 & 1 \\ 0 & 0 & -\beta \end{bmatrix} \begin{bmatrix} \Lambda \\ v \\ a_T \end{bmatrix} + \begin{bmatrix} 0 \\ -a_I \\ 0 \end{bmatrix} + \begin{bmatrix} 0 \\ 0 \\ w \end{bmatrix} \tag{3.12}$$

Thus, identifying the A matrix, from (3.12), to be

$$A = \begin{bmatrix} -\dfrac{v_R}{R} & \dfrac{1}{R} & 0 \\ 0 & 0 & 1 \\ 0 & 0 & -\beta \end{bmatrix}$$

and using the approximation of (3.3), with terms up to T^2, gives

$$\Phi \cong I + AT + \frac{A^2 T^2}{2} = \begin{bmatrix} 1 - \dfrac{v_R T}{R}\left(1 - \dfrac{v_R T}{2R}\right) & \dfrac{T}{R}\left(1 - \dfrac{v_R T}{2R}\right) & \dfrac{T^2}{2R} \\ 0 & 1 & T\left(1 - \dfrac{\beta T}{2}\right) \\ 0 & 0 & \rho \end{bmatrix}$$

where we have identified the exact solution for the third diagonal element to be

$$\rho = e^{-\beta T}$$

To complete the discrete representation of (3.2), we use (3.5) and the Markov representation for the target acceleration to give

$$f(k + 1|k) = \begin{bmatrix} \dfrac{-a_I T^2}{2R} \\ -a_I T \\ 0 \end{bmatrix}, \quad \psi w(k) = \begin{bmatrix} 0 \\ 0 \\ \sqrt{1 - \rho^2}\,\sigma_m r(k) \end{bmatrix} \triangleq q(k)$$

where

$r(k) \triangleq$ zero-mean, unit standard-deviation Gaussian random variable

$\sigma_m \triangleq$ target-acceleration standard deviation

Also,

$$\beta = 1/\tau_m$$

where τ_m is the target maneuver time constant.

Coupling with the range filter has been introduced through the range and range rate estimates used in Φ and f. The filtered estimates $(\hat{R}(k|k), \hat{v}_R(k|k))$ are used for prediction to the next $(k + 1)$ time frame. The initial estimates of Λ and v are the measured direction cosine and $-\hat{v}_I$, respectively. The required estimates $(\hat{v}_I, \hat{a}_I)$ of own-ship velocity and acceleration are available from the aircraft inertial navigation system. Finally, the Q matrix is, with one exception, as given in (2.17). The exception is that the elements associated with the first (direction cosine) state are modified by using the filtered range estimate, so that

$$q'_{11} = q_{11}/\hat{R}^2, \quad q'_{12} = q_{12}/\hat{R}, \quad q'_{13} = q_{13}/\hat{R}$$

where the q'_{1i} are the values appropriate for this application, and the q_{1i} values are as given in (2.17). This modification arises because of the necessity to convert the covariance elements that were derived for a Cartesian system for application to this tracking system which uses direction cosine for the first state.

Estimates of the target component of velocity are obtained noting that

$$v = v_T - v_I$$

and solving for v_T. A technique for improving the estimate of target velocity is presented below.

3.5.3 Use of Range Rate for Velocity Aiding in the ΛVA System

The accurate range rate estimate from the range rate filter can be used to improve the less accurate velocity estimates in the direction cosine filters. This approach, although potentially less accurate, avoids the complexity of a nonlinear filtering system that utilizes the range rate measurement more optimally. Farina and Pardini [10] discuss the nonlinear filtering approach for a two-dimensional case.

Given estimates of own-ship velocity components $(\hat{v}_{IN}, \hat{v}_{IE}, \hat{v}_{ID})$, estimated range rate $(\hat{v}_R)$ and direction cosines $(\hat{\Lambda}_N, \hat{\Lambda}_E, \hat{\Lambda}_D)$, an estimate of the target component of range rate is obtained from the equation (since $\hat{v}_{TR} = \hat{v}_R + \hat{v}_{IR}$):

$$\hat{v}_{TR} = \hat{v}_R + \hat{\Lambda}_N \hat{v}_{IN} + \hat{\Lambda}_E \hat{v}_{IE} + \hat{\Lambda}_D \hat{v}_{ID}$$

Then, define

$$RES = \hat{v}_{TR} - \hat{v}_{TRA}$$

where $\hat{v}_{TRA}$ is the estimate of the target radial component of velocity formed by using quantities from the angle filters:

$$\hat{v}_{TRA} = \hat{\Lambda}_N \hat{v}_{TN} + \hat{\Lambda}_E \hat{v}_{TE} + \hat{\Lambda}_D \hat{v}_{TD}$$

$$\hat{\Lambda}_N, \hat{\Lambda}_E, \hat{\Lambda}_D = \text{direction cosine estimates}$$

$$\hat{v}_{TN}, \hat{v}_{TE}, \hat{v}_{TD} = \text{estimates of the components of target velocity}$$

The quantity RES represents the difference between the estimated target component of range rate $(\hat{v}_{TR})$, which is derived from the usually accurate range rate measurements, and the estimated target component of range rate

($\hat{v}_{TRA}$), which is derived from the angle filters that only use angle measurements. Because the range filter estimate should be more accurate, correction terms can be applied. As derived in Appendix 3B, the corrections (or aiding terms) are defined as

$$\delta\hat{v}_N = C_N \cdot RES, \quad \delta\hat{v}_E = C_E \cdot RES, \quad \delta\hat{v}_D = C_D \cdot RES \tag{3.13}$$

where

$$C_N = \frac{\hat{\Lambda}_N \sigma_{v_N}^2}{C}, \quad C_E = \frac{\hat{\Lambda}_E \sigma_{v_E}^2}{C}, \quad C_D = \frac{\hat{\Lambda}_D \sigma_{v_D}^2}{C}$$

$$C = \hat{\Lambda}_N^2 \sigma_{v_N}^2 + \hat{\Lambda}_E^2 \sigma_{v_E}^2 + \hat{\Lambda}_D^2 \sigma_{v_D}^2 + \sigma_{v_R}^2$$

The variances ($\sigma_{v_N}^2, \sigma_{v_E}^2, \sigma_{v_D}^2$) on the prior velocity estimates are obtained from the Kalman filter covariance matrices. The variance on the range rate estimate from the range/range rate Kalman filter is $\sigma_{v_R}^2$.

The correction terms given by (3.13) are computed using the filtered estimates ($\hat{v}_R(k|k)$, $\hat{\Lambda}_N(k|k)$, $\hat{v}_{TN}(k|k)$, *et cetera*) at scan k given the data received on that scan. Then, the velocity correction term is added to the north target velocity estimate so that the new estimate becomes

$$\hat{v}_{TN}(k|k)_{NEW} = \hat{v}_{TN}(k|k) + \delta\hat{v}_N$$

and similar corrections are applied to east and down components.

The use of range rate for velocity aiding has been found to improve velocity estimation. This technique is also directly applicable for establishing initial ($k = 1$) velocity estimates in the angle filters using the initial measured range rate.

Finally, an estimate ($\hat{\omega}_p$) of the magnitude of the line-of-sight rate vector is required for the range filter. This estimate is given by

$$\omega_p^2 = \hat{v}_p^2 / \hat{R}^2$$

where, under the assumption that $\Lambda_D \ll 1$, valid for typical conditions in airborne radar tracking system, we write

$$\hat{v}_p^2 = (\hat{v}_N \hat{\Lambda}_E - \hat{v}_E \hat{\Lambda}_N)^2 + \hat{v}_D^2$$

3.5.4 Azimuth, Elevation Angle Filtering System

Next, we present a pair of angle filters that uses the azimuth and elevation angles, defined in (3.6), as states. The azimuth angle filter uses the component of velocity (v_H) that is perpendicular to the line of sight and located in the horizontal plane as the second state. Similarly, the elevation angle filter uses the component of velocity (v_V) that is perpendicular to the line of sight and located in the vertical direction as the second state. The third states are accelerations (a_H, a_V) that are perpendicular to the line of sight and located in the horizontal plane and the vertical direction, respectively.

Appendix 3A presents a detailed derivation of a coupled nine-state filter for use with range, range rate, azimuth angle, and elevation angle measurements. The derivation follows the general approach given by Pearson and Stear[11]. It shows how the resulting independent filters arise when coupling terms are ignored. This section briefly outlines the derivation and presents the uncoupled angle filters. The range/range rate filter was previously presented.

The polar coordinate system is a rotating coordinate system. Equation (3.14) gives the vector equations that relate target motion in this rotating coordinate system to motion observed in the inertial (NED) system:

$$\left.\frac{d\mathbf{x}}{dt}\right|_I = \left.\frac{d\mathbf{x}}{dt}\right|_r + \boldsymbol{\omega} \times \mathbf{x}$$

$$\left.\frac{d\mathbf{v}}{dt}\right|_I = \left.\frac{d\mathbf{v}}{dt}\right|_r + \boldsymbol{\omega} \times \mathbf{v}$$

$$(3.14)$$

where subscripts I and r refer to inertial and rotating, respectively. Also, ω is the angular rate of the rotating coordinate system with respect to the inertial system. Finally, $\mathbf{x}$ and $\mathbf{v}$ are the vector position and velocity.

The rotating coordinate system is defined by the following unit vectors:

$\mathbf{i}_R$ = unit vector in the direction of the range vector

$\mathbf{i}_H$ = unit vector in the horizontal plane perpendicular to the range vector

$\mathbf{i}_V$ = unit vector in the vertical plane perpendicular to the range vector (in the direction of $\mathbf{i}_R \times \mathbf{i}_H$).

Figure 3-4 illustrates the two coordinate systems. Note that the shaded area defined by the vectors $\mathbf{i}_R$ and $\mathbf{i}_D$ is a vertical plane and that this plane also contains the $\mathbf{i}_V$ and the $\mathbf{i}_{N'}$ vectors shown in the figure. The $\mathbf{i}_{N'}$ vector in Fig. 3-4 is the projection of the $\mathbf{i}_R$ vector onto the horizontal plane and defines the azimuth angle η.

As discussed in Appendix 3A, it is first necessary to identify the components of the vector ω. Then, solution of (3.14) leads to state equations of the form given in (3.1). The final step is to compute the transition matrix Φ. The approximate solution in the form

$$\Phi \cong I + AT + \frac{A^2 T^2}{2}$$

was used.

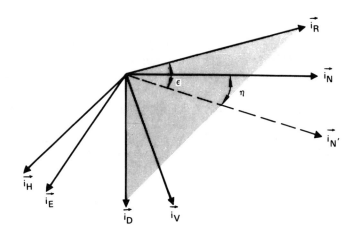

FIGURE 3-4. DEFINITION OF POLAR TRACKING COORDINATE SYSTEM

The two state vectors (x_H and x_V) are defined for motion perpendicular to the line-of-sight (radial) direction in the horizontal plane (along the H axis) and in the vertical direction (along the V axis), respectively. These state vectors are defined by

$$x_H = \begin{bmatrix} \eta \\ v_H \\ a_H \end{bmatrix}, \quad x_V = \begin{bmatrix} \epsilon \\ v_V \\ a_V \end{bmatrix}$$

where

η, ϵ = azimuth and elevation angles

v_H, v_V = velocity components perpendicular to the line of sight along the H and V axes, respectively

a_H, a_V = horizontal and vertical accelerations

The velocity (v_V) and acceleration (a_V) in the vertical direction are defined to be positive in the direction of increasing ϵ. Thus, v_V and a_V are defined to be positive in the direction of $-\mathbf{i}_V$. This final representation differs from the derivation in Appendix 3A where the velocity and acceleration were defined to be positive in the $\mathbf{i}_V$ direction. This form was chosen to eliminate unnecessary minus signs, and so that the form used for the vertical direction filter would be the same as that for the horizontal direction filter.

The transition matrix and the deterministic driving vector for the horizontal plane are

$$
\Phi_H = \begin{bmatrix} 1 & \dfrac{T}{R_H}C_R & \dfrac{T^2}{2R_H} \\[2ex] 0 & \rho_R & T\left(C_R - \dfrac{T\beta_H}{2}\right) \\[2ex] 0 & 0 & \rho_H \end{bmatrix}, \quad f_H = \begin{bmatrix} \dfrac{-T^2}{2R_H}a_{IH} \\[2ex] -TC_R a_{IH} \\[2ex] 0 \end{bmatrix}
$$

and for the vertical plane they are

$$
\Phi_V = \begin{bmatrix} 1 & \dfrac{T}{R}C_R & \dfrac{T^2}{2R} \\[2ex] 0 & \rho_R & T\left(C_R - \dfrac{T\beta_V}{2}\right) \\[2ex] 0 & 0 & \rho_V \end{bmatrix}, \quad f_V = \begin{bmatrix} \dfrac{-T^2}{2R}a_{IV} \\[2ex] -TC_R a_{IV} \\[2ex] 0 \end{bmatrix}
$$

where

$$
C_R = 1 - \frac{v_R T}{2R}, \quad R_H = R\cos\epsilon,
$$

$$
\rho_R = \exp(-v_R T/R), \quad \rho_H = \exp(-\beta_H T), \quad \rho_V = \exp(-\beta_V T)
$$

a_{IH}, a_{IV} = own-ship components of acceleration as projected on the H and V axes

The estimated values for the variable quantities (R, v_R, R_H, a_{IH}, a_{IV}) required for angle filtering are formed by using range-filtered estimates and inertial navigation system outputs. The standard form of the Q matrix is used with the appropriate modifications for range dependent terms. No initial ($k = 1$) estimates of the target velocity components can be formed. Thus, the initial velocity estimates are formed using only own-ship velocity component estimates ($\hat{v}_H(1|1) = -v_{IH}$, $\hat{v}_V(1|1) = -\hat{v}_{IV}$).

3.6 A COMPARATIVE STUDY OF ANGLE FILTERING METHODS

A study was performed to compare angle tracking performance of three filters using the angle tracking state models described above. This study used a two-dimensional Monte Carlo tracking simulation that examined the tracking of targets moving in the horizontal plane. The first filter used angle (η), angle rate ($\dot{\eta}$), and angle acceleration ($\ddot{\eta}$) as states. The second system used direction cosine filters (with states ΛVA) to estimate Λ_N and Λ_E. Then, the estimated azimuth angle was computed from

$$\hat{\eta} = \tan^{-1}(\hat{\Lambda}_E / \hat{\Lambda}_N)$$

This (direction cosine) method was evaluated with and without using range rate velocity aiding. The third method used the angle filter, defined in the previous section, with states (η, v_H, a_H). Table 3-1 summarizes the characteristics of the tracking methods.

TABLE 3-1
SUMMARY OF TRACKING METHODS EXAMINED

Method	Filtering Approach	Obtains Azimuth Angle Estimate (η)
One	One filter with states: ($\eta, \dot{\eta}, \ddot{\eta}$)	Directly
Two	(1) Two filters with states: (Λ_N, v_N, a_N) and (Λ_E, v_E, a_E)	$\hat{\eta} = \tan^{-1}(\hat{\Lambda}_E / \hat{\Lambda}_N)$
	(2) May use $\dot{R}$ aiding to improve velocity estimation	
Three	One filter with states (η, v_H, a_H)	Directly

Tracking in the horizontal plane ($\epsilon = 0$) was considered. Two geometries, shown in Fig. 3-5, were examined. For both geometries an initial range of 30 nmi was assumed, and both the own-ship and the target velocity magnitudes were chosen to be 1000 ft/sec. Also, for both geometries, the own-ship was taken to be flying due north ($v_I = 1000\, i_N$).

Random detection was simulated by using a constant probability of detection (P_D) of 0.7. The sampling interval (T) was taken to be 2.0 s. Measurements consisted of range, range rate, and direction cosines (Λ_N, Λ_E). The measurement errors were assumed to be zero-mean Gaussian, with standard deviations

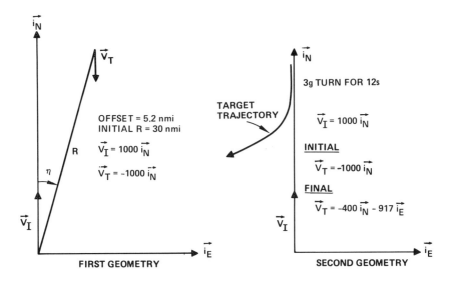

FIGURE 3-5. GEOMETRIES USED FOR FILTERING METHOD COMPARATIVE STUDY

$$\sigma_{R_o} = 1000 \text{ ft}, \quad \sigma_{\dot{R}_o} = 10 \text{ ft/sec}, \quad \sigma_{\lambda_o} = 0.01 \text{ rad}$$

Statistical results were based upon 500 Monte Carlo runs.

The first geometry had a constant target offset of 5.2 nmi, so that the initial azimuth angle was about 10 degrees. For this geometry the target velocity vector was $v_T = -1000\,i_N$ throughout the run. Tracking was examined until the azimuth angle reached 64 degrees. The angular rate $(\dot{\eta})$ was well below 1 deg/sec for most of the geometry, but reached 1.3 deg/sec at the end of the run.

Figure 3-6 summarizes results for the first geometry by giving the mean and standard deviation for the azimuth angle prediction error. As long as range rate velocity aiding was used for the direction cosine filters (method two), the results for the second and third methods were essentially indistinguishable. Thus, only the results for the direction cosine filtering method with $\dot{R}$ aiding are presented. Comparing performance, the first method showed an appreciable mean error, but had a slightly smaller prediction error standard deviation for most of the run. However, the smaller prediction error standard deviation is insignificant when compared with the large mean error that was developed.

The mean error for the first method becomes significant at about scan number 20. However, at scan 20 the azimuth angle and the azimuth angle rate are only about 17 degrees and 0.2 deg/sec, respectively. Even at scan 30

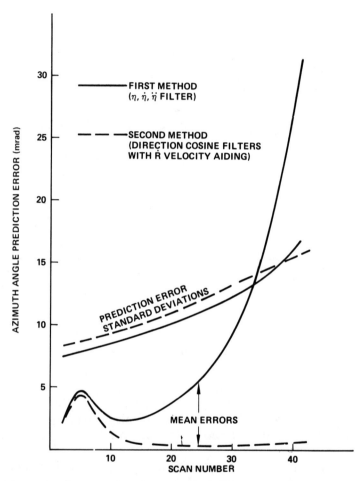

FIGURE 3-6. ANGLE TRACKING FOR CONSTANT OFFSET TARGET

the angle rate is only about 0.35 deg/sec. Thus, the inadequacy of the first method for target offset conditions where higher order angle derivatives are developed is apparent.

For the second geometry the target is assumed to perform a 3g maneuver perpendicular to its velocity vector and in the horizontal plane. The maneuver begins after scan 15 (at time 30 s) and lasts for 12 s. The result is that the target changes heading by about 66.5 degrees, so that the target velocity vector after the turn is

$$\mathbf{v}_T = -400\ \mathbf{i}_N - 917\ \mathbf{i}_E$$

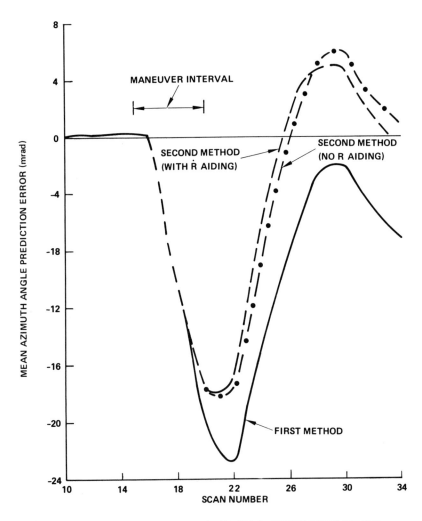

FIGURE 3-7. ANGLE TRACKING FOR 3g MANEUVERING TARGET

Figure 3-7 shows the mean azimuth prediction error for methods one and two, but this time we also consider the condition where range rate velocity aiding is not used for direction cosine filtering (method two). Again, angle, angle rate filtering (method one) is significantly less accurate. The use of range rate aiding shows somewhat better angle prediction accuracy, but the primary benefit was found to be in the estimation of the north component of velocity, which has little effect on azimuth angle estimation accuracy for this geometry. Again, methods two and three were indistinguishable if range rate velocity aiding was used for method two.

The angular prediction error standard deviations were about 12 mrad (0.012 rad) for all three methods for most of the encounter. The error standard deviation increased to a peak of about 15 mrad at scan 22 but returned to about 12 mrad at scan 25.

Methods two and three require the estimated range and range rate in the transition matrix. All three methods require estimated range in the matrix Q. Thus, sensitivity to range and range rate estimation error was studied. First, the range and range rate measurement error standard deviations were increased from 1000 ft and 10 ft/sec to 20,000 ft and 200 ft/sec, respectively. The increase in angular prediction error associated with the increased range and range rate measurement errors was found to be negligible for both geometries.

A second study was performed to simulate the condition where range and range rate measurements are unavailable, as in the case where ECM denies the radar range measurements. For this condition, nominal values $(R_n, \dot{R}_n)$ must be used for the range and range rate estimates that are required for angle tracking. The nominal values were chosen to be

$$\dot{R}_n = -1000 \text{ ft/sec}, \quad R_n = 8 \text{ nmi}$$

The values for R_n and $\dot{R}_n$ were chosen upon experimentation. It was found that a fairly small value for R_n was required in order to maintain acceptable dynamic response at shorter ranges. However, this led to larger random errors at ranges longer than R_n.

Simulation of the constant offset geometry shown in Fig. 3-5 was repeated with the three methods where the nominal values were then used. Figure 3-8 summarizes the results obtained for methods one and two. Again, method three gave essentially the same results as did method two, so that only the results for method two are presented.

Referring to the results in Fig. 3-8, method two now develops a large mean error, but the mean error for method one is about the same as was found when measured range was available (Fig. 3-6). Note that method one only uses estimated range to form the Q matrix and does not use estimated range rate. Thus, the only significant effect of the lack of range and range rate information is that the gains will be somewhat too large at ranges beyond R_n. Using an even smaller value of R_n would decrease the mean error for method two, but at the cost of a larger prediction error standard deviation. As it is, comparing Figs. 3-6 and 3-8, the prediction-error standard deviations are significantly larger for both methods when measured range and range rate are not available. The larger prediction-error standard deviations at ranges greater than R_n result from improper choice of Kalman gain. Using a nominal range that is smaller than the actual range makes the elements of Q too large with the eventual result that the gains are too large.

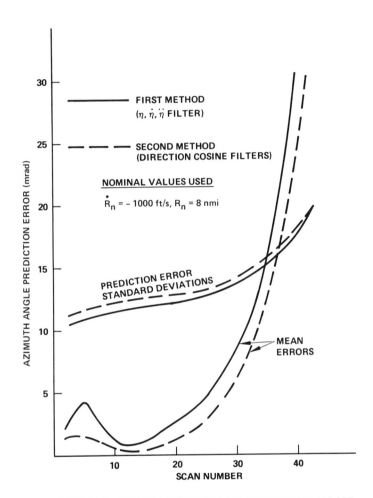

FIGURE 3-8. ANGLE TRACKING FOR CONSTANT OFFSET TARGET WITH NO MEASURED RANGE

Tracking performance in the absence of range rate measurement was also examined for the second (maneuvering target) geometry. Results for this case also showed a significant increase in angular prediction-error standard deviation. However, the lack of measured range and range rate did not significantly affect the mean prediction error for this geometry.

Conclusions for the typical conditions considered are that the direction cosine and (η, v_H, a_H) angle tracking filters performed well as long as reasonably accurate range and range rate were available. When range rate velocity aiding was used with the direction cosine filtering method, the two methods gave essentially identical performances. However, the angle/angle rate filter developed a large bias error for the offset target condition examined. Even if measured range and range rate were assumed to be unavailable, methods two and three were still superior to method one.

3.7 TRACKING WITH ANGLE-ONLY MEASUREMENTS

There is an increasing utilization in MTT of passive sensors that produce no range measurement. Also, the use of electronic countermeasures (ECM) can deny the radar range measurement. Thus, specific techniques are being developed for tracking when only angle is measured. The simplest approaches use either angle and angle rate as states or the polar coordinate systems discussed in Section 3.5 with nominal predetermined values for range and range rate. However, as shown in the previous section, these simple methods can lead to poor tracking performance. Thus, a variety of other, more complex techniques have been developed.

Several sets of coordinate systems have been proposed for angle-only filtering. However, in all cases, complex filtering (usually involving the extended Kalman filter) and changes (or maneuvers) in own-ship motion are required. Lindgren and Gong [12] discuss an application using the four Cartesian states (x, v_x, y, v_y) for tracking in the horizontal plane with angle-only measurements. The system is shown to be unobservable until the own-ship motion changes direction. Convergence may occur after own-ship maneuver, but (according to [13]) angle-only tracking performance is dependent upon the choice of ownship maneuver and upon the initialization method used.

Aidala and Hammel[14] present a modified polar (MP) coordinate system that uses bearing (azimuth) angle, bearing rate, range rate divided by range, and the reciprocal of range as states. This system was derived in order to avoid the erratic performance which may be associated with the use of Cartesian coordinates. An extended Kalman filter is proposed, and again an own-ship maneuver is required.

3.8 SUMMARY

The choice of tracking coordinates for an MTT system is very application dependent. This chapter has provided an overview of the wide variety of approaches that have been used. Further details on most of these methods can be found in the references.

The Cartesian system is probably the one most commonly applied. Based on experience with ground- and ship-based radars, Daum and Fitzgerald [15] present more details on proposed Cartesian coordinate systems, the sources of error and, in particular, the effects of decoupling. However, for airborne radar systems, the use of polar coordinates in which the range and angle filters are decoupled has proven most useful. This approach provides a convenient means of introducing the range rate measurement.

Our emphasis has been upon the development of relatively simple filtering systems. The use of simple filters allows the majority of the computer resources to be allocated to the most important function, data association.

The filtering techniques discussed in this chapter utilized statistical acceleration models that do not include physical constraints upon expected target maneuver. A more exact model should include the fact that dominant target accelerations are normal to the velocity vector and nearly normal to the wings [16]. These conditions imply the desirability of a more representative target maneuver model than the use of independent Gauss-Markov acceleration models for the three tracking coordinates, as has been assumed here.

Another alternative is to track in a target-oriented coordinate system such that one of the axes is aligned with the target velocity vector. This system may be chosen to model better target acceleration because the filter models for the directions perpendicular to the velocity vector can reflect the larger expected target maneuver potential. However, this type of coordinate system requires transformations for all target tracks so that all tracks can be referenced to a common coordinate system. The use of more exact target maneuver models is probably not computationally feasible at present for MTT but may be considered in the future.

REFERENCES

1. Fortmann, T.E., and S. Baron, "Problems in Multi-Target Sonar Tracking," *Proceedings of the 1978 IEEE Conference on Decision and Control*, San Diego, CA, Jan. 1979, pp. 1182–1188.

2. Gelb, A., *Applied Optimal Estimation*, Cambridge, MA: MIT Press, 1974.

3. Dorf, R.C., *Time-Domain Analysis and Design of Control Systems*, Reading, MA: Addison-Wesley, 1965.

4. Castella, F.R., and F.G. Dunnebacke, "Analytic Results for the X,Y Kalman Tracking Filter," *IEEE Transactions on Aerospace and Electronic Systems*, AES-10, Nov. 1974, pp. 891–895.

5. Ramachandra, K.V., and V.S. Srinivasan, "Steady-State Results for the XYZ Kalman Tracking Filter," *IEEE Transactions on Aerospace and Electronic Systems*, AES-13, July 1977, pp. 419–423.

6. Baheti, R.S., "A Sub-Optimal Kalman Filter Design for Target Tracking Applications," *Proceedings of the 1983 IEEE Conference on Decision and Control*, San Antonio, TX, Dec. 14–16, 1983, pp. 552–556.

7. Fitzgerald, R.J., "Comments on Position, Velocity and Acceleration Estimates from the Noisy Radar Measurements," *IEE Proceedings*, Vol. 123, Part F, No. 1, February 1985, pp. 65–67.

8. Brammer, K.G., "Stochastic Filtering Problems in Multiradar Tracking," *Nonlinear Stochastic Problems: Proceeding of the NATO Advanced Study Institute on Nonlinear Stochastic Problems*, edited by R.S. Bucy and J.M.F. Moura, May 16–28, 1982, Algarve, Portugal, pp. 533–552.

9. Bath, W.G., F.R. Castella, and S.F. Haase, "Techniques for Filtering Range and Angle Measurements from Colocated Surveillance Radars," *Proceedings of the 1980 IEEE International Radar Conference*, Arlington, VA, pp. 355–360.

10. Farina, A., and S. Pardini, "Track-While-Scan Algorithm in a Clutter Environment," *IEEE Transactions on Aerospace and Electronic Systems*, AES-14, Sept. 1978, pp. 769–779.

11. Pearson, J.B., and E.B. Stear, "Kalman Filter Applications in Airborne Radar Tracking," *IEEE Transactions on Aerospace and Electronic Systems*, AES-10, May 1974, pp. 319–329.

12. Lindgren, A.G., and K.F. Gong, "Position and Velocity Estimation via Bearing Observations," *IEEE Transactions on Aerospace and Electronic Systems*, AES-14, July 1978, pp. 564–577.

13. Aidala, V.J. "Kalman Filter Behavior in Bearings-Only Tracking Applications," *IEEE Transactions on Aerospace and Electronic Systems*, AES-15, Jan. 1979, pp. 29–39.

14. Aidala, V.J., and S.E. Hammel, "Utilization of Modified Polar Coordinates for Bearings-Only Tracking," *IEEE Transactions on Automatic Control*, AC-28, March 1983, pp. 283–294.

15. Daum, F.E., and R.J. Fitzgerald, "Decoupled Kalman Filters for Phased Array Radar Tracking," *IEEE Transactions on Automatic Control*, AC-28, March 1983, pp. 269–283.

16. Kendrick, J.D., P.S. Maybeck, and J.G. Reid, "Estimation of Aircraft Target Motion Using Orientation Measurements," *IEEE Transactions on Aerospace and Electronic Systems*, AES-17, March 1981, pp. 254–259.

Appendix 3A

Tracking Filter Development

Tracking Coordinate System

The tracking coordinate system to be considered is a polar coordinate system (defined to be the RHV system) that has one axis along the range vector (i_R). The other two axes (i_H, i_V) are perpendicular to the range vector and in the horizontal plane and the vertical direction, respectively. The system is illustrated in Fig. 3-4. The i_H axis is in the horizontal plane, is perpendicular to the $i_{N'}$ axis, and is rotated from the i_E axis by angle η. The i_V axis is in the vertical plane defined by i_R and i_D and is rotated from the i_D axis by angle ϵ. Note that the vectors i_R, i_V, $i_{N'}$ and i_D are all in the same vertical plane.

Next, coordinate transformations defining the RHV polar coordinate system axes (i_R, i_H, i_V) with respect to the NED system are

$$\begin{pmatrix} i_R \\ i_H \\ i_V \end{pmatrix} = T_1 T_2 \begin{pmatrix} i_N \\ i_E \\ i_D \end{pmatrix}, \quad \begin{pmatrix} i_N \\ i_E \\ i_D \end{pmatrix} = T_2^{-1} T_1^{-1} \begin{pmatrix} i_R \\ i_H \\ i_V \end{pmatrix}$$

where the transformation matrices are defined as

$$T_1 = \begin{bmatrix} \cos\epsilon & 0 & -\sin\epsilon \\ 0 & 1 & 0 \\ \sin\epsilon & 0 & \cos\epsilon \end{bmatrix}, \quad T_1^{-1} = \begin{bmatrix} \cos\epsilon & 0 & \sin\epsilon \\ 0 & 1 & 0 \\ -\sin\epsilon & 0 & \cos\epsilon \end{bmatrix}$$

$$T_2 = \begin{bmatrix} \cos\eta & \sin\eta & 0 \\ -\sin\eta & \cos\eta & 0 \\ 0 & 0 & 1 \end{bmatrix}, \quad T_2^{-1} = \begin{bmatrix} \cos\eta & -\sin\eta & 0 \\ \sin\eta & \cos\eta & 0 \\ 0 & 0 & 1 \end{bmatrix}$$

The components (x_R, x_H, x_V) of vector **x** expressed with respect to the RHV coordinate systems can be computed in terms of the NED vector components (x_N, x_E, x_D), and *vice versa*, through the transformations:

$$\begin{pmatrix} x_R \\ x_H \\ x_V \end{pmatrix} = T_1 T_2 \begin{pmatrix} x_N \\ x_E \\ x_D \end{pmatrix}, \quad \begin{pmatrix} x_N \\ x_E \\ x_D \end{pmatrix} = T_2^{-1} T_1^{-1} \begin{pmatrix} x_R \\ x_H \\ x_V \end{pmatrix} \tag{3A.1}$$

Equation (3A.1) provides a convenient transformation of quantities, such as velocity and acceleration, between the coordinate systems.

Using the coordinate system given above, the state variables used to define target motion will be range, range rate, angles (η and ϵ), velocities (v_H and v_V), and accelerations (a_H and a_V) in the i_H and i_V directions. In order to develop a tracking filter, it is first necessary to derive the equations of motion relating these variables. Then, using the equations of motion, the filtering equations can be developed.

Derivation of Equations of Motion

The tracking coordinate system is defined by the rotating axes (i_R, i_H, i_V). Because the coordinate system in which we will be representing target motion is rotating (as the range vector changes), it is necessary to relate motion in a rotating (r) coordinate system to that in an inertial (I) system. The position and velocity vector equations of motion are

$$\left. \frac{d\mathbf{x}}{dt} \right|_I = \left. \frac{d\mathbf{x}}{dt} \right|_r + \boldsymbol{\omega} \times \mathbf{x} \tag{3A.2}$$

$$\left. \frac{d\mathbf{v}}{dt} \right|_I = \left. \frac{d\mathbf{v}}{dt} \right|_r + \boldsymbol{\omega} \times \mathbf{v} \tag{3A.3}$$

The vector $\boldsymbol{\omega}$ represents the angular rate of the rotating coordinate frame relative to the inertial frame. Next, we derive expressions for the components of $\boldsymbol{\omega}$ along the axes of the RHV coordinate system. These components can be expressed in terms of the angular rate variables $\dot{\eta}$ and $\dot{\epsilon}$.

The rate of change ($\dot{\epsilon}$) of elevation angle is in the vertical direction leading to a rotation about the i_H axis, so that $\omega_H = \dot{\epsilon}$. The other rotation ($\dot{\eta}$) is about the i_D axis. Thus, the $\boldsymbol{\omega}$ vector is

$$\boldsymbol{\omega} = \dot{\epsilon} i_H + \dot{\eta} i_D \tag{3A.4}$$

Expressing i_D in terms of i_R and i_V,

$$i_D = -i_R \sin\epsilon + i_V \cos\epsilon$$

Equation (3A.4) becomes

$$\boldsymbol{\omega} = \omega_R i_R + \omega_H i_H + \omega_V i_V$$

with

$$\omega_R = -\dot{\eta} \sin\epsilon, \quad \omega_H = \dot{\epsilon}, \quad \omega_V = \dot{\eta} \cos\epsilon \qquad (3A.5)$$

Using (3A.5) and noting that $\mathbf{x} = R\,\mathbf{i}_R$ gives

$$\boldsymbol{\omega} \times \mathbf{x} = \begin{vmatrix} \mathbf{i}_R & \mathbf{i}_H & \mathbf{i}_V \\ \omega_R & \omega_H & \omega_V \\ R & 0 & 0 \end{vmatrix} = R\omega_V \mathbf{i}_H - R\omega_H \mathbf{i}_V$$

Thus, using (3A.2), and the relationships

$$\left.\frac{d\mathbf{x}}{dt}\right|_I = v_R\,\mathbf{i}_R + v_H\,\mathbf{i}_H + v_V\,\mathbf{i}_V, \quad \left.\frac{d\mathbf{x}}{dt}\right|_r = \dot{R}\,\mathbf{i}_R$$

gives the identity $\dot{R} = v_R$. Also, the other two equations of motion become

$$\begin{aligned} v_H &= R\omega_V = R\dot{\eta}\cos\epsilon, \quad \dot{\eta} = v_H/R_H \\ v_V &= -R\omega_H = -R\dot{\epsilon}, \quad \dot{\epsilon} = -v_V/R \end{aligned} \qquad (3A.6)$$

where $R_H = R\cos\epsilon$ is the projection of the range onto the horizontal plane. Finally, from (3A.5) and (3A.6), the following relationships are presented for later use:

$$\omega_R = -\dot{\eta}\sin\epsilon = -\frac{v_H \tan\epsilon}{R}, \quad \omega_H = \dot{\epsilon} = -\frac{v_V}{R}, \quad \omega_V = \frac{v_H}{R} \qquad (3A.7)$$

Consider the equation for the rate of change of the velocity vector as given by (3A.3). First, we define the components (A_R, A_H, A_V) of $\boldsymbol{\omega} \times \mathbf{v}$ to be

$$\boldsymbol{\omega} \times \mathbf{v} \triangleq A_R\,\mathbf{i}_R + A_H\,\mathbf{i}_H + A_V\,\mathbf{i}_V = \begin{vmatrix} \mathbf{i}_R & \mathbf{i}_H & \mathbf{i}_V \\ \omega_R & \omega_H & \omega_V \\ v_R & v_H & v_V \end{vmatrix}$$

so that, using (3A.7), we have

$$A_R = \omega_H v_V - \omega_V v_H = -\frac{v_H^2 + v_V^2}{R} \triangleq -\omega_p^2 R$$

$$A_H = \omega_V v_R - \omega_R v_V = \frac{v_R v_H}{R} + \frac{v_H v_V}{R}\tan\epsilon$$

$$A_V = \omega_R v_H - \omega_H v_R = \frac{v_R v_V}{R} - \frac{v_H^2}{R} \tan \epsilon$$

The quantity $\omega_p = \sqrt{v_H^2 + v_V^2} / R$ is the magnitude of the line-of-sight rate vector. Finally,

$$\left. \frac{d\mathbf{v}}{dt} \right|_I = a_R \mathbf{i}_R + a_H \mathbf{i}_H + a_V \mathbf{i}_V$$

$$\left. \frac{d\mathbf{v}}{dt} \right|_r = \dot{v}_R \mathbf{i}_R + \dot{v}_H \mathbf{i}_H + \dot{v}_V \mathbf{i}_V$$

where a_R, a_H, and a_V are the accelerations as seen by an observer in the inertial coordinate system. Thus, from (3A.3), the equations of motion for velocity become

$$\dot{v}_R = a_R - A_R = a_R + \omega_p^2 R$$

$$\dot{v}_H = a_H - A_H = a_H - \frac{v_R}{R} v_H - U(R, \epsilon, v_H) v_V$$

$$\dot{v}_V = a_V - A_V = a_V - \frac{v_R}{R} v_V + U(R, \epsilon, v_H) v_H \qquad (3A.8)$$

where

$$U(R, \epsilon, v_H) = \frac{v_H}{R} \tan \epsilon \qquad (3A.9)$$

The acceleration terms represent the relative (target minus own-ship) accelerations. Thus,

$$a_R = a_{TR} - a_{IR}, \quad a_H = a_{TH} - a_{IH}, \quad a_V = a_{TV} - a_{IV} \qquad (3A.10)$$

where the own-ship accelerations transformed from the inertial NED coordinate system are

$$a_{IR} = a_{IN} \cos\eta \cos\epsilon + a_{IE} \sin\eta \cos\epsilon - a_{ID} \sin\epsilon$$

$$a_{IH} = -a_{IN} \sin\eta + a_{IE} \cos\eta$$

$$a_{IV} = a_{IN} \cos\eta \sin\epsilon + a_{IE} \sin\eta \sin\epsilon + a_{ID} \cos\epsilon$$

Finally, we assume independent target acceleration components as defined by the Singer model, given in Chapter 2, whence we have

$$\dot{a}_{TR} = -\beta_R\, a_{TR} + w_R$$
$$\dot{a}_{TH} = -\beta_H\, a_{TH} + w_H \qquad\qquad (3A.11)$$
$$\dot{a}_{TV} = -\beta_V\, a_{TV} + w_V$$

Using (3A.6), (3A.8), (3A.10), and (3A.11), the process can be put into the standard state equation form of (3.1), with the following identifications:

$$
x = \begin{bmatrix} R \\ v_R \\ a_{TR} \\ \eta \\ v_H \\ a_{TH} \\ \epsilon \\ v_V \\ a_{TV} \end{bmatrix}, \quad
Gw = \begin{bmatrix} 0 \\ 0 \\ w_R \\ 0 \\ 0 \\ w_H \\ 0 \\ 0 \\ w_V \end{bmatrix}, \quad
Lu = \begin{bmatrix} 0 \\ -a_{IR} \\ 0 \\ 0 \\ -a_{IH} \\ 0 \\ 0 \\ -a_{IV} \\ 0 \end{bmatrix}
$$

and

$$
A = \begin{bmatrix}
0 & 1 & 0 & & & & & & \\
\omega_p^2 & 0 & 1 & & & 0 & & 0 & \\
0 & 0 & -\beta_R & & & & & & \\
& & & 0 & 1/R_H & 0 & 0 & 0 & 0 \\
& 0 & & 0 & -v_R/R & 1 & 0 & -U & 0 \\
& & & 0 & 0 & -\beta_H & 0 & 0 & 0 \\
& & & 0 & 0 & 0 & 0 & -1/R & 0 \\
& 0 & & 0 & U & 0 & 0 & -v_R/R & 1 \\
& & & 0 & 0 & 0 & 0 & 0 & -\beta_V
\end{bmatrix}
$$

$$(3A.12)$$

Referring to (3A.12), range and angle become essentially uncoupled. However, velocity estimates from the angle filters form the ω_p^2 estimate used in the range filter transition matrix. Also, estimates of v_R and R from the range filter are used for the angle filter transition matrix.

The decoupling into three separate filters occurs if terms involving $U(R, \epsilon, v_H)$, as defined in (3A.9), can be neglected. This term can be neglected for small values of ϵ, but typically it is small, even when ϵ is not small. For example, for $\epsilon = 15$ deg, $v_H = 1000$ ft/sec, and $R = 20$ nmi:

$$U = \frac{1000\ (0.27)}{20\ (6076)} \cong 0.002$$

so that

$$U v_H \sim 2$$

This is a rather small contribution to $\dot{v}_V$, defined in (3A.8), that can, in effect, be absorbed in the acceleration estimate a_{TV}.

The transition matrices given in the text (Φ_R, Φ_H, Φ_V) were derived upon assuming U to be negligible and using A of (3A.12) in the approximation:

$$\Phi \cong I + AT + \frac{A^2 T^2}{2}$$

One minor modification was to define v_V and a_{TV} to be positive in the direction of $-\mathbf{i}_V$. This removes some minus signs that otherwise might appear, but, of course, it does not change the filter form. Finally, the deterministic inputs resulting from own-ship motion (f_R, f_H, f_V) were found directly using $L\mathbf{u}$ defined above and the relationship of (3.5).

Appendix 3B

Use of Range Rate for NED Velocity Component Estimation

The target component of range rate (v_{TR}) can be expressed in terms of the total range rate (v_R) and own-ship velocity as

$$v_{TR} = v_R + \Lambda_N v_{IN} + \Lambda_E v_{IE} + \Lambda_D v_{ID} \tag{3B.1}$$

Define

$$RES = \hat{v}_{TR} - (\hat{\Lambda}_N v_{TN} + \hat{\Lambda}_E \hat{v}_{TE} + \hat{\Lambda}_D \hat{v}_{TD}) \tag{3B.2}$$

The quantity RES represents the difference between two, essentially independent estimates of the target component of range rate. The first is formed from (3B.1) using the estimated direction cosines and the typically accurate estimates of range rate ($\hat{v}_R$) and own-ship velocity components ($\hat{v}_{IN}, \hat{v}_{IE}, \hat{v}_{ID}$).

The second estimate is the projection of the estimated target velocity in the line-of-sight direction. The contributions to RES will be predominately from errors in the estimates of the target components of velocity. Thus, we can approximate the direction cosine and own-ship velocity estimates by the true quantities ($\hat{\Lambda}_N \cong \Lambda_N$, $\hat{v}_{IN} \cong v_{IN}$, *et cetera*). Then, the estimate of the target's north component of velocity ($\hat{v}_{TN}$) can be expressed in terms of the true quantity (v_{TN}):

$$v_{TN} = \hat{v}_{TN} + \delta v_N$$

with similar expressions for east, down, and radial velocities. Finally, (3B.2) can be expressed as

$$RES = \hat{\Lambda}_N \, \delta v_N + \hat{\Lambda}_E \, \delta v_E + \hat{\Lambda}_D \, \delta v_D - \delta v_R \qquad (3B.3)$$

where

$$\delta v_N, \delta v_E, \delta v_D = \text{components of velocity estimation error}$$

$$\delta v_R = \text{error in range rate estimate}$$

Estimates of the components of velocity estimation error will be derived from RES through the linear relationships:

$$\delta \hat{v}_N = C_N \cdot RES, \quad \delta \hat{v}_E = C_E \cdot RES, \quad \delta \hat{v}_D = C_D \cdot RES \qquad (3B.4)$$

Then, (3B.3) and (3B.4) can be used to compute the values for C_N, C_E, and C_D that minimize the mean squared error terms, which, for example, for C_N are of the form:

$$E\,[\delta v_N - C_N \cdot RES]^2 = (1 - \hat{\Lambda}_N \, C_N)^2 \, \sigma_{v_N}^2 + C_N^2 \,(\hat{\Lambda}_E^2 \sigma_{v_E}^2 + \hat{\Lambda}_D^2 \sigma_{v_D}^2 + \sigma_{v_R}^2)$$

The resulting minimizations give

$$C_N = \frac{\hat{\Lambda}_N \, \sigma_{v_N}^2}{C}, \quad C_E = \frac{\hat{\Lambda}_E \, \sigma_{v_E}^2}{C}, \quad C_D = \frac{\hat{\Lambda}_D \, \sigma_{v_D}^2}{C}$$

where

$$C = \hat{\Lambda}_N^2 \, \sigma_{v_N}^2 + \hat{\Lambda}_E^2 \, \sigma_{v_E}^2 + \hat{\Lambda}_D^2 \, \sigma_{v_D}^2 + \sigma_{v_R}^2$$

Also, the velocity variances ($\sigma_{v_N}^2, \sigma_{v_E}^2, \sigma_{v_D}^2, \sigma_{v_R}^2$) are the variances, obtained from the Kalman filters on the prior velocity and range rate estimates.

Chapter 4

Gating and Data Association

4.1 INTRODUCTION

This chapter will consider the process of associating observations with tracks. We assume the existence of a set of tracks at the time a new observation or set of observations is received. These observations may be used for updating the existing tracks or for initiating new tracks. The next two chapters will discuss measurement formation and track initiation. Here, we discuss the manner in which the observations (once generated) are chosen for track updating.

The track updating process typically begins with a gating procedure that is used to eliminate unlikely observation-to-track pairings. Section 4.2 discusses the general techniques that have been proposed for gating and Appendix 4A summarizes the probabilistic expressions associated with correlation using rectangular and ellipsoidal gating. Some of the results of of Appendix 4A are presented in Section 4.2. Also, the expressions derived in Appendix 4A will be used more extensively in Chapter 7.

The simplest MTT systems use sequential data processing and the nearest-neighbor (NN) association rule. For example, this is normally the approach used with a TWS system. With this approach, processing is done at each scan using only data received on that scan to update the results of previous processing. The NN assignment algorithm assigns observations to existing tracks in a manner that minimizes some overall distance criterion. This process usually leads to the assignment matrix, the solution for which is discussed in Section 4.3

Simple assignment techniques, such as the sequential nearest-neighbor approach, can lead to miscorrelation with poor tracking as a consequence. Chapter 1 presented a simplified interpretation of the MTT data association problem (Fig. 1-4) in which an unstable region was identified. This interpretation can be used intuitively to describe the effects of the commonly employed techniques for data association. Thus, use of the optimal solution to the assignment matrix, discussed in Section 4.3, and the branching technique, introduced in Section 4.4, represent techniques for expanding the region of unambiguous correlation.

Section 4.4 discussed the intuitively appealing idea of deferring difficult association decisions until more data is received. The initial methods proposed for this approach were denoted branching or track splitting. These methods are outlined here with the understanding that the multiple hypothesis tracking technique, which will be discussed in Chapter 10, represents a more powerful general approach.

It has long been recognized that the use of standard Kalman filtering tecniques in the dense MTT environment can lead to divergence because the covariance matrix may not reflect the increased error due to miscorrelation. Thus, Section 4.5 discusses techniques whereby the Kalman filter covariance matrix can be increased to account for miscorrelation effects.

4.2 GATING TECHNIQUES

Gating is a technique for eliminating unlikely observation-to-track pairings. A gate is formed around the predicted track position. Then, if a single observation is within the gate, and if that observation is not within the gate of any other track, the observaton will be correlated with the track and used to update the track filters. If more than one return is within the track gate, or if the observation is within the gates of more than one track, further correlation logic is required.

We begin this section by reviewing the definitions of quantities to be used in gating. The use of Kalman filtering, with its associated covariance matrix, is assumed. However, as discussed in Chapter 2, if constant-coefficient filtering is used, it is still possible to compute corresponding covariance terms from the filtering coefficients and the measurement noise variance.

At scan $k - 1$, the filter forms the prediction $\hat{x}(k|k-1)$ of the state vector for use at time kT. The measurement at scan k is

$$y(k) = Hx(k) + v(k)$$

where H is the measurement matrix and $v(k)$ is zero-mean, white Gaussian measurement noise with covariance matrix R_c. The vector difference between measured and predicted quantities, $\tilde{y}(k) = y(k) - H\hat{x}(k|k-1)$, is defined to be the residual vector with residual covariance matrix, $S = HPH^T + R_c$, where P is the one step prediction covariance matrix. The time subscripts k will be dropped for notational convenience. Assume that the measurement is of dimension M. Then, defining d^2 to be the norm of the residual (or innovation) vector, $d^2 \triangleq \tilde{y}^T S^{-1} \tilde{y}$, the M-dimensional Gaussian probability density for the residual is

$$f(\tilde{y}) = \frac{e^{-\frac{d^2}{2}}}{(2\pi)^{M/2} \sqrt{|S|}} \tag{4.1}$$

where

$$|S| \triangleq \text{the determinant of } S$$

In either of the special cases where the probability of detection is unity or there are no expected extraneous returns, the gate size should be infinite for optimal correlation performance. However, insofar as one primary purpose of gating logic is to reduce the number of observation-to-track pairings that must be considered, a finite gate size would be appropriate even in these cases. Also, for non-unity probability of detection or during the presence of extraneous returns, an optimal, non-infinite gate size can be defined. We start by considering rectangular gates and then we shall discuss ellipsoidal gates.

4.2.1 Rectangular Gates

Probably, the simplest gating technique is to define rectangular regions such that an observation is said to satisfy the gates of a given track if all elements, $\tilde{y}_l$, of the residual vector $\tilde{y}$ satisfy the relationship:

$$|y_l - \hat{y}_l| = |\tilde{y}_l| \leq K_{Gl}\sigma_r \tag{4.2}$$

where σ_r is the residual standard deviation as defined in terms of the measurement (σ_o^2) and the prediction (σ_p^2) variances:

$$\sigma_r = \sqrt{\sigma_o^2 + \sigma_p^2}$$

Finally, note that the prediction variance (σ_p^2) is typically taken from the Kalman covariance matrix.

Assuming the Gaussian error model, we next consider choice of the gating constants K_{Gl}. The theoretical probability of a valid observation satisfying the gating test can be computed from standard Gaussian probability relationships. Assume the same gate size in all dimensions ($K_{Gl} = K_G$ for all l). Then, given an M-dimensional measurement and assuming independence of the residual errors, the probability (P_G) of a valid observation satisfying the gating relationship is

$$P_G = [1 - \text{Pr}(|t| \geq K_G)]^M \cong 1 - M\,\text{Pr}(|t| \geq K_G) \tag{4.3}$$

where $\text{Pr}(|t| \geq K_G)$ is the probability of the magnitude of a standard, normalized Gaussian random variable ($t \sim N(0,1)$) exceeding K_G. The approximation is valid given the typically small values chosen for the probability that a valid observation will not satisfy the gating relationship. For example, if K_G is chosen to be the typical value of 3, we write

$$\text{Pr}(|t| \geq 3) = 2\text{Pr}(t \geq 3) = 2(0.00135) = 0.0027$$

Thus, for the typical four-dimensional radar measurement (azimuth, elevation, range, and range rate), the theoretical probability of a valid observation satisfying the gating test for K_G of 3 is about 99 percent.

The theoretical relationship given in (4.3) is based upon the assumption of perfect filter models for the target dynamics and the measurement noise. This assumption can be optimistic, particularly in the presence of target maneuver. Also, a one percent probability of rejecting a valid return per update opportunity can lead to a much larger cumulative value (>20 percent) over the life of a typical track. Thus, larger values ($K_G \gtrsim 3.5$) may be used. An alternative approach is to define two levels (standard and maneuver) of gating. This will be discussed in more detail below.

Sea [1] discusses the correlation statistics associated with rectangular gating. These relationships (as well as the relationships for ellipsoidal gates) are summarized in Appendix 4A. Here, for purposes of illustration, we consider a two-dimensional measurement where it is assumed that the residual errors are uncorrelated for the two measured variables.

The probability of correct decision (P_{CD}) is given by

$$P_{CD} = P_D P_{CC/D} + (1 - P_D) P_{NE}$$

where P_D is the probabilty of detection, and

$P_{CC/D}$ = probability of a correct correlation, given that a true target detection occurs;

P_{NE} = probability of no correlation, given that the target is not detected. This is the probability of no extraneous returns within the gate volume.

The probability of correct decision is the sum of two terms. The first term is the product of P_D times the probability of making a correct decision (a correct correlation), given that the target is detected. The second term is the probability of no detection times the probability of correctly making no correlation. In the latter case no correlation will occur if there are no extraneous returns (either from new targets or false alarms) within the gate volume.

For the two-dimensional measurement case (assuming the same K_G for both dimensions and as presented in [1] and Appendix 4A), we have

$$P_{CC/D} = [C \operatorname{erf}(K_G/\sqrt{2C})]^2$$
$$P_{NE} = e^{-n_{TF}K_G^2}$$

where, for no correlation between residual errors,

$$C = \frac{1}{\sqrt{1 + \dfrac{\pi}{2} n_{TF}}}$$

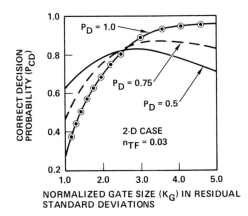

FIGURE 4–1. CORRECT DECISION PROBABILITY
VERSUS GATE SIZE AND P_D

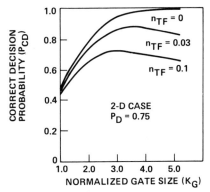

FIGURE 4–2. CORRECT DECISION PROBABILITY
VERSUS GATE SIZE AND NORMALIZED
NEW SOURCE DENSITY (n_{TF})

The quantity n_{TF} is a dimensionless variable that is defined as the expected number of false returns within M-dimensional boxes with sides of two residual standard deviations in length. Define the new source density β to be the expected number of new sources (true targets and false alarms) that arise per unit volume per unit scan time. Then, for the two-dimensional case (with residual standard deviations σ_{r1} and σ_{r2}), n_{TF} is given by

$$n_{TF} = \beta \, (2\sigma_{r1}) \, (2\sigma_{r2}) \qquad (4.4)$$

Figure 4-1 gives P_{CD} as a function of the gate size for cases with $P_D=0.5$, 0.75, and 1.0. The value chosen for n_{TF} is 0.03, so that for $K_G=3.0$, the probability of at least one return falling within the gate volume is $1-P_{NE}=1-e^{-0.27}$ (approximately 0.24). Note that in order to maximize P_{CD}, the gate size should decrease significantly as P_D decreases ($K_G \cong 5$ is appropriate for $P_D=1.0$, but $K_G \cong 3$ maximizes P_{CD} for $P_D=0.5$). A similar relationship exists whereby the gate size should decrease as the false target density increases. Figure 4-2 shows the manner in which P_{CD} varies with n_{TF} and K_G.

Note that the gate size should also decrease as the uncertainty in predicted position or the measurement noise increases. With respect to P_{CD}, an increase in the residual standard deviation is seen through (4.4) to be equivalent to an increase in n_{TF}, which, as shown in Fig. 4-2, requires a reoptimization in the choice of K_G. Thus, for example, K_G should decrease as the filter prediction variance increases with extrapolation. This principle will also be illustrated with the ellipsoidal gate discussed next.

Finally, for future reference, the volume of an M-dimensional rectangular gate normalized with respect to the residual variances is

$$V_{G1}(M)=(2K_G)^M \tag{4.5}$$

4.2.2 Ellipsoidal Gates

Define a gate (G) such that correlation is allowed if the following relationship is satisfied by the norm (d^2) of the residual vector:

$$d^2=\tilde{y}^T S^{-1} \tilde{y} \leqq G \tag{4.6}$$

Following References [2,3], a maximum likelihood gate (G_o) can be defined such that an observation falling within that gate is more likely from the track in question than from an extraneous source. This gate is defined in terms of the probability of detection (P_D), the new source density (β), the measurement dimension (M), and the residual statistics as represented by the determinant of the residual covariance matrix ($|S|$):

$$G_o=2 \ln \left[\frac{P_D}{(1-P_D)\beta(2\pi)^{M/2} \sqrt{|S|}} \right] \tag{4.7}$$

Note that G_o approaches infinity as P_D approaches unity or β approaches zero. Also, G_o decreases as P_D decreases or the residual error increases such as would occur during extrapolation. At the point where G_o approaches zero, continuing the track and attempting further correlation become futile.

A simpler, but less adaptive, method is to choose G based on the chi-square (χ_M^2) distribution with M degrees of freedom. As shown in Appendix 4A, the quantity d^2 is the sum of the squares of M independent Gaussian random variables with zero means and unit standard deviations. Thus, d^2 will have the χ_M^2 distribution for correct observation-to-track pairings and a gate on d^2 can be defined using the properties of the χ_M^2 distribution. Using the χ_M^2 distribution and assuming an allowable probability ($\bar{P}_G = 1 - P_G$) of a valid observation falling outside the gate, the value of G can be determined using a χ^2 table and the relationship:

$$\text{Pr}\{\chi_M^2 > G\} = \tilde{P}_G \tag{4.8}$$

The probability (P_G) that a valid observation will fall within the gate G can be found using the χ^2 table. Alternatively, the relationship given in (4.6) defines a constant likelihood ellipsoid, such that

$$P_G = \int \ldots \int f(\tilde{y}) \, d\tilde{y}_1, \ldots, d\tilde{y}_M \tag{4.9}$$
$$\text{over ellipsoidal}$$
$$\text{volume } (V_G)$$

Following the derivation outlined in Appendix 4A, solutions of the integral in (4.9) for values of M from one to six have been obtained and are summarized in Table 4-1.

TABLE 4-1
PROBABILITY, P_G, OF VALID OBSERVATION FALLING WITHIN M-DIMENSIONAL GATE OF SIZE G

M	$P_G(M)$
1	$2\,gc\,(\sqrt{G})$*
2	$1 - \exp(-G/2)$
3	$2\,gc\,(\sqrt{G}) - \sqrt{2G/\pi}\,\exp(-G/2)$
4	$1 - (1 + G/2)\exp(-G/2)$
5	$2\,gc\,(\sqrt{G}) - (1 + G/3)\sqrt{2G/\pi}\,\exp(-G/2)$
6	$1 - 1/2\,(G^2/4 + G + 2)\exp(-G/2)$

$$*gc\,(x) \triangleq \frac{1}{\sqrt{2\pi}} \int_0^x \exp(-u^2/2)\,du = \text{standard Gaussian probability}$$
$$\text{integral.}$$

Finally, the volume within the ellipsoidal gate is

$$V_G(M) = C_M \sqrt{|S|}\,G^{M/2}$$

Thus, the normalized volume is

$$V_{G2}(M) = C_M G^{M/2}$$

where

$$C_M = \cfrac{\pi^{M/2}}{\Gamma\left(\cfrac{M}{2}+1\right)} = \begin{cases} \cfrac{\pi^{M/2}}{\left(\cfrac{M}{2}\right)!} & , M \text{ even} \\[3em] \cfrac{2^{M+1}\left(\cfrac{M+1}{2}\right)!\,\pi^{\frac{M-1}{2}}}{(M+1)!} & , M \text{ odd} \end{cases} \qquad (4.10)$$

4.2.3 Comparison of Gating Volumes

Using (4.3) and (4.8), we choose K_G and G such that the probability ($\tilde{P}_G$) of rejecting a valid observation is 0.01 for both gating techniques. Table 4-2 gives the appropriate values for K_G and G as functions of the measurement dimension. It also gives the ratio of the volumes $r(M)$ defined as

$$r(M) = \frac{V_{G1}(M)}{V_{G2}(M)}$$

The probability that at least one false observation will satisfy the gating relationship is approximately proportional to the gate volume. Thus, the quantity $r(M)$ approximates the ratio of the probabilities of the gates accepting an extraneous observation for the two gating techniques considered.

TABLE 4-2
COMPARATIVE PROBABILITIES OF ACCEPTING EXTRANEOUS OBSERVATIONS
($P_G = 0.99$ for true observation)

M	K_G	G	$r(M)*$
2	2.81	9.21	1.09
3	2.94	11.34	1.28
4	3.04	13.28	1.59
5	3.09	15.09	2.0

* Ratio of the probability of accepting an extraneous observation using rectangular gating to that for ellipsoidal gating.

Referring to Table 4-2, the relative volume required by the rectangular gating method increases rapidly as the measurement dimension increases. The ellipsoidal gating method decreases the required gating volume, thus decreasing the probability of an extraneous observation falling within the gates. Also, as shown by (4.7), the ellipsoidal gate can be conveniently used to vary gate volume with the environment (P_D, β, *et cetera*). However, use of the ellipsoidal gate requires somewhat more computation because the normalized distance function must be computed using (4.6). Finally, note that an efficient alternative is to do coarse gating first, using relatively large ($K_G \sim 4.0$) rectangular gates, and then to use ellipsoidal gates for those observation-to-track pairings that survive the coarse gating. This process has been found to decrease significantly the number of required calculations.

4.2.4 Other Gating Techniques

As illustrated by Fig. 2-5 in Chapter 2, one common technique is to use two or three levels of gating. The inner gates are defined using the covariance matrix while a large, or maneuver, gate can be based on a more detailed model of possible target trajectories. Wong and Korsak [4] define a complex gate based on aircraft maneuver capability. We next outline the manner in which the large gate shown in Fig. 2-5 was defined using an intuitive approach.

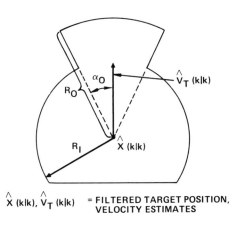

$\hat{X}$ (k|k), $\hat{V}_T$ (k|k)   = FILTERED TARGET POSITION, VELOCITY ESTIMATES

FIGURE 4-3. DEFINITION OF A MANEUVER GATE
FOR A SHIP TRACKING PROBLEM

Figure 4-3 shows how a large (or maneuver) gate was defined for a ship tracking problem. First, the inner radius R_I is computed based on the assumption that if a large heading change occurs, the ship's speed will not also change significantly. Thus, R_I represents a maximum range for the constant speed assumption, given that the heading change occurred at the time of the last sample. The outer radius, R_o, represents the locus of points resulting from the maximum expected large velocity increase with no heading change. A large speed change cone is defined by the angle $\pm\alpha_o$ about the estimated heading to account for uncertainties in the heading estimate. Finally, a portion of the large heading change circle is deleted to the rear of the previously estimated ship's heading. This is to account for the low probability of such a large heading change occurring right at the previous sampling interval.

As noted in Chapter 2, a filter modification is usually appropriate when an observation assigned to a track falls outside a standard gate, but within the maneuver gate. For the gate defined by Fig. 4-3, the approach was to predict the future target position by estimating a point when an abrupt turn occurred, and extrapolating, using that point and the present measured position. Also, the covariance matrix was reinitialized. Finally, branching, which will be discussed in Section 4.4, was used, with one branch including the large maneuver gate observation and the other branch continuing the previous track extrapolation.

4.3   THE ASSIGNMENT PROBLEM

In a dense target environment, gating only begins to solve the problem of associating observations with tracks. Additional logic is required when an observation falls within the gates of multiple target tracks or when multiple observations fall within the gates of a target track. Figure 4-4 illustrates a typical situation in which both types of conflict occur.

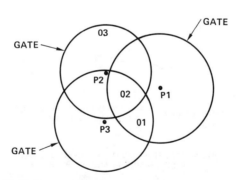

01, 02, 03 = OBSERVATION POSITIONS
P1, P2, P3 = PREDICTED TARGET POSITIONS

FIGURE 4-4.   EXAMPLE OF A COMPLEX CONFLICT SITUATION

There are basically two approaches to conflict resolution. First, the nearest-neighbor (NN) approach looks for a unique pairing, so that, at most, one observation can be used to update a given track. NN correlation can be done most efficiently when, using the branching or multiple hypothesis techniques discussed below, difficult decisions can be deferred until further data are received. Here, we will consider the sequential NN approach in which irrevocable assignments are all made after each scan of data is received. The alternative all-neighbors approach, as shall be discussed in Chapter 10, allows a track to be updated with a composite of all the observations within its gates.

The problem of assigning observations to tracks in the sequential NN approach is an example of the classical assignment problem [5]. The optimal assignment minimizes a total distance function, which is the sum of the distances for all the individual assignments. Thus, it is first necessary to define a distance measure from the predicted position of track *i* to observation *j*. This quantity is termed a normalized or statistical distance function*, and there are several different ways of defining it. One convenient definition is given in Section 4.3.1. A more complex distance function is discussed in Chapter 9.

4.3.1 Normalized Distance Function

Assuming the Gaussian distribution for the residual, the likelihood function associated with the assignment of observation *j* to track *i* (for measurement dimension *M*) is

$$g_{ij} = \frac{e^{-\frac{d_{ij}^2}{2}}}{(2\pi)^{M/2} \sqrt{|S_i|}} \tag{4.11}$$

where S_i is the residual covariance matrix for track *i*, and

$$d_{ij}^2 = \tilde{y}_{ij}^T S_i^{-1} \tilde{y}_{ij}$$

$\tilde{y}_{ij}$ = residual vector from observation *j* to track *i*

The basic goal is to choose assignments that maximize the g_{ij} terms. By taking the logarithm of (4.11) it is seen that maximization of g_{ij} is equivalent to minimization of the quantity:

$$d_{G_{ij}}^2 = d_{ij}^2 + \ln|S_i| \tag{4.12}$$

Thus, assuming the same measurement dimension for all observations, the quantity $d_{G_{ij}}^2$ is a convenient distance function for use in the problem of assigning observations to tracks. Chapter 9 discusses more complex distance functions, but for most applications $d_{G_{ij}}^2$ has been found to be adequate.

---

*Again note that the function will actually represent a squared distance, but it will be referred to simply as a *distance*.

4.3.2   Solution of the Assignment Matrix

The typical assignment method [6, 7] is to form an assignment matrix
with non-zero elements as the appropriate distance functions. Either a zero
or some other element can be chosen to identify observation-to-track pairings
that are unacceptable because of the gating criteria. The classical approach
has been to consider only the assignment of observations to existing tracks.
As will be discussed in Chapter 9, a more general approach is to allow also
the assignment of observations to new sources within the framework of the
assignment matrix. However, for this chapter's discussion, we will maintain
the classical approach.

OBSERVATIONS TRACKS	01	02	03
T1	⑨	6	X
T2	X	3	⑩
T3	8	④	X

X = OBSERVATION OUTSIDE GATE

◯ = OPTIMAL SOLUTION

FIGURE 4-5.   ASSIGNMENT MATRIX FOR EXAMPLE OF FIGURE 4-4

Figure 4-5 shows the assignment matrix for the example given in Fig. 4-4.
We have chosen the rows to represent tracks and columns to represent
observations. This choice (as opposed to columns for tracks, *et cetera*), of
course, has no effect on the solution. The non-zero elements are hypothetical
distance functions that will be used for illustration.

It is generally accepted that the desired (or optimal) solution to an
assignment matrix, such as that given in Fig. 4-5, will give the maximum
number of possible assignments. Then, of those solutions satisfying that
constraint, the desired solution is the one that minimizes the summed total
distance. For simple cases, such as two or three conflicting observations and
tracks, the optimal solution can easily be found by enumeration. In general,
enumeration is too time consuming, but algorithms have been developed to
obtain the optimal solution more efficiently. One of these, Munkres algorithm [8, 9], will be discussed in more detail in Chapter 14.

A number of approximate solutions to the assignment problem have been developed. These solutions are not guaranteed to be optimal for all conditions, but they are simpler than algorithms guaranteed to give the optimal solution. The rules (applied in order) that define two of these suboptimal solutions are given below. For the purpose of defining the rules for the first method, the term "validate" is defined to mean satisfaction of the gating test.

- *Suboptimal Solution One*

    1. An observation that validates with a singly validated track is rejected by any multiply validated track.
    2. A multiply validated observation is rejected by any track that validates with a singly validated observation.
    3. Whether or not a track is multiply validated is determined again after each application of *Rule 1* affecting it. A track that becomes singly validated is again subject to *Rule 1*.
    4. Whether or not an observation is multiply validated is determined again after each application of *Rule 2* affecting it. An observation that becomes singly validated is again subject to *Rule 2*.
    5. For each remaining multiply validated track, choose the observation with minimum distance.
    6. For each remaining multiply validated observation, choose the track with minimum distance.

- *Suboptimal Solution Two*

    1. Search the assignment matrix for the closest (minimum distance) observation-to-track pair and make the indicated assignment.
    2. Remove the observation-to-track pair identified above from the assignment matrix and repeat *Rule 1* for the reduced matrix.

Considering the assignment matrix shown in Fig. 4-5, it is of interest to compare the solutions obtained by the optimal and two suboptimal methods discussed above. The example, of course, was chosen to be particularly difficult and to emphasize differences. For most simpler cases, the three solutions will agree. However, as shown later, the use of different assignment methods can lead to significant overall performance differences for certain multiple target geometries.

The optimal assignment for the matrix is indicated by the circled entries in Fig. 4-5. The total distance for the optimal assignment is 23. Using the first suboptimal method, the initial assignment is $O3$ to $T2$ because $O3$ is singly validated. Then, processing $T1$ first will lead to the assignment of $O2$ to $T1$ because the corresponding distance, 6, is less than the distance, 9, from $O1$ to $T1$. Finally, the remaining assignment is $O1$ to $T3$. This leads to three assignments, but the total distance is 24, which exceeds that of the optimal solution.

The second suboptimal solution begins by making the minimum distance (3) assignment of *O*2 to *T*2. Then, *O*1 is assigned to *T*3, but *O*3 is left without an assignment. Thus, the second suboptimal solution leads to less than the maximum number of possible assignments.

4.3.3 Comparative Performance for Two Assignment Methods*

Next, we present comparative results showing the effects of assignment method upon overall system performance for a typical radar TWS system with a sampling interval of about 3.0s. Results were obtained using the optimal solution, Munkres algorithm [8, 9], and the first suboptimal solution presented above. The assumed geometry had four targets flying directly toward the tracking radar so as to maintain a constant spacing in azimuth angle as seen by the radar. Target separation occurred only in azimuth angle. The angular separation was chosen to be about three times the angular measurement error standard deviation. Range, range rate, and elevation angle were essentially the same for all targets.

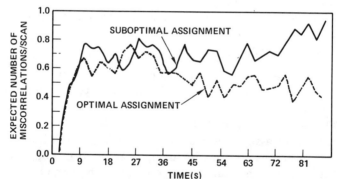

FIGURE 4-6.   COMPARATIVE MISCORRELATION PROBABILITY-OPTIMAL VS. SUBOPTIMAL ASSIGNMENT

The statistics examined were the number of deleted tracks, the expected number of miscorrelations, and the normalized azimuth angle prediction error. The results were obtained using a Monte Carlo simulation (described in Chapter 8) with 100 runs. A miscorrelation was defined to occur when an observation from a given target was assigned to a track that was last updated by an observation generated by a different target. Figure 4-6 shows the comparative number of expected miscorrelations per scan. Note that

*Results in this section are based on a study performed by Ms. Elana Dror of Hughes Aircraft Company.

because there generally were about four tracks (per the four targets), the probability of miscorrelation was about 0.12 per track using optimal assignment. This is a fairly typical large value for a difficult tracking environment.

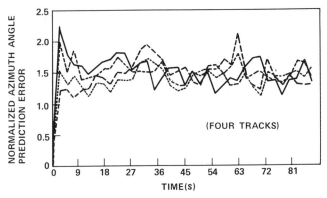

FIGURE 4-7. ANGULAR PREDICTION ERROR FOR OPTIMAL ASSIGNMENT SYSTEM

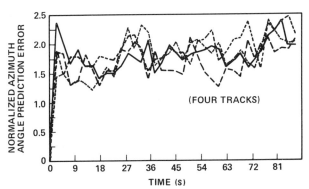

FIGURE 4-8. ANGULAR PREDICTION ERROR FOR SUBOPTIMAL ASSIGNMENT SYSTEM

Figures 4-7 and 4-8 show the normalized azimuth prediction-error standard deviations for the cases where the optimal and the suboptimal assignment methods were used. The prediction error is defined to be the difference between the true and the predicted position. The normalized angular prediction error is defined to be the angular prediction error divided by the angular measurement error standard deviation. The four lines in each figure represent the errors for the tracks on each of the four targets. All track errors are fairly large compared to the typical prediction-error standard deviations that were found for a single target (with no miscorrelation) to be less than the measurement error standard deviation. Thus, the effects of miscorrelation act to nearly double the prediction-error standard deviation for this geometry.

Referring to Figs. 4-6 through 4-8, use of the optimal assignment algorithm clearly leads to an improvement in correlation and tracking performance. The most significant performance improvement appeared in the track retention statistics, where the total number of deleted tracks was decreased from 75 for the suboptimal assignment system to 35 for the system using optimal assignment. Miscorrelation leads to degraded tracks that eventually are deleted. This occurs when the predicted position deviates from the true target position so that observations are no longer assigned to the track. Thus, decreasing the probability of miscorrelation can significantly reduce the number of prematurely deleted tracks.

4.4 SIMPLE BRANCHING OR TRACK SPLITTING

Correlation performance can be improved if certain difficult assignment decisions are deferred until more data are collected. This is an improvement upon simple sequential decision-making. Correlation performance can be improved by the efficient formation and evaluation of alternative correlation hypotheses. As shown in Figs. 4-9 and 4-10, a simple branching method applied to the tracking of two closely spaced targets illustrates the principle. Referring to Fig. 4-9, without branching, the track oscillates between the two targets and there is a significant probability that the track would eventually be extrapolated away from either true target position. Referring to Fig. 4-10, when branching is employed, a tentative track is initiated on the observation from the second target and the two-target hypothesis is accepted when another observation is received from the first target.

A simple branching logic designed for the problem described above is discussed in [10]. A Monte Carlo simulation was developed in which this branching logic was evaluated by considering two aerial targets with range separation of 3,000 to 4,000 feet and angular separation of about two degrees. With detection probability of 0.5, the probability of miscorrelation occurring before two tracks are formed is $1/3$ if branching is not used. From the Monte Carlo results of the example, without branching, incorrect correlation decisions ocurred 29 times in 85 Monte Carlo runs. With the use of branching, the number of miscorrelations was reduced to 12. Thus, for these cases, the probability of correctly establishing two target tracks without miscorrelation has increased from about $2/3$ to 0.86. Also, the logic was tested in 80 Monte

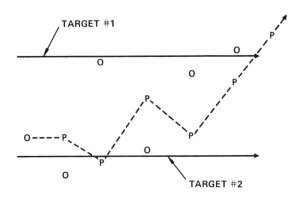

O = OBSERVATION
P = PREDICTED TRACK POSITION

FIGURE 4-9. WITHOUT BRANCHING TARGET OBSERVATIONS ARE MISCORRELATED

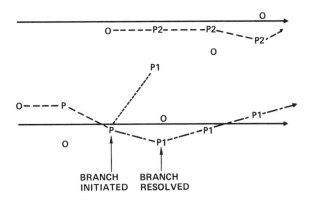

FIGURE 4-10. BRANCHING REDUCES MISCORRELATION

Carlo runs against a single maneuvering target, and it yielded the formation of only one false track.

Smith and Buechler [11] have defined a more general branching technique based upon three relatively simple rules. First, it is necessary to define a convenient notation. Here, following [11], we use j to denote the measurement number for scan k. The measurements are renumbered on each scan so that measurement j on scan k is not related to measurement j on scan $k+1$. Also, index i is used to denote the track number (defined in [11] to be a mode). Then, a support function $C_{ij}(k)$ associated with the assignment of observation j to track i on scan k can be computed, using the generalized distance $d_{G_{ij}}$ from (4.12). The recursive relationship defining the support function is

$$C_{ij}(k) = C_i(k-1) - \frac{1}{2} d_{G_{ij}}^2(k) \qquad (4.13)$$

where $C_i(k-1)$ is the support associated with track i from the previous scan, and $C_i(0)$ is the logarithm of the *a priori* probability associated with track i. Thus, a support function can be computed recursively for each track using residual information together with (4.12) and (4.13).

The support function defined in (4.13) is the log-likelihood function, which is found by taking the logarithm of the likelihood of validity of the track and ignoring constant terms. It is a simplified version of the score function, discussed in Chapter 9. The complete score function includes terms related to potential missing observations and to the option of initiating new tracks, rather than using all observations to update existing tracks.

Kalman filtering is assumed to be used for each track. The branching method is defined by (4.13) and the use of three rules. First, a gating relationship, such as that defined by (4.6), is used to eliminate unlikely observation-to-track pairings. Second, if two or more tracks have similar state estimates, only the most likely, as measured by the support function, is maintained. This reduces the number of multiple tracks on the same target and the total number of tracks is also limited. Third, tracks are eliminated if the support function falls below a threshold value.

The branching algorithm given in [11] and outlined above represents a highly simplified version of the multiple hypothesis tracking (MHT) approach that was later formulated by Reid [12] and which will be discussed in Chapter 10. The first simplifications are that missing detections ($P_D < 1$) and false alarms are not included. This deficiency could be remedied in a fairly straightforward manner by using a more complete support function, such as the score function defined in Chapter 9.

The major drawback to this simplified branching approach arises from the fact that the association constraint, which states that an observation cannot truly belong to several different target tracks, is not used. A track can be updated with all observations within its gate and an observation can be used to update several tracks. Thus, it is possible that this method may present the user with data-association hypotheses which are not mutually exclusive, nor consistent with each other, because the same observation may be used in several tracks. It is the use of the association constraint that distinguishes the more accurate (and more complex) MHT method discussed in Chapter 10.

This section introduced the concept of simple branching. The more general MHT approach is preferable if sufficient computational resources are available. However, it is often useful to devise simple branching algorithms to handle specific problems that may occur in a particular MTT system design. The problem of track initiation with closely spaced targets, illustrated in Figs. 4-9 and 4-10, is one example. Another is the problem of jet engine modulation (JEM) associated with the Doppler (range rate) return from aircraft. For this phenomenon, the angle is unaffected so that branching occurs in range and range rate when a suspect range rate return is received.

4.5 METHODS FOR STATE ESTIMATION AND COVARIANCE MODIFICATION TO ACCOUNT FOR MISCORRELATION

It has been recognized that miscorrelation represents a source of error that should be included in the Kalman filtering covariance matrix [13, 14]. Use of the unmodified standard Kalman filter in an environment where false track updates occur leads to poor performance because the theoretical covariance matrix can be very optimistic. This, in turn, leads to problems in gating and track maintenance, as well as in filtering and prediction, because the gate sizes are not likely to be optimal. Then, track updates may be lost and the tracks prematurely deleted.

Assume the sequential NN method for data association. Thus, it is desirable to modify the covariance matrix to reflect the additional error source associated with miscorrelation. This modification should be done in an *a posteriori* manner so that the probability of the given data association being incorrect is reflected. Following Jaffer and Bar-Shalom [15] and Willman [16], two methods for doing this will be described next.

Assume NN correlation and define the variable γ with respect to an observation-to-track pairing such that:

$\gamma = 1 \rightarrow$ observation originated from the target in track;

$\gamma = 0 \rightarrow$ observation did not originate from the target in track. It could be a false return or a return from another target in track.

Then, the Kalman filtering equations from (2.11) are modified to give [15]:

$$\hat{x}(k\,|\,k,\gamma) = \hat{x}(k\,|\,k-1) + \gamma K(k)\,[y(k) - H\hat{x}(k\,|\,k-1)]$$

$$P(k\,|\,k,\,\gamma) = [I - \gamma K(k)H]\,P(k\,|\,k-1)$$

(4.14)

Note that, in general, $\gamma = \gamma(k)$, but the subscripts will be omitted for notational convenience. Finally, note that

$p(\gamma = 1) = $ probability of correct correlation $= P_{CC}$
$p(\gamma = 0) = 1 - P_{CC}$

A suboptimal estimator that does not require branching forms the composite estimate of $\hat{x}(k|k)$ from the weighted sums of the estimates based upon the validity ($\gamma=1$) or nonvalidity ($\gamma=0$) of the observation. This estimate is

$$\hat{x}(k|k) = P_{CC}\hat{x}(k|k,\ \gamma=1)+(1-P_{CC})\ \hat{x}(k|k,\gamma=0) \qquad (4.15)$$

The covariance equation corresponding to the use of (4.14) and (4.15) is shown in Appendix 4B to be

$$P(k|k)= \sum_{\gamma=0}^{1} [P(k|k,\gamma)+\hat{x}(k|k,\gamma)\hat{x}^T(k|k,\gamma)]$$
$$\times p(\gamma)-\hat{x}(k|k)\hat{x}^T(k|k) \qquad (4.16)$$

Equation (4.16) allows the provision to increase the covariance as a function of the difference in the estimates provided by the two correlation alternatives. For example, consider the problem of estimating a scalar position, where

$$\hat{x}(k|k,\ \gamma=1) = 2, \quad \hat{x}(k|k,\ \gamma=0) =- 1, \quad p(\gamma=1) = 0.6,$$
$$p(\gamma=0) = 0.4$$

so that

$$\hat{x}(k|k)=0.6(2)+0.4(-1)=0.8$$

Then, the additional term (δP), which is added to the covariance in order to account for positional estimation discrepancy, becomes

$$\delta P=0.4(1)+0.6(4)- 0.64=2.16$$

The techinique discussed above requires knowledge of, or an estimate for, the probability of correct correlation (P_{CC}). Methods for estimating P_{CC} will be discussed later. First, we present another technique [16], which uses a similar approach, but differs from the above method in several ways.

Again, assume an estimate of P_{CC} to be available. For this method, the estimate of P_{CC} and the measurement that was assigned to a given track are saved from the previous data association (at scan k). Then, the updated track state vector is extrapolated forward in the usual manner. This estimate, based on the assumption of a valid observation-to-track pairing ($\gamma=1$), is defined to be $\hat{x}(k+1|k,\ \gamma=1)=x_A$. Next, the observation that was received on the previous scan and paired with the track in question is also extrapolated forward in the same manner as if it were a newly initiated track. The extrapolated observation is defined to be x_B. Finally, a composite estimate is formed from

$$\hat{x}(k+1|k)= P_{CC}x_A+(1-P_{CC})x_B \stackrel{\Delta}{=} \hat{x} \qquad (4.17)$$

Willman [16] also presents a technique for modifying the covariance matrix. Again, one covariance matrix is extrapolated ahead as would be done for the standard Kalman filter under the assumption of a correct data assignment. This covariance is defined to be $P(k+1 \mid k, \gamma = 1) = P_A$. A second covariance is computed as if the observation were the first point in a newly initiated track and is denoted P_B. Then, the resulting covariance for the estimate defined by (4.17) (again following Appendix 4B) is

$$P(k+1 \mid k) = P_{CC}[P_A + (x_A - \hat{x})(x_A - \hat{x})^T] + (1 - P_{CC})$$
$$\times [P_B + (x_B - \hat{x})(x_B - \hat{x})^T]$$
$$= P_{CC}\left(P_A + x_A x_A^T\right) + (1 - P_{CC})\left(P_B + x_B x_B^T\right) - \hat{x}\,\hat{x}^T$$

(4.18)

Note that the methods defined by (4.15) and (4.16), and by (4.17) and (4.18), respectively, are quite similar. In effect, both methods combine the standard Kalman estimate, derived under the assumption of correct correlation, with a second estimate. For the first method [15] this estimate is the non-updated extrapolation, while the second method uses the questionable updating observation to effectively initiate a new track. Both methods lead to the same form of term used to increase the covariance matrix. Also, both methods must use an estimate ($\hat{P}_{CC}$) of the probability that the assignment is correct. Thus, we next discuss computation of $\hat{P}_{CC}$.

OBSERVATIONS TRACKS	01	02
T1	g_{11}	g_{12}
T2	g_{21}	g_{22}
NEW SOURCE	β	β

FIGURE 4-11. ASSIGNMENT MATRIX
USING LIKELIHOOD FUNCTIONS

To begin, consider an assignment matrix with entries g_{ij}, as given by (4.11), representing the Gaussian likelihood function associated with the assignment of observation j to track i. Also, a final row with entries equal to the new source density β is added to represent the event that each observation is from a new source. Figure 4-11 gives an example for the two-track, two-observation case.

Assume that a solution to the assignment matrix has been obtained and that we wish to determine the probability that one of the assignments is correct. As an example, from Fig. 4-11, consider the assignment of $O1$ to $T1$. The estimated probability of correct correlation (P_{CC}) is found by forming the ratio of the likelihood of this assignment to the likelihood of all assignments involving $O1$. Thus, also including detection probability (P_D), we write

$$\hat{P}_{CC}= \frac{P_Dg_{11}[P_Dg_{22}+(1-P_D)\beta]}{P_Dg_{11}[P_Dg_{22}+(1-P_D)\beta]+P_Dg_{21}[P_Dg_{12}+(1-P_D)\beta]+(1-P_D)\beta}$$
$$\times[P_D(g_{12}+g_{22})+(1-P_D)\beta] \qquad (4.19)$$

where the term P_Dg_{11} represents detection and assignment of $O1$ to $T1$ and the term $[P_Dg_{22}+(1-P_D)\beta]$ represents the options allowed for $O2$ given that $O1$ is assigned to $T1$. The other terms have similar interpretation.

As illustrated by (4.19), the general *a posteriori* probability expression becomes quite complex even for the simple two-by-two case. For a greater number of observations and tracks, the enumeration of likelihood expressions for all feasible assignment matrix solutions also requires considerable logic. For a particular solution, the following rules (Reference [17] gives more detail) can be used:

1. Scan all columns (observations) and pick one assignment from either a track for which the gating relationships is satisfied or the new source alternative.

2. Maintain the constraint that, at most, one observation can be assigned to a track. The number of new source assignments is unlimited.

However, because of the complexity involved, simplifications are sought.

One simplification is to approximate P_{CC} by considering only the likelihoods associated with the given observation and track. Then, as recommended in [16], P_{CC} can be approximated as the ratio of the likelihood associated with the particular observation-to-track assignment to the sum of the likelihoods associated with all possible assignments for that observation. For the assignment of $O1$ to $T1$ in the example given in Fig. 4-11, this becomes

$$\hat{P}_{CC}= \frac{g_{11}}{g_{11}+g_{21}+\beta}$$

In general, for assignment of observation j to track i and with a total of N_T tracks for which the gate is satisfied, the expression becomes

$$\hat{P}_{CC}= \frac{g_{ij}}{\sum_{l=1}^{N_T} g'_{lj}+\beta} \qquad (4.20)$$

Following [16], to account for the fact that an assignment algorithm has been used, a constraint is applied for the terms in the sum of (4.20), so that,

$$g'_{lj} = \text{MIN}[g_{ij}, g_{lj}] \tag{4.21}$$

The constraint defined by (4.21) is to account for the fact that (considering only the observation by itself) if there is a more likely assignment ($g_{lj} > g_{ij}$) for observation j, this assignment was probably rejected by the assignment algorithm because of a better overall assignment. Thus, the assignment of observation j to track l must lead to other more unlikely assignments, when considering other observations and tracks. Therefore, a penalty is applied so that g'_{lj} cannot exceed g_{ij}.

The expression given in (4.20) will be most inaccurate for the case where there are several observations within the gate of a single track while not within the gates of other tracks. For this situation in which there are N_o observations within the gate of track i, an alternative expression giving the relative likelihood associated with track update by observation j is

$$\hat{P}_{CC} = \frac{g_{ij}}{\sum_{l=1}^{N_o} g'_{il}}$$

where the constraint $g'_{il} = \text{MIN}[g_{ij}, g_{il}]$ is applied.

A third technique for increasing the filter covariance is to increase the measurement noise covariance matrix (R_c). This also has the effect of decreasing the gain K so that the measurement is given less weight. For example, in the case of a conflict situation, the measurement covariance matrix would be incremented by a multiplicative factor s where ($s > 1$). The factor s could be chosen from the distance functions associated with the conflict situation or from the probability $\hat{P}_{CC}$.

4.6 SUMMARY

The purpose of this chapter has been to outline the "classical" techniques that have been proposed for gating and data association with existing tracks. The techniques discussed here are most applicable when computational resources are limited so that basically sequential processing is required. As in other areas of MTT, a great many techniques have been developed for gating and data association, and the choice of particular techniques is always highly application-dependent.

As shown in Table 4-2, the use of ellipsoidal (rather than rectangular) gates becomes more important as the measurement dimension (M) increases. For $M \geq 4$, the decreased volume associated with the ellipsoidal gate appears to be worth the increased computational effort.

Figure 1-4 showed the manner in which an unstable region occurs for certain target spacings. One general approach for decreasing the unstable region is to use methods for improving correlation. Two relatively simple and effective methods are the use of an improved assignment algorithm and the use of branching. Section 4.3 discussed the assignment problem and illustrated the considerable improvement in tracking performance that was associated with the use of an optimal assignment algorithm for a particular application. Chapter 14 will discuss implementation of an optimal assignment algorithm. Section 4.4 outlined a branching algorithm that can also be used to improve correlation without requiring the detailed logic associated with the full hypothesis tree implementation.

Section 4.5 discussed methods for modifying the Kalman covariance matrix in order to account for the increased error expected due to miscorrelation. Typically, in the presence of miscorrelation, the covariance matrix is too optimistic and the result is that subsequent correlations are missed because the gates, set using covariance terms, are too small. Thus, by appropriately modifying the covariance matrix, the effects of miscorrelation are reduced and the unstable tracking region is decreased.

REFERENCES

1. Sea, R.G., "An Efficient Suboptimal Decision Procedure for Associating Sensor Data with Stored Tracks in Real-Time Surveillance Systems," *Proceedings of the 1971 IEEE Conference on Decision and Control.*, Dec. 15–17, 1971, Miami Beach, FL, pp. 33–37.
2. Sea, R.G., "Optimal Correlation of Sensor Data with Tracks in Surveillance Systems," *Proceedings of the Sixth International Conference on Systems Sciences,* Jan. 9–11, 1973, Honolulu, HI, pp. 424–426.
3. Stein, J.J., and S.S. Blackman, "Generalized Correlation of Multi-Target Track Data," *IEEE Transactions on Aerospace and Electronic Systems,* AES-11, Nov. 1975, pp. 1207–1217.
4. Wong, P.J., and A.J. Korsak, "Reachable Sets for Tracking," *Operations Research,* Vol. 22, May-June 1974, pp. 497–508.
5. Marty, K., *Linear and Combinatorial Programming*, New York: John Wiley and Sons, 1976.
6. Hovanessian, S.A., *Radar System Design and Analysis*, Dedham, MA: Artech House, 1984.
7. Bridgewater, A.W., "Automatic Tracking Techniques for Surveillance Radars," CRC Report 1357, Communication Research Center, Department of Communications, Ottawa, Canada, July 1982.

8. Bourgeois, F., and J.-C. Lassalle, "An Extension of the Munkres Algorithm for the Assignment Problem to Rectangular Matrices," *Communications of the ACM*, Vol. 14, Dec. 1971, pp. 802–804.

9. Bourgeois, F., and J.-C. Lassalle, "Algorithm for the Assignment Problem," *Communications of the ACM*, Vol. 14, Dec. 1971, pp. 805–806.

10. Blackman, S.S., T.J. Broida, and M.F. Cartier, "Applications of a Phased Array Antenna in a Multiple Maneuvering Target Environment," *Proceedings of the 1981 IEEE Conference on Decision and Control*, San Diego, CA, Dec. 16–18, 1981, pp. 1413–1418.

11. Smith, P., and G. Buechler, "A Branching Algorithm for Discriminating and Tracking Multiple Objects," *IEEE Transactions on Automatic Control*, AC-20, Feb. 1975, pp. 101–104.

12. Reid, D.B., "An Algorithm for Tracking Multiple Targets," *IEEE Transactions on Automatic Control*, AC-24, Dec. 1979, pp. 843–854.

13. Nahi, N.E., "Optimal Recursive Estimation with Uncertain Observation," *IEEE Transactions on Information Theory*, IT-15, July 1969, pp. 457–462.

14. Singer, R.A., and J.J. Stein, "An Optimal Tracking Filter for Processing Sensor Data of Imprecisely Determined Origin in Surveillance Systems," *Proceedings of the 1971 IEEE Conference on Decision and Control*, Miami Beach, FL, Dec. 1971, pp. 171–175.

15. Jaffer, A.J., and Y. Bar-Shalom, "On Optimal Tracking in Multiple Target Environments," *Proceedings of the Third Symposium on Non-Linear Estimation Theory and Its Applications*, San Diego, CA, Sept. 11–13, 1972, pp. 112–117.

16. Willman, W.W., "Some Performance Results for Recursive Multitarget Correlator-Tracker Algorithms," NRL Report 8423, Naval Research Laboratory, Washington, DC, July 23, 1980.

17. Fortmann, T.E., Y. Bar-Shalom, and M. Scheffe, "Sonar Tracking of Multiple Targets Using Joint Probabilistic Data Association," *IEEE Journal of Oceanic Engineering*, OE-8, July 1983, pp. 173–184.

Appendix 4A

Summary of Correlation Statistics

We consider a single track with potential returns from that track and from new sources that may fall within the gate of the track. Conflict situations with interacting tracks are not considered. Probabilities associated with the correlation situations that can occur are computed below under the conditions of rectangular and ellipsoidal gates.

Two preliminaries are required for the derivation. First, the relationship $d^2 = \tilde{y}^T S^{-1} \tilde{y} \leq Z$ defines an M-dimensional hyperellipsoid with volume

$$V(M,Z) = C_M \sqrt{|S|}\, Z^{M/2} \tag{4A.1}$$

and C_M as given by (4.10). Second, assuming a Poisson distribution for the new sources with new source density β, the probability of n new sources arising within a volume element V per unit time is

$$p(n) = \frac{(\beta V)^n}{n!}\, e^{-\beta V}$$

so that

$$p(0) = e^{-\beta V}, \qquad p(n \geq 1) = 1 - e^{-\beta V} \cong \beta V \tag{4A.2}$$

Now consider the various correlation situations that may occur.

1. *Probability of Correct Return Falling Within the Track Gate* (P_G)

The quantity P_G is defined as the probability that a valid return will fall within the track gates. For the M-dimensional measurement case, the expression for P_G becomes

$$P_G(M) = \int_{V_G} \cdots \int f(\tilde{y})\, d\tilde{y}_1, \ldots, d\tilde{y}_M \tag{4A.3}$$

where

$$f(\tilde{y}) = \frac{e^{-\frac{1}{2} \tilde{y}^T S^{-1} \tilde{y}}}{(2\pi)^{M/2} \sqrt{|S|}} \tag{4A.4}$$

and the integral is over the gated volume V_G. Equation (4A.3) is, in general, difficult to evaluate for the case of rectangular gates. However, if independence of the residual errors can be assumed, the expression simplifies to

$$P_G(M) = \int_{-K_{G1}}^{K_{G1}} \frac{e^{-\frac{U_1^2}{2}}}{\sqrt{2\pi}} \, dU_1 \dots \int_{-K_{GM}}^{K_{GM}} \frac{e^{-\frac{U_M^2}{2}}}{\sqrt{2\pi}} \, dU_M$$

where U_l is the ratio of the lth component residual error to the corresponding residual error standard deviation:

$$U_l = \frac{\tilde{y}_l}{\sigma_{rl}}$$

Then, taking $K_{G1} = K_{G2} = \dots K_{GM} = K_G$ gives (4.3) from the text of Chapter 4.

For the case of ellipsoidal gates, V_G is defined as the volume element such that $\tilde{y}^T S^{-1} \tilde{y} \leq G$. Then, after transforming from $\tilde{y}$ to principal axes W such that off-diagonal elements of the residual covariance matrix vanish, the gating relationship becomes

$$\frac{W_1^2}{\sigma_{W_1}^2} + \frac{W_2^2}{\sigma_{W_2}^2} + \dots + \frac{W_M^2}{\sigma_{W_M}^2} \leq G$$

Further transforming to $V_i = W_i / \sigma_{Wi}$ gives for the gating relationship:

$$r^2 = V_1^2 + V_2^2 + \dots + V_M^2 \leq G$$

The quantity r^2 can be recognized as an M-dimensional chi-square variable (χ_M^2) such that, letting $Z = r^2$, we derive

$$f(Z)dZ = \frac{Z^{\frac{M}{2}-1} e^{-\frac{Z}{2}} \, dZ}{2^{\frac{M}{2}} \Gamma\left(\frac{M}{2}\right)} \tag{4A.5}$$

Thus, for ellipsoidal gating, we have

$$P_G(M) = \int_0^G f(Z) \, dZ \tag{4A.6}$$

Table 4.1 presents the results of evaluating (4A.6) for values of M from one to six.

2. *Probability of Correct Correlation Given Detection of True Target Return* ($P_{CC/D}$)

A correct correlation occurs if the true target return is within the gate, and if there are no false returns that have smaller normalized distance and are also within the gate. Consider the case where the true target return is within the gate. Then, for ellipsoidal gates, any false return with smaller normalized distance function must also be within the gate. For rectangular gates, there may be some small probability that a false return can have smaller normalized distance and still be outside the gate. However, for simplicity in evaluating the resulting expressions, this unlikely event will not be considered.

Assume that the true target return has normalized distance $Z = \tilde{y}^T S^{-1} \tilde{y}$. Then, using (4A.2), the probability that there are no false returns with smaller normalized distance is

$$p(0) = e^{-\beta V(M,Z)}$$

where $V(M,Z)$ is given by (4A.1). Thus, in general, the probabilty ($P_{CC/D}$) of a correct correlation given a detection becomes

$$P_{CC/D} = \int \cdots \int_{V_G} e^{-\beta V(M,Z)} f(\tilde{y}) \, d\tilde{y}_1, \ldots, d\tilde{y}_M \tag{4A.7}$$

Evaluation of (4A.7) for rectangular gates, in general, is very difficult and would require numerical integration. However, for the special case of a two-dimensional ($M=2$) measurement and uncorrelated residuals, in which

$$\rho = \frac{E[\tilde{y}_1 \tilde{y}_2]}{\sigma_{r1} \sigma_{r2}} \equiv 0$$

Reference [1] gives the solution

$$P_{CC/D}(M=2, \rho=0) = C^2 \operatorname{erf}(K_{G1}/C\sqrt{2}) \operatorname{erf}(K_{G2}/C\sqrt{2})$$

where

$$C^2 \triangleq \frac{1}{1 + \dfrac{\pi}{2} n_{TF}}, \qquad n_{TF} \triangleq \beta(2\sigma_{r1})(2\sigma_{r2})$$

The quantity $P_{CC/D}$ can be placed in a more convenient form when the use of ellipsoidal gates is assumed. For this case we again note that $Z = \tilde{y}^T S^{-1} \tilde{y}$ has the χ_M^2 distribution given by (4A.5). Then, the expression for $P_{CC/D}$ becomes

$$P_{CC/D} = \int_0^G f(Z) \, e^{-\beta V(M,Z)} \, dZ \tag{4A.8}$$

In order for reasonably effective system operation with the use of NN correlation, it would be required that the expected number of false alarms (βV) be sufficiently small so that the conservative approximation $e^{-\beta V} \cong 1 - \beta V$ is valid. In these circumstances, Equation (4A.8) becomes

$$P_{CC/D} \cong \int_0^G [1 - \beta V(M,Z)] f(Z)\, dZ = P_G(M) - \frac{\beta\, C_M \sqrt{|S|}}{2^{\frac{M}{2}}\, \Gamma\left(\dfrac{M}{2}\right)}$$

(4A.9)

$$\times \int_0^G Z^{M-1}\, e^{-\frac{Z}{2}}\, dZ \triangleq P_G(M) - \frac{\beta\, C_M \sqrt{|S|}}{2^{\frac{M}{2}}\, \Gamma\left(\dfrac{M}{2}\right)} I(M,G)$$

where

$$I(M,G) \triangleq 2^M (M-1)! - e^{-\frac{G}{2}}$$
$$\times \left[2G^{M-1} + 2^2(M-1)\, G^{M-2} + \ldots + 2^M(M-1)! \right]$$

3. *Probability of No False Return Within Gate Volume* (P_{NE})

Using (4A.2), the probability that no false (or extraneous) return falls within the gate volume is

$$P_{NE} = e^{-\beta V_G} \qquad\qquad\qquad (4A.10)$$

In the case of rectangular gates V_G is given by

$$V_G = (2K_{G1}\sigma_{r1})(2K_{G2}\sigma_{r2})\ldots(2K_{GM}\sigma_{rM})$$

Thus, using the convenient definition of (4.4),

$$n_{TF} = \beta(2\sigma_{r1})(2\sigma_{r2})\ldots(2\sigma_{rM})$$

gives

$$P_{NE} = e^{-n_{TF}K_{G1}\cdots K_{GM}}$$

For the ellipsoidal gating case, V_G is given by

$$V_G = C_M \sqrt{|S|}\, G^{M/2}$$

and this expression is substituted directly in (4A.10).

Appendix 4B

Derivation of Covariance Considering Uncertain Correlation

The desired covariance matrix is defined

$$P(k|k) = E\left[(x-\hat{x})(x-\hat{x})^T\right] = \sum_{\gamma} p(\gamma) E\gamma\left[(x-\hat{x})(x-\hat{x})^T\right] \qquad (4B.1)$$

where

$$\gamma = \begin{cases} 1, \text{ event that a correct correlation occurred} \\ \\ 0, \text{ event that an incorrect correlation occurred} \end{cases}$$

$$p(\gamma) = \begin{cases} \text{Probability of correct correlation} \stackrel{\Delta}{=} P_{CC}, \ \gamma = 1 \\ \\ 1 - P_{CC}, \ \gamma = 0 \end{cases}$$

$$E\gamma(A) = \quad \text{expected value of } A \text{ given that event } \gamma \text{ occurs}$$

Also, note that

$$x = x(k) \text{ and } \hat{x} = \hat{x}(k|k)$$

but these subscripts have been omitted for notational convenience.

We can rewrite $\hat{x}$ to be

$$\hat{x} = \hat{x}(\gamma) + (\hat{x} - \hat{x}(\gamma))$$

where

$$\hat{x}(\gamma) = \text{estimate conditioned upon the event } \gamma$$

Then,

$$E\gamma\left[(x-\hat{x})(x-\hat{x})^T\right] = E\gamma$$

$$\times \left\{ \left[(x-\hat{x}(\gamma)) - (\hat{x}-\hat{x}(\gamma)) \right] \left[(x-\hat{x}(\gamma)) - (\hat{x}-\hat{x}(\gamma)) \right]^T \right\} \qquad (4B.2)$$

The individual terms of (4B.2) become

$$E\gamma\left[(x-\hat{x}(\gamma))(x-\hat{x}(\gamma))^T\right] \equiv P(k|k,\gamma)$$

$$E\gamma\left[(\hat{x}-\hat{x}(\gamma))(x-\hat{x}(\gamma))^T\right] = (\hat{x}-\hat{x}(\gamma))\,E\gamma\left[(x-\hat{x}(\gamma))^T\right] \equiv 0$$

$$E\gamma\left[(x-\hat{x}(\gamma))(\hat{x}-\hat{x}(\gamma))^T\right] \equiv 0$$

$$E\gamma\left[(\hat{x}-\hat{x}(\gamma))(\hat{x}-\hat{x}(\gamma))^T\right] = (\hat{x}-\hat{x}(\gamma))(\hat{x}-\hat{x}(\gamma))^T$$

Thus, (4B.1) becomes

$$P(k|k) = \sum_{\gamma} p(\gamma)\left[P(k|k,\gamma) + (\hat{x}-\hat{x}(\gamma))(\hat{x}-\hat{x}(\gamma))^T\right] \qquad (4B.3)$$

In order to further simplify (4B.3) note that

$$\sum_{\gamma} p(\gamma)\hat{x}(\gamma)\hat{x}^T = \left[p(\gamma=0)\hat{x}(\gamma=0) + p(\gamma=1)\hat{x}(\gamma=1)\right]\hat{x}^T = \hat{x}\hat{x}^T$$

Similarly,

$$\sum_{\gamma} p(\gamma)\hat{x}\hat{x}^T(\gamma) = \hat{x}\hat{x}^T$$

Thus, (4B.3) becomes

$$P(k|k) = \sum_{\gamma} p(\gamma)\left[P(k|k,\gamma) + \hat{x}(\gamma)\hat{x}^T(\gamma)\right] - \hat{x}\hat{x}^T$$

Chapter 5

Measurement Formation and Processing for Multiple-Target Tracking

5.1 INTRODUCTION

This chapter discusses how sensor design and measurement data processing relate to the overall MTT problem. The emphasis will be on radar system design, but the general techniques discussed for adaptive threshold setting and target resolution are also applicable to infrared (IR) devices.

Section 5.2 presents an overview of the potential ways in which results from the MTT tracking loop can be used as feedback to effect the detection and observation formation processes [1]. Then, Section 5.3 gives a discussion of probably the most important use of feedback, adaptive threshold control. Section 5.4 outlines processing techniques that have been proposed for use in the presence of heavy background clutter.

An extremely important, but difficult, problem for MTT is multiple-target resolution. This problem presents a trade-off issue between the determination of the presence of multiple targets *versus* the false declaration of multiple targets given that only a single target is present. Section 5.5 discusses techniques for observation redundancy elimination. These techniques are required so that multiple observations from a single target can be combined.

Sections 5.6 and 5.7 discuss several techniques for sensing the presence of multiple targets within a radar beamwidth. However, solution of this problem is highly complex and system/sensor-dependent. Also, detailed signal processing techniques may be required.

Section 5.6 outlines the processing techniques that are applicable in the presence of closely spaced targets that may be resolvable in range or range rate. Section 5.7 gives a detailed discussion of a monopulse angle processing technique for determining the presence of multiple targets within the beamwidth under the condition that these targets are not resolvable in range or range rate.

The radar signal return is frequently corrupted by spurious returns resulting from jet engine (or turbine) modulation (JEM). The resulting range rate measurement can be highly disruptive to the tracking process [2]. The radar signal return may also be corrupted by electronic countermeasures (ECM), again leading to track disruption. These subjects are generally classified. Thus, we can only present a brief overview, as given in Section 5.8, of possible techniques for eliminating, or at least reducing, the effects of these corrupting signals.

5.2 OVERVIEW OF FEEDBACK BETWEEN TRACKING AND DETECTION FUNCTIONS

As illustrated by Fig. 1-1, the observation process and the rest of the tracking loop are often designed independently for MTT systems. This dichotomy can also be seen in the design specializations where one group of analysts is concerned with sensor design and another group with tracking. However, the tracking and detection functions should be interrelated. Thus, following [1], Fig. 5-1 shows how information (feedback) from the tracking loop can be incorporated into the detection process.

Feedback can first be applied to determine antenna positioning, resource allocation, and transmission control. For example, Chapter 12 discusses the advantages of adaptive sampling for an agile beam radar, and Chapter 13 outlines a technique for sensor allocation. Basically, the approach is to sample important tracks more frequently and increase the time on target in order to improve the detection probability. In addition, the tactical situation may dictate that covertness be maintained. Thus, the transmitted power can be controlled so that tracks are maintained while minimizing the probability that the transmitted radar signal is detected by hostile aircraft or ground-based tracking systems. Possible techniques include limiting the system to

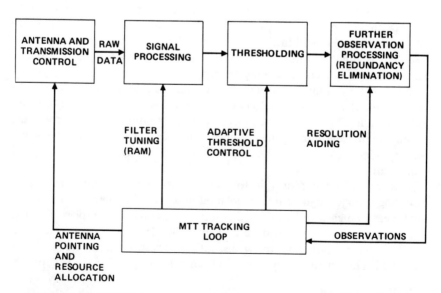

FIGURE 5-1 FEEDBACK FROM MTT LOOP TO OBSERVATION FORMATION PROCESS

intermittent search and adjusting the transmitted power according to the target range during track update illuminations.

A more complex, but potentially important, application of feedback is to affect signal processing. Special processing that cannot feasibly be done everywhere may be performed in the limited regions of expected target returns. One application in this area is to form finer Doppler (range rate) filters in the region of an expected target return. For example, in a radar raid assessment mode (RAM) the size of the Doppler filters can be reduced so that multiple targets traveling in formation can be resolved based on small differences in range rate. Another example is the performance of detailed signal processing for the purpose of determining target signature, thus indicating target type. However, typically, these techniques must also be accompanied by an increased time on target. Another application would be to apply special processing to recognize and reduce the effects of JEM returns in the vicinity of the expected target range rate.

Sections 5.3 and 5.4 will discuss techniques for adaptive detection threshold setting. Basically, the approach is to reduce the threshold in the region of expected target return (higher probabilities of detection (P_D) and false alarm (P_{FA})) and to increase it in regions of greater than average background (clutter) power (reduced P_{FA}, but also reduced P_D). Thus, by selective choice of the threshold it may be possible to obtain the required false alarm rate without loss of tracking performance.

Another application of feedback is towards the final process of determining the number of targets present in a given return or set of returns. Because a single target can generate several detections in adjacent range, range rate cells, or angular positions, a redundancy elimination (or merging) logic is required. This logic can be aided by the track-file information regarding the number of expected target returns within the region being processed. Thus, for example, merging of observations would be made less likely in regions where multiple targets are known to exist.

5.3   ADAPTIVE THRESHOLDING FOR ENHANCED DETECTION AND TRACKING PERFORMANCE

Several techniques (discussed in this section) have been proposed for choosing the detection threshold based upon expected MTT performance. Burlage [1] introduced the idea of "coached" detection, whereby the detection threshold was reduced in the region of an expected target return. This region was chosen using the filter covariance matrix to identify the detection cells in the vicinity of the expected target return. The lowered threshold in this region led to an increase in the probability of false alarm (P_{FA}) from 5×10^{-5} to 5×10^{-3}. However, a typical resulting increase in probability of detection (P_D), was, at 17 km, from about 0.5 to 0.9. The conclusion was that tracking range was increased by about 10 to 15 percent as a result of the use of adaptive thresholding.

References [3] and [4] have addressed the problem of adaptive thresholding by using the minimization of expected tracking error as the criterion for threshold setting. The method of [3] is based on the all-neighbors PDA correlation technique discussed in Chapter 10, while [4] assumes nearest-neighbor correlation.

Although the techniques differ, both [3] and [4] indicate that a threshold setting exists so that the tracking error can be minimized. This is true, first, because if the threshold setting is too high, P_D will be too small and not enough data will be received for accurate tracking. Conversely, if the threshold is too low, false alarms will corrupt tracking accuracy. Thus, it seems clear that an intermediate threshold setting that will minimize tracking error can be found.

5.3.1 Threshold Setting Based on Covariance Analysis

Fortmann [3] uses covariance analysis to determine the appropriate threshold setting. Using this analysis, the effects of missed detections and miscorrelation are represented by an average contribution to the covariance iteration (Ricatti) equation. Then, the threshold setting is chosen to minimize tracking error given the constraint of the set of feasible values for P_D *versus* P_{FA} as defined by the receiver operating characteristic (ROC) curve of the system.

The method given in [3] is based on use of the all-neighbors PDA tracking method discussed in Chapter 10. Complete details of the method are given in [3], but a number of approximations and some rather complex computations are involved. The method of [4], discussed next, provides a less complex alternative means for adaptive threshold selection.

5.3.2 Adaptive Threshold Setting Using One-Step Error Minimization

The approach presented by McLane [4] is to vary the threshold setting adaptively so that the expected tracking error after the next detection attempt is minimized. The appropriate setting is based on target SNR and position uncertainty, and the derivation uses a standard detection model. This approach is used here with a slightly different false alarm model than was used in [4].

Consider the filtered tracking error in coordinate x immediately after a target illumination is performed. The estimation error is defined as

$$\epsilon^2 \leqq E\{[x(k) - \hat{x}(k|k)]^2\} P_D + E\{[x(k) - \hat{x}(k|k-1)]^2\} (1 - P_D)$$
$$+ E\{[x(k) - \hat{x}_F(k|k)]^2\} P_{FAT} \tag{5.1}$$

where

$\hat{x}_F(k|k)$ = estimate of target position based on the assignment of a false alarm to the track

P_{FAT} = total probability of false alarm over all detection cells (or bins) = $N_B P_{FA}$ (for $N_B P_{FA}$ small)

N_B = number of detection bins within the track gate

The three terms in (5.1) represent the conditional expectation of the errors after update with a true target return, no update, and update with a false alarm. This expression is conservative because it effectively assumes that if a false alarm occurs, it will be chosen for update. Also, the factor $(1 - P_{FAT})$, which should multiply the first two terms, has been approximated by unity. Thus, as indicated by the inequality sign, this expression represents an upper bound on the error.

Define $\alpha = K_1(k)$ to be the first Kalman gain, at time step k. Then, as shown in Appendix 5A, (5.1) becomes

$$\epsilon^2 \leqq \alpha \sigma_o^2 P_D + \frac{\alpha}{1 - \alpha} \sigma_o^2 (1 - P_D) + P_{FAT} \sigma_{SFA}^2 \tag{5.2}$$

where $\sigma^2{}_{SFA}$ is the filtered variance given that a false alarm is used for track update. Also, using a standard (Swerling I) detection model [5]

$$P_{FA} = e^{-\lambda}, \quad P_D = (P_{FA})^{\frac{1}{1+SNR}} = \exp(-\alpha_s \lambda) \tag{5.3}$$

where λ is the threshold setting, and

SNR = target signal-to-noise ratio = $(R_o/R)^4$

R = target range

R_o = range at which target signal and noise power are equal

$$\alpha_s \triangleq \frac{1}{1 + SNR}$$

Following the general approach of [4], Appendix 5A computes the threshold setting (λ_M) that minimizes the expected error ϵ^2. First, the error variance resulting from update with a false alarm is computed and is expressed in terms of the rectangular gating constant (K_G of Chapter 4).

Then, using (5.3), (5.2) can be expressed in terms of the variable λ and known parameters (SNR, α, *et cetera*). A standard minimization procedure is performed and algebraic simplifications are made with the result that the desired threshold setting is

$$\lambda_M = \frac{1 + SNR}{SNR} \ln \left\{ (1 + SNR) N_B \left[\frac{(1 - \alpha)^2}{\alpha} + \frac{K_G^2}{3} \right] \right\} \qquad (5.4)$$

The derivation of (5.4) was based on the assumption of rectangular gating, discussed in Chapter 4, with gating constant K_G, typically $K_G \cong 3$. Finally, the expression given in (5.4) differs somewhat from that of [4] because of the false alarm model used here.

Referring to (5.4) and the simulation results given in Fig. 5-2, the threshold setting is a complex function of several factors. First, for low SNR the threshold may decrease with increasing SNR but, in general, the threshold increases slowly with increasing SNR. As uncertainty in the target's predicted position increases (such as through missing data) N_B will grow because the gate volume expands. Thus, increasing uncertainty in target position estimation will lead (as shown in Fig. (5-2)) to increasing threshold (and thus decreased P_{FA}). Finally, although not directly reflected in (5.4), an increase

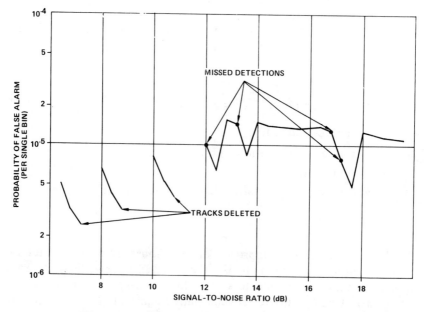

FIGURE 5-2 TYPICAL TIME HISTORY OF PFA FOR ADAPTIVE THRESHOLDING

in measurement noise variance will also increase N_B, so that the threshold will increase (and P_{FA} decrease). To summarize, the threshold generally increases with increasing SNR and, for a given SNR, the threshold also increases as target position uncertainty or measurement noise increase.

Next, results obtained from simulation of two hypothetical radar systems are summarized. The primary difference between the systems was that the second had somewhat more transmitted power (about 2.5 dB). Both used standard fixed confirmation and deletion criteria. A single target in a false alarm background was considered.

For both systems the nominal threshold setting was such that P_{FA} was 10^{-9} for each detection bin. This low value of P_{FA} ensures an acceptably low false alarm rate in search, even though many detection bins are considered. However, as will be shown, the nominal threshold setting also leads to track maintenance problems for true targets. The purpose of the study was to determine the sensitivity of tracking performance to the detection threshold.

Figure 5-2 plots the P_{FA} that was computed using the adaptive threshold for a typical case using the parameters of the second system. For this case, three tentative tracks were prematurely deleted using the fixed confirmation/deletion rule. Noting the behavior of P_{FA} (P_{FA} decreases with increasing threshold λ_M), we see that λ_M initially decreases with increasing SNR (decreasing range). Later, λ_M increases slightly as SNR increases. After missed detection attempts, P_{FA} decreases. Thus, it can be seen that λ_M increases with the increased tracking uncertainty associated with extrapolation.

Note from Fig. 5-2 that P_{FA} remains around 10^{-5}. Thus, for this system it appears that a constant threshold setting at this level may suffice for track update. Indeed, results given in Table 5-1 will indicate that the fixed threshold setting at $P_{FA} = 10^{-5}$ gives nearly the same performance as does use of the fully adaptive threshold setting. Table 5-1 presents results for the fixed threshold settings that give P_{FA} values of 10^{-9} and 10^{-5} for the adaptive thresholding system. The results are summarized through use of the following performance measures:

N_{DEL} = number of tracks deleted (including tentative)

N_{FC} = expected number of false correlations

P_{CD} = probability of a correct correlation decision. This includes the probability that no observation will be assigned to the track in the event of no return from the true target. Chapter 7 derives the expressions used to compute P_{CD} and N_{FC}

T_{90} = range at which there exists a 90 percent probability that there will be a true target track that will not later be deleted

$\sigma_{\tilde{x}}$ = standard deviation of filtered estimation error for quantity x

TABLE 5-1
TRACKING PERFORMANCE AS FUNCTION OF THRESHOLD SETTING
(based upon 100 Monte Carlo runs)

System	Threshold Setting	N_{DEL}	N_{FC}	P_{CD}	T_{90}	Normalized Values		
						$\sigma_{\bar{\eta}}$	$\sigma_{\bar{R}}$	$\sigma_{\dot{\bar{R}}}$
1	Nominal ($P_{FA} = 10^{-9}$)	99	6.2	0.994	1.0	1.0	1.0	1.0
	Fixed ($P_{FA} = 10^{-5}$)	55	21.4	0.978	1.06	0.84	0.89	0.84
	Adaptive	53	14.4	0.987	1.09	0.82	0.88	0.81
2	Nominal ($P_{FA} = 10^{-9}$)	170	4.5	0.996	1.0	1.0	1.0	1.0
	Fixed ($P_{FA} = 10^{-5}$)	100	20.8	0.982	1.03	0.90	0.96	0.89
	Adaptive	98	16.9	0.988	1.06	0.87	0.93	0.87

Tracking error was examined for azimuth angle (η), range (R), and range rate ($\dot{R}$). The results in Table 5-1 were obtained using a combination of Monte Carlo and covariance methods, and using correlation formulas derived in Appendix 4A and Chapter 7. The results were derived using 100 Monte Carlo runs. The values given for tracking range (T_{90}) and tracking error standard deviation ($\sigma_{\tilde{x}}$) are normalized with respect to the values for the nominal setting.

Table 5-1 indicates that use of an appropriately chosen fixed threshold does nearly as well overall as the full adaptive method. However, P_{CD} is somewhat better for the adaptive threshold method. Also, a significant increase in the expected number of false correlations results from use of the fixed ($P_{FA}=10^{-5}$) *versus* the full adaptive threshold method. Note that P_{CD} is highest (and N_{FC} the lowest) for the nominal setting ($P_{FA} = 10^{-9}$) because there are so few false alarms to mistake for true target returns. However, the nominal setting leads to many more track deletions and larger tracking error because of missed detections. Similar conclusions were also obtained when an improved confirmation and deletion logic, based on methods developed in Chapter 9, was used.

To summarize, use of the fully adaptive threshold setting, in preference to using the search threshold setting always, led to an improvement from six to nine percent in tracking range. This is somewhat below the 10 to 15 percent improvement predicted in [1], but this appears to be attributable to the differing detection models. The present study also indicates significant improvements in track deletion and estimation error statistics. For this system it appears that much of the improvement as a result of the adaptive threshold setting can be achieved by using a fixed (at $P_{FA}=10^{-5}$) approximation to the adaptive threshold setting for track update. Note that this threshold setting would only be used in the region of expected target return. The normal value (such that $P_{FA}=10^{-9}$ for this case) would be used elsewhere. However, the performance found with the fully adaptive threshold setting was found to be consistently better than that derived using the fixed approximation.

5.3.3 Combined Adaptive Thresholding and Branching

An appealing approach is to lower the threshold in the search area of an established track and then to apply branching for any questionable returns [6]. What might be considered "questionable" could be made a function of available computer resources (empty track files). The lowered threshold will improve track maintenance and the branching can be used to maintain tracking accuracy in the presence of the inevitable increased number of false alarms. This approach is particularly applicable to maintaining tracks moving through patches of clutter.

Results given in [6] indicate that the combination of a lowered threshold and branching can lead to an improvement in track maintenance performance that is equivalent to an increase in signal power of about 2 dB. It has been found that a 2 dB increase in signal power is worth about a 10-percent increase in tracking range as measured by T_{90}.

5.4 MEASUREMENT PROCESSING FOR A CLUTTER BACKGROUND

Ideally, the threshold setting within a given detection cell could be calculated from the returns in surrounding reference cells on the same scan. This approach is valid when the background interference is uncorrelated from scan-to-scan, and when the reference cells are independent and representative of the background. However, when the ground is illuminated, the same large amplitude clutter returns may persist over many scans and may be contained in several reference cells. In this case, more complex processing is required so that the processing of the return within a given detection cell will also be based on the returns found within the cell on previous scans. Using this approach, the goal is for the tracking system at least to have interclutter visibility, so that it can detect and track targets that are between large clutter returns.

The clutter background is nonhomogeneous and typically contains extraneous sources that produce returns which can easily be mistaken for true target returns. This section outlines some special techniques that are applicable when targets must be tracked through a clutter environment.

Following [7, 8, 9], Fig. 5-3 gives an overview of the combined detection and tracking processes that can be used for a clutter background. First, a constant false alarm rate (CFAR) logic is used to adjust the threshold according to the observed background signal level. One technique used is to estimate parameters of the background signal level for use in setting the threshold so that the required false alarm rate is achieved [10]. Also, the threshold should be adjusted based on the number of threshold crossings. This is required in order to compensate for modeling errors, such as the occurrence of non-Rayleigh clutter statistics when the Rayleigh model is used.

In addition to the overall threshold control provided by the CFAR algorithm, it may be necessary to develop quantitative measures of activity within local regions so that local threshold adjustments can be made. Also, the local false target density can be passed to the MTT tracking loop for use in determining the track confirmation criterion. For example, the false target density (β_{FT}) can be adjusted according to the local clutter density

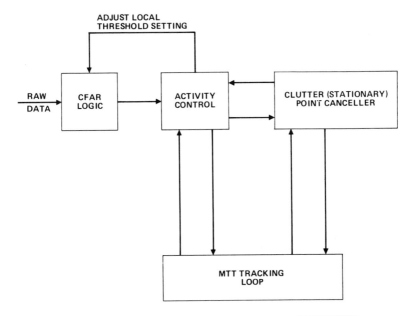

FIGURE 5-3 PROCESSING FLOW DIAGRAM FOR CLUTTER BACKGROUND

and used in the track confirmation algorithms, presented in Chapters 6 and 9, and in the multiple hypothesis tracking method, discussed in Chapter 10.

In general, feedback from the MTT tracking loop to the activity control function will also exist. This is so that tentative tracks, which are later deleted (and thus declared to be false returns), can be used in the activity control statistics. Also, the number of stationary points, as determined by the logic discussed below, can be fed back and used to aid in estimation of the local clutter density.

The clutter point canceller (or clutter map) technique establishes tracks on persistent returns from stationary objects. Returns within a gated region of a stationary point track can be removed from further processing. Input returns that are not associated with either an existing stationary point or a regular moving track are used to initiate tentative stationary and moving tracks. Then, later data are used to determine which (if either) hypothesis is correct. If the return is a false alarm that is from neither a clutter point nor a new target, the tentative stationary and moving tracks will be deleted.

A convenient method [9] for maintaining a stationary point track is to keep a counter with the track. The counter is incremented by amount γ whenever an observation associates with the stationary track and decremented by amount δ whenever there is a scan with no association. The track is deleted when the counter reaches zero. The counter is limited to maximum value M so that tracks can be deleted within a reasonable length of time.

Using this scheme, the probability of a clutter return reaching the output is a function of the defining parameters (γ, δ, M) and the probability of detection of the clutter at the input. Clutter points with intermediate probabilities of detection are the most likely to escape the stationary point tracker because they will be detected intermittently, but they may not be seen frequently enough to maintain a stationary point track.

The MTT processing loop may also be designed to adapt to the clutter environment. In addition to the appropriate choice of β_{FT} for use in a simplified sequential track confirmation algorithm, a more complex track confirmation algorithm may be required in a dense clutter environment. The next chapter will discuss track confirmation algorithms in more detail.

It may also be appropriate to vary the form of the correlation and tracking algorithms as a function of the clutter background. For example, Bar-Shalom and Tse [11] have shown the effectiveness of the probabilistic data association (PDA) method (discussed in Chapter 10) for the case of a single target being tracked against a clutter background. Thus, the PDA method might be used within a region of heavy clutter density, whereas a nearest-neighbor or multiple hypothesis tracking method (also discussed in Chapter 10) could be more appropriate in a less dense environment. Alternatively, target tracks can merely be extrapolated across a dense clutter environment.

5.5 OBSERVATION REDUNDANCY ELIMINATION (OBSERVATION MERGING)

Figures 5-4 and 5-5 illustrate typical radar scan patterns for a mechanically

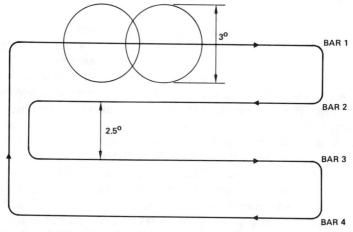

FIGURE 5-4 TYPICAL MSA TWS SCAN PATTERN

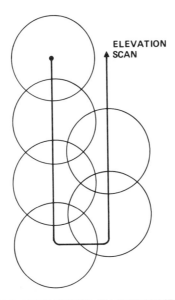

FIGURE 5-5 TYPICAL ESA SCAN PATTERN

scanned antenna (MSA) and an agile-beam electronically scanned antenna (ESA). The MSA is shown scanning a bar pattern so that a constant elevation angle is maintained while the azimuth coverage is up to 60 degrees. For tactical airborne radar applications, two to six elevation bars are typically used, with the spacing between bars about 2 degrees. The turnaround time required by the MSA dictates that a relatively long uninterrupted search segment be performed before the direction of the antenna is changed. A more continuous coverage (as illustrated by Fig. 5-5) can be provided by the ESA. Because there is essentially no turnaround time, it can conveniently scan several elevation angles at a constant azimuth angle and then move on to the next azimuth portion.

For both MSA and ESA systems, as well as for other sensor systems, a single, large target may be detected several times. These detections typically occur in adjacent azimuth and elevation beam positions, but they can also occur in adjacent range and range rate cells. Thus, a centroiding scheme must be developed to merge individual detections into a centroided detection.

For an MSA system, the centroiding will typically first occur in azimuth. As the antenna sweeps along at a constant elevation angle, adjacent azimuth detections (that also satisfy range and range rate gating criteria) will be centroided according to rules based on the anticipated target signal return and the width of the antenna beam. Resolution between adjacent targets can be obtained by using a "peak-and-valley" type of logic as illustrated in Fig. 5-6. As target spacing increases, a notch (or valley) develops between the two

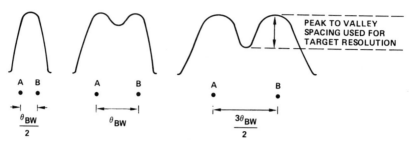

A, B = TARGET ANGULAR POSITIONS

θ_{BW} = ANTENNA BEAMWIDTH

FIGURE 5-6 AS TARGET SPACING INCREASES PEAK AND VALLEY
PROCESSING BECOMES FEASIBLE

peaks and the differences between the peaks and the valley are used to determine the presence of multiple targets. This typically occurs for target spacings of about 1 to 1.5 times the antenna's 3-dB beamwidth θ_{BW}).

The MSA system also requires a bar-to-bar centroiding logic so that returns on adjacent elevation bars are centroided if azimuth, range, and range rate gating criteria are satisfied. Peak-and-valley type logic is usually not applicable here because the amplitude from a single target can vary as a result of scintillation and eclipsing (discussed in Chapter 8) during the time between bars. Thus, patterns such as shown by the third case (spacing equals $3\theta_{BW}/2$) of Fig. 5-6 can occur in elevation by looking at three adjacent elevation bars in which the target return is eclipsed or scintillated down during the middle bar.

Finally, target range, range rate, and azimuth angle can change during the time between bars so that fine resolution using these quantities is also difficult. Thus, resolution of closely spaced targets that differ primarily in elevation is limited for the MSA system scanning pattern shown in Fig. 5-4.

Trunk [12] presents an algorithm for merging detections received using a scan pattern such as shown in Fig. 5-5. Using this algorithm, a set of adjacent detections is formed and a new detection is added to the set if it is adjacent to any existing set member. The rules presented in [12] define two detections to be adjacent if two of the three parameters (range, azimuth, and elevation) are within a resolution element and the other parameter differs by only one resolution element. The resolution elements are defined to be the range cell and the antenna beamwidth in azimuth and elevation angles. A straightforward extension of the logic could be made in order to include range rate. Also, a peak-and-valley type logic could be added, but this would greatly increase the complexity of the algorithm.

Centroiding logics tend to be defined so that a single target will rarely produce multiple observations. The price paid for this property is the lack of resolution for closely spaced targets. The next sections discuss techniques for resolving multiple targets, or at least recognizing the presence of multiple targets, even if separate measurements cannot be obtained.

5.6 METHODS FOR DETERMINING TARGET MULTIPLICITY (RANGE/RANGE RATE RESOLUTION)*

The question of unresolved detections is one of the major issues in MTT. For the radar application, this first involves the problems of detecting and resolving multiple targets within adjacent detection elements. Also, it is important at least to determine the presence of multiple targets within the radar beamwidth when these targets cannot be resolved by using differences in range or range rate.

Techniques have been developed for processing the radar range, range rate (Doppler), and angle returns to determine target multiplicity. This section begins by discussing detection issues for closely spaced targets and then discusses resolution in range or range rate. The next section discusses a general technique for determining target multiplicity through processing of the monopulse angle measurements.

The presence of closely spaced targets can lead to problems in detection as well as resolution. Typically, the threshold within a given detection cell will be determined by the returns in adjacent cells that are used to form an estimate of the local noise level. Thus, the presence of one or more interfering targets within the reference cells will lead to an increased threshold and a resulting loss of detectability within a given detection cell. For example, Rickard and Dillard [13] consider the case of two targets with proportional cross sections. Proportionality constants of 0.5 and 1.0 were examined. The threshold setting was chosen to give $P_{FA} = 10^{-5}$. Results showed that as the average received power from the primary target increases (such as through decreased range), the probability of detection still remains below 0.5. This is because SNR for the interfering target will increase, along with the SNR of the primary target, and the threshold formed using the return from the interfering target will also increase.

A partial solution to the above problem can be achieved by ranking techniques and by removing large returns from the reference cells. Using the method developed in [13], the amplitudes in the reference cells are ranked and the reference cells with the k largest amplitudes are not used in the threshold determination. The case of closely spaced targets with proportional cross sections was re-examined using this method for $k = 1$ and $k = 2$, and with a single interfering target. The effect was to require about 1 dB in

---

*The author wishes to acknowledge the contribution of Ms. H. Shyu to this section.

additional *SNR* to achieve detection performance comparable to the case of no interfering target and $k = 0$.

Trunk [12] addresses the problem of range resolution, given the typical centroiding scheme discussed in the previous section. Results presented there indicate a range resolution of approximately two and one-half pulsewidths. However, Trunk obtains improved resolution (less than a pulsewidth) using a generalized likelihood approach developed in [14]. Several more easily implemented *ad hoc* approaches are also presented in [14].

The frequency discrimination capabilities of modern high pulse repetition frequency (HPRF) radars produce very accurate range rate estimates. Typical HPRF range rate measurement errors are on the order of only a few feet per second. This capability has led to the design of a raid assessment mode (RAM), which will be outlined next. This mode is periodically entered during the tracking process to determine if a given track represents a single target, or if it actually is a single track on several closely spaced targets.

A radar MTT system may have difficulty resolving a stream raid or a wave raid scenario. A stream raid or wave raid threat consists of several closely spaced aircraft or missiles traveling at nearly the same velocity. The raid assessment mode (RAM) is used to search for targets in a designated location in space, and to determine if a return represents a single target or a cluster of targets. The purpose of a RAM mode is to provide an estimate of the number of targets in the cluster. Resolution of the elements of the cluster is possible by utilizing longer time on target and frequency agility.

Using longer time on target allows the formation of finer range-range rate detection bins. Thus, even closely spaced targets can be placed in different detection bins. Finally, frequency agility refers to the use of several different transmitted frequencies, so that the effects of scintillation, described in Chapter 8, are minimized, and the detection of multiple targets is enhanced.

5.7 TARGET MULTIPLICITY DETECTION THROUGH MONOPULSE ANGLE PROCESSING*

The technique presented in this section addresses the important problem of detecting unresolved targets through angle processing. The basic technique is general and can also be applied to processing in Doppler (range rate) and potentially range as well. This section requires detailed signal processing, and those readers wishing to avoid these mathematical details may skip this section without loss of continuity with the rest of the book.

Previous discussion has not considered use of the radar monopulse angle-

---

*Section contributed by Dr. P. Bogler of Hughes Aircraft Company and based upon a paper accepted for publication in the *IEEE Transactions on Aerospace and Electronic Systems* (AES).

measurement technique. The monopulse technique (discussed in more detail by Sherman [15]) can provide angular accuracies to within a fraction of a beamwidth. However, as also pointed out in [15], the presence of multiple targets within the beamwidth (unresolved in range or range rate) can completely distort the monopulse measurement. This is because in the presence of multiple unresolved targets, the monopulse technique essentially measures on the average the group *centroid* of any collection of objects that may lie within its field of view. Unfortunately, the position of any single individual target may differ substantially from this averaged centroid position. Thus, the monopulse measurement is not immediately applicable to tracking any given single target.

To obtain a meaningful angle measurement in the case of multiple targets in the beam, an additional technique must be introduced. This is achieved by estimating the angular *extent* of the target collection as well as the angular *centroid*. Joint centroid-extent estimation* can be accomplished because the presence of more than a single point target in the beam tends to produce extra degrees of freedom in the observables. From this an estimate can be obtained which corresponds to a measure of angular extent. If the individual targets themselves can be safely assumed to be of negligible angular extent, a large estimated value of extent serves to indicate the presence of multiple targets. In addition, the estimated value of extent is itself a measure of target separation (which can be used to ascertain individual target locations if relative target cross sections are known or can be assumed).

Asseo [16] has developed a target multiplicity detector derived from the "quadrature"(or imaginary) estimator. A more generalized approach is taken here, which includes Asseo's approach as a special case. It will be shown in the case of a single received pulse that this approach and Asseo's are entirely equivalent. However, the use of frequency agility allows several independent pulses ("looks" at the target) to be integrated into a single solution. This additional information is not efficiently handled by Asseo's approach. Frequency agility will be shown to improve greatly the detector's performance, thereby permitting feasible operation at moderate signal-to-interference ratios (SIR).

To briefly review the traditional monopulse radar concept, both the "sum" and "difference" signals are received simultaneously in the monopulse radar. Given a single point target at an angle θ_T off-boresight (for θ_T measured in fractional antenna beamwidths), and utilizing an idealized antenna model, a signal voltage proportional to $\cos^2(\theta_T)$ is generated in the sum channel, and a voltage proportional to $\sin(\theta_T)\cos(\theta_T)$ is generated in the difference channel. These two voltages can be inverted to obtain target position because

---

*The concept of joint centroid-extent estimation was originally proposed by Dr. S. Thaler of Hughes Aircraft Company.

the difference-to-sum ratio, $\tan(\theta_T)$, is functionally dependent on target position, θ_T. However, in the presence of multiple targets, a more detailed statistical model is required.

5.7.1 The Statistical Model

We begin by developing a detailed model for the monopulse measurement process. The observed outputs consist of two complex-valued voltage samples from the sum (S) and difference (D) channel outputs, respectively:

$$\mathbf{S} = S_R + jS_I, \quad \mathbf{D} = D_R + jD_I$$

for (R, I) the real (in-phase) and imaginary (quadrature phase) components, respectively; $j = \sqrt{-1}$ is the imaginary number, and the boldface denotes complex value. Assuming a Swerling II target model, these two complex-valued voltage samples, $\mathbf{S}$ and $\mathbf{D}$, can be modeled as zero-mean Gaussian random variables. When consideration is given that N Swerling II pulses are transmitted and received, the returning sum and difference signals comprise a set $\{\mathbf{S}_i; 1 \leq i \leq N\}$ and $\{\mathbf{D}_i; 1 \leq i \leq N\}$ of observed voltages.

The random observables, $\mathbf{S}_i$ and $\mathbf{D}_i$, can be written in a convenient form by way of Cholesky's decomposition [17] as shown below:

$$\begin{bmatrix} \mathbf{S}_i \\ \mathbf{D}_i \end{bmatrix} = \begin{bmatrix} A & 0 \\ B & C \end{bmatrix} \times \begin{bmatrix} \mathbf{S}_i \\ \mathbf{T}_i \end{bmatrix} \tag{5.5}$$

By definition of a Cholesky decomposition, the deterministic Cholesky parameters A, B, and C can be chosen so that the random Cholesky variable $\mathbf{T}_i$ is statistically independent of $\mathbf{S}_i$ and of equal variance to $\mathbf{S}_i$. Thus, squaring (5.5), and taking the expected value:

$$\begin{bmatrix} E[\mathbf{S}_i^* \mathbf{S}_i] & E[\mathbf{S}_i^* \mathbf{D}_i] \\ E[\mathbf{D}_i^* \mathbf{S}_i] & E[\mathbf{D}_i^* \mathbf{D}_i] \end{bmatrix} = E[\mathbf{S}_i^* \mathbf{S}_i] \begin{bmatrix} A & 0 \\ B & C \end{bmatrix} \times \begin{bmatrix} A & B \\ 0 & C \end{bmatrix}$$

where $E[\ ]$ denotes the expected value or ensemble average of the quantity between the brackets, and $\mathbf{S}_i^*$ is the complex conjugate of $\mathbf{S}_i$. For example, $E[\mathbf{S}_i^* \mathbf{S}_i]$ is written as

$$E[\mathbf{S}_i^* \mathbf{S}_i] = E[(S_{Ri} - jS_{Ii})(S_{Ri} + jS_{Ii})] = E[S_{Ri}^2 + S_{Ii}^2]$$

Finally, from the above decomposition, three expressions are produced for the unknown parameters A, B, and C:

$$A = 1.0 \tag{5.6a}$$

$$B = \frac{E[D_i^*S_i]}{E[S_i^*S_i]} = \frac{E[S_i^*D_i]}{E[S_i^*S_i]} \tag{5.6b}$$

$$C^2 = \frac{E[D_i^*D_i]}{E[S_i^*S_i]} - B^2 \tag{5.6c}$$

The parameters B and C are related to the target geometry in the following manner:

B = measure of target angular position off-boresight, or, in the case of multiple targets, a measure of group-target angular centroid. The relation $E[D_i^*S_i] = E[S_i^*D_i]$ assumed in (5.6b) is valid provided that the antenna is correctly calibrated;

C = measure of target angular extent.

The nature of C is best illustrated by the following simple example. Consider a case with two targets of equal average power present in the beam (target 1 and target 2). Assume a target angular separation $\Delta\theta$, such that the targets are symmetrically located about the boresight at $\pm\Delta\theta/2$, respectively, for $\Delta\theta$ expressed in fractional antenna beamwidths. Therefore, using our previous idealistic monopulse antenna model,

$$\begin{aligned} S_i &= V_1\cos^2(\Delta\theta/2) + V_2\cos^2(-\Delta\theta/2) \\ &= (V_1 + V_2)\cos^2(\Delta\theta/2) \end{aligned} \tag{5.7a}$$

with V_1 and V_2 the instantaneous random voltage strengths for targets 1 and 2, respectively. Similarly,

$$\begin{aligned} D_i &= V_1\cos(\Delta\theta/2)\sin(\Delta\theta/2) + V_2\cos(-\Delta\theta/2)\sin(-\Delta\theta/2) \\ &= (V_1 - V_2)\cos^2(\Delta\theta/2)\tan(\Delta\theta/2) \end{aligned} \tag{5.7b}$$

Therefore, inserting these equations in (5.6),

$$B = \frac{E[D_i^*S_i]}{E[S_i^*S_i]} = 0$$

so that

$$C^2 = \frac{E[D_i^*D_i]}{E[S_i^*S_i]} = \tan^2(\Delta\theta/2) \tag{5.7c}$$

Note that both B and C are real-valued and deterministic. In addition, C is directly dependent on target angular separation $\Delta\theta$, and is positive-valued. Also note, from (5.5) and (5.7), that $\mathbf{T}_i$ is given by $\mathbf{T}_i = (\mathbf{V}_1 - \mathbf{V}_2) \cos^2(\Delta\theta/2)$, so that $\mathbf{T}_i$ and $\mathbf{S}_i$ are independent random variables of equal variance:

$$E[\mathbf{S}_i^*\mathbf{S}_i] = E[\mathbf{T}_i^*\mathbf{T}_i]$$

$$E[\mathbf{S}_i^*\mathbf{T}_i] = 0.0$$

5.7.2 Joint Centroid-Extent Estimation

In the approach taken here, the above Cholesky parameters will be the primary target measures of interest. In the previous idealistic example, it was shown that the Cholesky parameters B and C reduce on the average to the power centroid and extent, respectively. In the general case, this is no longer true, but C still retains a direct dependency on target multiplicity that can be exploited to detect the presence of multiple targets.

To begin, in an actual implementation, the parameters B and C are not known and must be estimated from the observables. Straightforwardly estimating $E[\mathbf{S}_i^*\mathbf{S}_i]$, $E[\mathbf{D}_i^*\mathbf{D}_i]$ and $E[\mathbf{S}_i^*\mathbf{D}_i] = E[\mathbf{D}_i^*\mathbf{S}_i]$ and substituting these quantities into (5.6), a resulting estimator is found for the angular centroid B and angular extent C (denoted here as $\hat{B}$ and $\hat{C}$), as given by (using the observed $\mathbf{S}_i$ and $\mathbf{D}_i$):

$$\hat{B} = \frac{\sum\limits_{i=1}^{N} \text{Re}\,[\mathbf{D}_i^*\mathbf{S}_i]}{\sum\limits_{i=1}^{N} \mathbf{S}_i^*\mathbf{S}_i} \tag{5.8a}$$

$$\hat{C}^2 = \frac{\sum\limits_{i=1}^{N} \mathbf{D}_i^*\mathbf{D}_i}{\sum\limits_{i=1}^{N} \mathbf{S}_i^*\mathbf{S}_i} - \hat{B}^2, \quad \text{for } \hat{C} > 0$$

where Re[ ] denotes the real part of the quantity between the brackets.

Assuming a Swerling II model for the fluctuating target cross section, the estimates in (5.8) can be shown to be equivalent to the maximum likelihood estimates of B and C. Also, the angular accuracy of these estimates approaches the Cramer-Rao lower bound as $N \to \infty$. Moreover, as shown in Appendix 5B, the C^2 estimator is equivalent to the quadrature estimator of Asseo [16] in the special case of $N = 1$.

5.7.3 Detection of Target Multiplicity through Angular Extent

To discriminate against returns from noise (clutter or thermal), the value of $\hat{C}^2$ is required to exceed a threshold,

$$\hat{C}^2 > \lambda_C^2 \tag{5.9}$$

before target multiplicity is declared. To determine λ_C^2, it is necessary to consider the effects of noise on the behavior of the C^2 estimator. In the presence of additive noise, Appendix 5B shows that

$$C^2 = \frac{C_t^2\,SIR + 1 + B^2\,(SIR + 1)/SIR}{SIR + 1} \tag{5.10}$$

where

C_t = true target angular extent, $C \rightarrow C_t$ as $SIR \rightarrow \infty$

SIR = signal-to-interference ratio (per pulse), equal to the signal in the sum channel minus the noise, for example,

$SIR = E[\mathbf{S}_i^*\mathbf{S}_i] - 1.0$

assuming that the signal has been normalized to unity noise power; i.e., $E[\mathbf{N}_i^*\mathbf{N}_i] \triangleq 1.0$. (Note that the quantity SIR is simply a generalization of SNR.)

Also, as shown in Appendix 5B, the quantity $\hat{C}^2/C^2$ equals the ratio of two chi-square (χ^2) random variables with $2N-1$ and $2N$ degrees of freedom in the numerator and denominator, respectively. Thus,

$$\frac{\hat{C}^2}{C^2} = \frac{\chi_{2N-1}^2}{\chi_{2N}^2}$$

where N equals the number of independent pulses taken. For the case of a single point target C_t equals zero, so that

$$\lim_{C_t \rightarrow 0} C^2 = C_0^2 \triangleq \frac{1 + B^2\,(SIR + 1)/SIR}{SIR + 1} \tag{5.11}$$

Equation (5.11) implies that, in the case of a single point target,

$$\lim_{C_t \rightarrow 0} \hat{C}^2 = C_0^2\,\frac{\chi_{2N-1}^2}{\chi_{2N}^2} = C_0^2\,\frac{2N}{2N-1}\,F_{2N-1,2N} \tag{5.12}$$

where $F_{2N-1,2N}$ is an F distributed random variable with $2N - 1$ and $2N$ degrees of freedom.

Define P_{FD} to be the probability of falsely declaring multiple targets when a single target is present. Then, given an allowable value for P_{FD}, an appropriate value for the threshold λ_C^2 can be defined from (5.9) and (5.12), using the relationship:

$$P_{FD} = \Pr\left[\; C_0^2 \,\frac{2N}{2N-1}\, F_{2N-1,2N} > \lambda_C^2 \;\right]$$

which can be solved using a standard look-up table for the F distribution. Note that the threshold λ_C^2 will implicitly depend, through C_0^2, on the estimated target-off-boresight angle B and the estimated SIR.

Finally, given λ_C^2, the probability of detecting a true condition of target multiplicity, P_{DMT}, is given by

$$P_{DMT} = \Pr\left[\; C^2 \,\frac{2N}{2N-1}\, F_{2N-1,2N} > \lambda_C^2 \;\right]$$

where C^2 is the value from (5.10) when more than a single target is present.

Alternatively, closed-form expressions have been obtained for the above quantities P_{FD} and P_{DMT}. Appendix 5B derives

$$P_{FD} = 1 - \sum_{i=0}^{N-1} \frac{\Gamma(N+i-1/2)}{\Gamma(N-1/2)\, i!} \; \frac{[C_0^2/\lambda_C^2]^i}{[1 + C_0^2/\lambda_C^2]^{N+i-1/2}} \tag{5.13}$$

and

$$P_{DMT} = 1 - \sum_{i=0}^{N-1} \frac{\Gamma(N+i-1/2)}{\Gamma(N-1/2)\, i!} \; \frac{[C^2/\lambda_C^2]^i}{[1 + C^2/\lambda_C^2]^{N+i-1/2}} \tag{5.14}$$

Following Asseo [16], a convenient parametric form for P_{FD} and P_{DMT} can be obtained by introducing the following notation:

$$\mu \triangleq \sqrt{\frac{C_t^2\, SIR}{1 + B^2\,(SIR + 1)/SIR}}$$

Then, on noting that

$$C^2 = C_0^2\,[1 + \mu^2]$$

the receiver operating characteristic (ROC), P_{DMT} *versus* P_{FD}, can be obtained as a function of μ by mutually eliminating the common variable C_0^2/λ_C^2 from (5.13) and (5.14). Figure 5-7 presents this ROC curve for $N=1$.

To illustrate the use of Fig. 5-7, return to the example discussed previously (for which $N=1$). In this example, we showed that

$$B = 0, \quad C_t = \tan(\Delta\theta/2)$$

Thus, if the targets are separated by one-half beamwidth ($\Delta\theta = 1/2$),

$$\mu = C_t \sqrt{SIR} = 0.255 \sqrt{SIR}$$

For a moderate value of $SIR = 18$ dB (or 61.5), the appropriate curve would be $\mu = 2.0$. As shown in Fig. 5-7, the performance is not good for $\mu = 2.0$ and $N=1$ (for example, $P_{DMT} = 0.2$ at $P_{FD} = 0.05$). In conclusion, at moderate SIR values, something more is required to achieve acceptable system performance; namely, increasing the system's diversity number, N.

Figure 5-8 shows the detector performance as N is allowed to become larger than 1, fixing the allowable P_{FD} at 0.05. Also, for comparison, Fig. 5-8 shows the performance of Asseo's single-pulse quadrature detector given the 1-out-of-N declaration scheme proposed in [16]. Note the rapid performance improvement in the C^2 detector as N increases, whereas the quadrature method shows relatively little improvement. Taking the parameter values $N=5$ and $\mu = 2.0$, the C^2 estimator gives $P_{DMT} = 0.77$ with $P_{FD} = 0.05$.

In conclusion, for $N > 1$, use of the C^2 estimator permits feasible operation

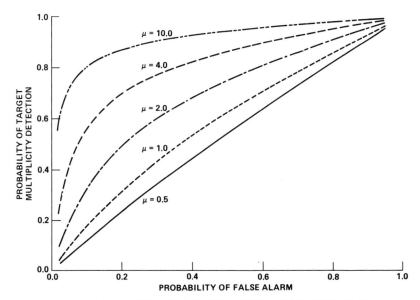

FIGURE 5-7 RECEIVER OPERATING CHARACTERISTICS FOR SINGLE PULSE (N=1)

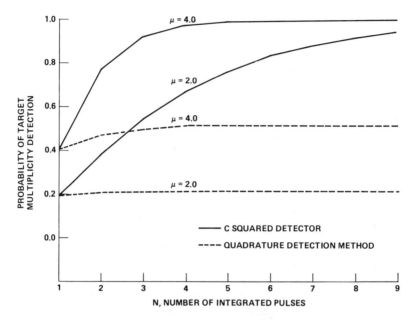

FIGURE 5-8 COMPARATIVE PERFORMANCE VERSUS NUMBER OF INTEGRATED PULSES

at levels of SIR significantly beyond that of the quadrature estimator. The value of N in (5.8) should be as large as possible in order to realize these benefits.

The technique presented above was developed assuming Rayleigh fluctuating Swerling II targets, which corresponds to assuming maximum entropy for the target model. The C^2 estimator can be shown equivalent to the maximum likelihood estimate of target separation and is asymptotically efficient; this property is achieved by forming estimates on the full set of data rather than basing them on each individual pulse. Thus, it is the maximum likelihood estimate of target separation which is the quantity of interest in the detection logic. This amounts to making the best use of the available information.

5.8 MEASUREMENT DEGRADATION DUE TO JET ENGINE MODULATION AND ELECTRONIC COUNTERMEASURES

Jet engine modulation (JEM) has been shown to have potentially degrading effects upon tracking performance [2]. Also, it is known [18, 19] that a number of electronic countermeasures (ECM) techniques have been developed to corrupt the radar return, and thus disrupt tracking. This section briefly describes some of the most relevant characteristics of JEM and ECM, and outlines approaches that may be helpful in reducing their effects for the MTT problem. However, these techniques typically require either extensive signal processing to recognize the corrupting effects during observation, or extensive additions to the MTT tracking logic in order to reduce the ultimate effects of the corrupting measurements.

5.8.1   MTT Modifications for JEM

The use of pulse Doppler radar provides a range rate measurement for tracking. However, in practice, the returns from a single aircraft target often lead to multiple observations at the same range and angle, but with different range rates. Unfortunately, the correct range rate may not even be included in the observation set. The spurious range rate observations are the result of modulation produced by the motion of internal components of the jet engine. This modulation (JEM) tends to be of highest amplitude for head-on geometries and begins at about two-thirds of the usual tracking range. The modulation is also typically characterized by harmonic relationships among the returns.

The exact pattern of JEM returns is dependent upon the particular aircraft being observed and the range. However, the deviations of the JEM returns from the true target range rate (skin return) are often about the same as the expected deviations between true and expected returns during the conditions of target maneuver. Thus, in the absence of a skin return, a JEM return may correlate with the track and lead to a false indication of maneuver. Conversely, if the target does maneuver, a JEM return can appear closer to the predicted range rate than is the true skin return, and thus be correlated with the track in question. In this case, the true target maneuver may go undetected. Finally, because multiple spurious returns are generated from the single target, there is the potential to form multiple tracks on the same target.

There are basically two approaches to the JEM problem. The first approach is to examine the signature of the components using harmonic processing and amplitude information in order to identify returns that are likely to have been produced by JEM. Thus, once relative likelihoods of validity are determined, the correlation and track initiation processes are designed so that they heavily favor returns which have been designated as likely to be from the skin. However, this approach is highly complex.

An alternative (or complementary) approach is to modify the MTT logic to account for the potential presence of JEM. For example, one technique uses the principle that observations which satisfy gates with existing tracks in range and angle, but differ in range rate, can be identified as likely JEM returns. This logic reduces spurious track initiations. Under certain conditions of ambiguity, range rate observations either can be ignored or branch-

ing type logic can be used to defer decisions on the true range rate measurement until further data are received. However, note that range and angle
information can be used for track update (or new track initiation), even if
the range rate observation is questionable.

As discussed by Nelson [2], a time-delay maneuver detector can be used
so that consistency between the range rate measurements and the target flight
path is established before the potentially spurious range rate is accepted.
Other techniques include the use of more complex range-range rate gating
procedures and the maintenance of tracks on the JEM lines in addition to
the target skin return. Then, using the latter method, spurious returns
corresponding to JEM line estimates can be identified, and it may also be
possible to update estimated target range rate using a JEM return and the
expected offset, even though the skin return is not present.

5.8.2   MTT Modifications for ECM

A wide variety of deception techniques have been developed for denying
or confusing the measurements of range, range rate, or angle [18, 19]. The
simplest technique is noise (or barrage) jamming, which can deny the
measurement of range and range rate. As stated in Chapter 3, the tracking
coordinate system must be chosen so that track can be maintained in the
presence of angle-only measurements. This constraint favors the use of polar
coordinates over the Cartesian system. When range and range rate estimates
are used in the angle tracking filters, it is necessary to provide "nominal"
values for the cases where no direct range or range rate measurements are
available. However, crude estimates of range can be obtained from the
original range estimate (or measurements) and the line-of-sight rate. Then,
eventually burn-through may occur so that a range measurement can be
obtained. Finally, special filtering techniques (outlined in Chapter 3) have
been developed for tracking with angle-only measurements.

Sophisticated ECM devices can corrupt the returning radar signal so that
incorrect range, range rate, and angle information are received. Furthermore,
these corrupting signals may be generated in a systematic manner with the
intent of confusing the tracking system. For example, the RGPO (range gate
pull-off) device can delay the returning radar pulses so that the tracking
system "sees" the target as moving away.

A never-ending game exists between the designers of ECM techniques and
those designing electronic counter-countermeasures (ECCM) techniques to
counter ECM. A variety of ECCM techniques exists in order to design the
transmitted radar signal and the processing techniques for the received signal
to be resistant to ECM [18]. However, the techniques developed by the MTT
system designer represent the last line of defense for the total ECCM system.

For the MTT system to operate successfully in the ECM environment, it is necessary that models be developed to describe potential ECM returns. Then, as with JEM, measures of likelihood for the validity of returning observation can be used to aid the track initiation and correlation processes. Also, extensive consistency tests between the state estimates can be used to detect track degradation due to ECM before track is lost. For example, independent filters can be used to estimate range rate through measured range alone and through measured range rate alone. Consistency checks can then be used to determine the presence of range or range rate deception ECM. The important principle for the design of military systems is that ECCM (and JEM) logic should be an integral portion of the MTT system design from inception.

5.9 SUMMARY

This chapter has presented a number of ways in which measurement data processing can be used to affect MTT performance. The principle of lowering the detection threshold in the vicinity of the predicted target position is very appealing and several approaches for determining threshold setting have been proposed. One approach (discussed in detail here) leads to a convenient adaptive recursive formulation. Results indicate feasibility, but this remains an area for research.

Special measurement processing techniques are required when tracking occurs in a heavy clutter (or false alarm) background. Adaptive threshold settings are typically determined using constant false alarm rate (CFAR) algorithms. In addition, special techniques should be used so that returns from stationary clutter sources are recognized before being allowed to cause potential miscorrelation with true target tracks. Also, the false target density, β_{FT}, should be estimated for use in the correlation and track confirmation logic. Special techniques for track initiation and confirmation may also be required, such as the batch processing techniques to be discussed in Chapter 6. Finally, use of an all-neighbors correlation approach, such as the PDA discussed in Chapter 10, may be appropriate for regions of heavy background clutter.

It is important to inhibit the formation of multiple tracks on a single target. Thus, observation redundancy logic, such as discussed in Section 5.5, is required so that a single target will not produce more than one observation per scan. However, it is also important to recognize the presence of multiple closely spaced targets. These conflicting requirements are best satisfied by the design of special modes or processing techniques for determining target multiplicity.

Target multiplicity can be determined by special processing in range and range rate or angle. Either technique requires an increased time on target, beyond that normally required for the detection of a single target. A typical approach would be to schedule a track for special update periodically in order to determine if more than one target is present in the return. This, of course, requires more time on target to collect the required information and special processing. One approach is to form special, narrow, range-range rate detection cells. Another approach is to perform special processing, using multiple "looks" at the target, of the monopulse angle-measurement data.

Spurious measurements caused by JEM or ECM are potentially very disruptive to the MTT process. False tracks, false maneuver indications, and premature track deletions can result as a single target produces multiple incorrect returns. A brief outline was given of suggested approaches for designing MTT logic to operate in JEM and ECM environments.

REFERENCES

1. Burlage, D.W., *et al.*, "Automatic Track-While-Scan Radar Systems with Feedback," *SOUTHEASTCON '78: Proceedings of the Southeast Region 3 Conference,* Atlanta, GA, April 10–12, 1978, pp. 398–401.
2. Nelson, N., "Aircraft Tracking Problems from Range Rate Turbine Modulation," *NAECON '77, Proceedings of the National Aerospace and Electronics Conference,* Dayton, OH, May 17–19, 1977, pp. 679–682.
3. Fortmann, T.E., *et al.*, "Detection Thresholds for Multi-Target Tracking in Clutter," *Proceedings of the 1981 IEEE Conference on Decision and Control,* San Diego, CA, Dec. 16–18, 1981, pp. 1401–1408.
4. McLane, P.J., P.H. Wittke, and C.K.S. Ip, "Least Mean-Square-Error Adaptation of Parameters in Track-While-Scan Radar Systems," *Proceedings of the 1980 IEEE International Radar Conference,* Arlington, VA, April 28–30, 1980, pp. 451–457.
5. Di Franco, J.V., and W.L. Rubin, *Radar Detection,* Dedham, MA: Artech House, 1980.
6. Miller, R.J., and R. Treciokas, "Tracker Feedback for Adaptive Threshold Control," *Proceedings of the IEE Colloquium on Adaptive Thresholding 1981,* London, March 25, 1981, pp. 10.1–10.4.
7. Bath, W.G., *et al.*, "False Alarm Control in Automated Radar Surveillance Systems," *Proceedings of the IEE 1982 International Radar Conference,* London, 1982, pp. 71–75.
8. Tunnicliffe, R.J., "An Automatic Tracking System Based on

the Stationary Plot Filter," *AGARD Conference Proceedings No. 252, Strategies for Automatic Track Initiation*, Monterey, CA, Oct. 1978, pp. 1-1 to 1-20.

9. Fleskes, W., "Automatic Track Initiation for a Phased Array Antenna Using a Clutter Map," *AGARD Conference Proceedings No. 252, Strategies for Automatic Track Initiation*, Monterey, CA, Oct. 1978, pp. 10-1 to 10-9.

10. Tugnart, J.K., and S. Prasad, "Adaptive Radar Detection with Asymptotically Regulated False-Alarm Rate," *IEEE Transactions on Aerospace and Electronics Systems*, AES-13, July 1977, pp. 390-394.

11. Bar-Shalom, Y., and E. Tse, "Tracking in a Cluttered Environment with Probabilistic Data Association," *Proceedings of the 4th Symposium on Nonlinear Estimation*, San Diego, CA, September 1973, pp. 13-21.

12. Trunk, G.V., "Range Resolution of Targets Using Automatic Detectors," *IEEE Transactions on Aerospace and Electronic Systems*, AES-14, Sept. 1978, pp. 750-755.

13. Rickard, J.T., and G.M. Dillard, "Adaptive Detection Algorithms for Multiple-Target Situations," *IEEE Transactions on Aerospace and Electronic Systems*, AES-13, July 1977, pp. 338-343.

14. Trunk, G.V., "Range Resolution of Targets," *IEEE Transactions on Aerospace and Electronic Systems*, AES-20, November 1984, pp. 789-797.

15. Sherman, S.M., *Monopulse Principles and Techniques*, Dedham, MA: Artech House, 1984.

16. Asseo, S.J., "Detection of Target Multiplicity Using Monopulse Quadrature Angle," *IEEE Transactions on Aerospace and Electronic Systems*, AES-17, March 1981, pp. 271-280.

17. Bierman, G.J., *Factorization Methods for Discrete Sequential Estimation*, New York: Academic Press, 1977.

18. Johnston, S.L., *Radar Electronics Counter-Countermeasures*, Dedham, MA: Artech House, 1979.

19. Bernhard, R., "Electronic Countermeasures," *IEEE Spectrum*, Volume 19, October 1982, pp. 59-62.

Appendix 5A

Derivation of Optimal Threshold Setting

Given the detection model of (5.3), we wish to find the threshold setting (λ_M) that minimizes the error expression (ϵ^2) of (5.1). First, define

σ_o^2 = observation variance

σ_p^2 = prediction variance = $p_{11}(k|k-1) = E\{[x(k) - \hat{x}(k|k-1)]^2\}$

σ_s^2 = filtered variance = $p_{11}(k|k) = E\{[x(k) - \hat{x}(k|k)]^2\}$

Then, using the Kalman filtering equations:

$$\alpha \stackrel{\Delta}{=} K_1(k) = \frac{\sigma_p^2}{\sigma_p^2 + \sigma_o^2}, \qquad \sigma_s^2 = (1 - \alpha)\,\sigma_p^2$$

so that

$$\sigma_p^2 = \frac{\alpha}{1 - \alpha}\,\sigma_o^2, \qquad \sigma_s^2 = \alpha\sigma_o^2$$

Thus, (5.1) becomes

$$\epsilon^2 \leqq \sigma_s^2\,P_D + \sigma_p^2\,(1 - P_D) + P_{FAT}\,\sigma_{SFA}^2$$

$$= \alpha\sigma_o^2\,P_D + \frac{\alpha}{1 - \alpha}\,\sigma_o^2\,(1 - P_D) + P_{FAT}\,\sigma_{SFA}^2 \tag{5A.1}$$

The term σ_{SFA}^2 is the filtered variance given that a false alarm is used for track update using the Kalman filtering update with observation $y(k)$. Using the update equation

$$\hat{x}(k|k) = (1 - \alpha)\,\hat{x}(k|k-1) + \alpha y(k)$$

gives

$$\sigma_{SFA}^2 = (1 - \alpha)^2\,\sigma_p^2 + \alpha^2\,\sigma_{FA}^2 = \alpha\sigma_o^2\left[(1 - \alpha) + \alpha\,\frac{\sigma_{FA}^2}{\sigma_o^2}\right] \tag{5A.2}$$

where σ_{FA}^2 is the variance of the difference between the position of the measured false alarm and the true target position. Substituting (5A.2) into (5A.1) and using (5.3) gives

$$\epsilon^2 \leqq \alpha\sigma_o^2\left\{\exp(-\alpha_s\lambda) + \frac{1 - \exp(-\alpha_s\lambda)}{1 - \alpha} + N_B\exp(-\lambda)\left[(1 - \alpha) + \alpha\,\frac{\sigma_{FA}^2}{\sigma_o^2}\right]\right\}$$

$$\tag{5A.3}$$

Differentiation of (5A.3) with respect to λ gives the threshold setting (λ_M) that minimizes ϵ^2. First, define

$$Q \stackrel{\triangle}{=} N_B \left[(1 - \alpha) + \alpha \; \frac{\sigma_{FA}^2}{\sigma_o^2} \right]$$

Then, taking

$$\frac{\partial \epsilon^2}{\partial \lambda} = \alpha \sigma_o^2 \left\{ \left[-\alpha_s + \frac{\alpha_s}{1 - \alpha} \right] e^{-\alpha_s \lambda} - Q e^{-\lambda} \right\} = 0$$

gives

$$\frac{\alpha \alpha_s}{1 - \alpha} e^{-\alpha_s \lambda_M} = Q e^{-\lambda_M}$$

Using the identifications

$$\alpha_s = \frac{1}{1 + SNR}, \quad \frac{1 - \alpha}{\alpha \sigma_o^2} = \frac{1}{\sigma_p^2}$$

and solving for λ_M gives

$$\lambda_M = \frac{(1 + SNR)}{SNR} \ln \left\{ (1 + SNR) \, N_B \left[\frac{(1 - \alpha)^2}{\alpha} + \alpha \; \frac{\sigma_{FA}^2}{\sigma_p^2} \right] \right\} \qquad (5A.4)$$

The final step in the derivation is to determine σ_{FA}^2 in terms of other parameters that can be conveniently specified. First, the residual variance σ_r^2 is given by

$$\sigma_r^2 = \sigma_o^2 + \sigma_p^2$$

Next, assume rectangular gating (with gate constant K_G) so that the false alarms are uniformly distributed over the interval $(-K_G \sigma_r, K_G \sigma_r)$. Then,

$$\frac{\sigma_{FA}^2}{\sigma_p^2} = \frac{K_G^2 \, \sigma_r^2}{3 \sigma_p^2} = \frac{K_G^2 \, (\sigma_o^2 + \sigma_p^2)}{3 \sigma_p^2} = \frac{K_G^2}{3\alpha} \qquad (5A.5)$$

Thus, combining (5A.4) and (5A.5) gives (5.4):

$$\lambda_M = \frac{(1 + SNR)}{SNR} \ln \left\{ (1 + SNR) \, N_B \left[\frac{(1 - \alpha)^2}{\alpha} + \frac{K_G^2}{3} \right] \right\} \qquad (5.4)$$

Appendix 5B

Derivations for Target Multiplicity Detection Method

First, we show that the extent estimator C^2 behaves as the ratio of two χ^2 random variables with $2N - 1$ and $2N$ degrees of freedom in the numerator and denominator, respectively. To begin, from (5.5):

$$\mathbf{D}_i = B\,\mathbf{S}_i + C\,\mathbf{T}_i$$

so that

$$\sum_{i=1}^{N} \mathbf{D}_i^*\mathbf{D}_i = B^2 \sum_{i=1}^{N} \mathbf{S}_i^*\mathbf{S}_i + C^2 \sum_{i=1}^{N} \mathbf{T}_i^*\mathbf{T}_i + 2BC \sum_{i=1}^{N} \mathrm{Re}(\mathbf{T}_i^*\mathbf{S}_i)$$

and

$$\sum_{i=1}^{N} \mathrm{Re}(\mathbf{D}_i^*\mathbf{S}_i) = B \sum_{i=1}^{N} \mathbf{S}_i^*\mathbf{S}_i + C \sum_{i=1}^{N} \mathrm{Re}(\mathbf{T}_i^*\mathbf{S}_i)$$

Inserting the above into (5.8b), and cancelling common terms, results in

$$\hat{C}^2 = C^2 \frac{\displaystyle\sum_{i=1}^{N} \mathbf{T}_i^*\mathbf{T}_i - \left[\displaystyle\sum_{i=1}^{N} \mathrm{Re}(\mathbf{T}_i^*\mathbf{S}_i)\right]^2 \Big/ \displaystyle\sum_{i=1}^{N} \mathbf{S}_i^*\mathbf{S}_i}{\displaystyle\sum_{i=1}^{N} \mathbf{S}_i^*\mathbf{S}_i} \tag{5B.1}$$

$$= C^2 \frac{\text{numerator}}{\text{denominator}}$$

The denominator of (5B.1) is seen to be a $2N$ chi-square random variable. Considering the numerator, first note that

$$\sum_{i=1}^{N} \mathbf{T}_i^*\mathbf{T}_i$$

is invariant to a change of coordinates. Therefore, the coordinates of $\{\mathbf{T}_i\}$ can be changed so that one of its new N components, for example $\mathbf{T}_N$, lies congruent with $\{\mathbf{S}_i\}$. In this new coordinate frame, we have

$$\mathbf{T}_N \triangleq N\text{th element of } \{\mathbf{T}_i\} \triangleq \frac{\displaystyle\sum_{i=1}^{N} \mathbf{T}_i^*\mathbf{S}_i}{\sqrt{\displaystyle\sum_{i=1}^{N} \mathbf{S}_i^*\mathbf{S}_i}}$$

Thus,

$$\text{Re}(\mathbf{T}_N) = \frac{\displaystyle\sum_{i=1}^{N} \text{Re}[\mathbf{T}_i^*\mathbf{S}_i]}{\sqrt{\displaystyle\sum_{i=1}^{N} \mathbf{S}_i^*\mathbf{S}_i}}$$

so that

$$\text{numerator} = \sum_{i=1}^{N} \mathbf{T}_i^*\mathbf{T}_i - |\text{Re}(\mathbf{T}_N)|^2$$

$$= \sum_{i=1}^{N} [\text{Im}(\mathbf{T}_i)]^2 + \sum_{i=1}^{N-1} [\text{Re}(\mathbf{T}_i)]^2$$

$$\triangleq 2N - 1 \text{ chi-square random variable}$$

in this new coordinate frame. Hence, the numerator can be identified as a $2N-1$ chi-square random variable, whereas the denominator, as mentioned previously, is of order $2N$.

Next, we show that the C^2 estimator is equivalent to the quadrature estimator of Asseo for $N = 1$. First, note that for the special case of $N = 1$ (single pulse), we can write

$$\text{numerator} = |\text{Im}(\mathbf{T}_{N=1})|^2 \triangleq \frac{[\text{Im}(\mathbf{T}_1^*\mathbf{S}_1)]^2}{\mathbf{S}_1^*\mathbf{S}_1} \tag{5B.2}$$

Then, for $N = 1$, using (5B.1), (5B.2), and (5.5) gives

$$\hat{C}^2 = C^2 \frac{[\text{Im}(\mathbf{T}_1^*\mathbf{S}_1)]^2}{|\mathbf{S}_1^*\mathbf{S}_1|^2} = \frac{[\text{Im}(\mathbf{D}_1^*\mathbf{S}_1 - B\mathbf{S}_1^*\mathbf{S}_1)]^2}{|\mathbf{S}_1^*\mathbf{S}_1|^2} = \frac{[\text{Im}(\mathbf{D}_1^*\mathbf{S}_1)]^2}{|\mathbf{S}_1^*\mathbf{S}_1|^2}$$

Thus, in the case of a single pulse, the C^2 estimator is equivalent to the square of the quadrature estimator.

Next, the net effect of introducing an additive noise term will be shown to be equivalent to a change in one of the variables. To begin, the presence of additive noise causes the random observable S_i to be composed of a random signal component, Q_i, and an additive noise component, N_i, so that

$$S_i = Q_i + N_i$$

where N_i is modeled as a zero-mean independent identically-distributed (i.i.d.) additive noise waveform with Gaussian statistics. The variance of N_i will be normalized to unity (i.e., the variance of Q_i will be normalized to be the signal-to-interference ratio).

Similarly,

$$D_i = B_t Q_i + C_t T_i' + M_i \tag{5B.3}$$

where M_i is modeled as a i.i.d. noise waveform independent of N_i and of unity variance. As $SIR \to \infty$, then B and C will approach B_t and C_t, respectively.

To determine the relationship between the target parameters B_t and C_t and the Cholesky parameters B and C, first note that the random variable T_i' is uncorrelated with Q_i and of equal variance. Then, equating the relationships, from (5.5) and (5B.3), we have

$$D_i = B_t Q_i + C_t T_i' + M_i \overset{\triangle}{=} BS_i + CT_i \tag{5B.4}$$

Multiplying both sides by S_i and taking the expected value:

$$B_t E[Q_i^* Q_i] = BE[S_i^* S_i] = B\, E[Q_i^* Q_i] + E[N_i^* N_i]$$

Therefore, normalizing the result to $E[N_i^* N_i] = 1.0$,

$$B_t = B \left[\frac{(SIR + 1)}{SIR} \right] \tag{5B.5}$$

which is then used to prove

$$C\, T_i = C_t\, T_i' + M_i + B[Q_i / SIR - N_i] \tag{5B.6}$$

Squaring (5B.6), and taking the ensemble average, the expression (5.10) results.

Next, the expressions for P_{FD} and P_{DMT} ((5.13) and (5.14)) are derived from (5.12). The derivation is strictly valid only if pulse-to-pulse independence can be assured. However, this is a valid assumption to make for many tracking systems.

To begin, define a to be a χ^2_{2N} distributed random variable and b to be a χ^2_{2N-1} distributed random variable. Therefore,

$$P_{FD} = \Pr[a < bC_0^2/\lambda_C^2]$$

$$= \int_0^\infty db\, f(b) \int_0^{bC_0^2/\lambda_C^2} da\, f(a)$$

$$= \int_0^\infty db\, b^{N-3/2} \exp(-b) \int_0^{bC_0^2/\lambda_C^2} da\, a^{N-1} \exp(-a)/\Gamma(N)\,\Gamma(N-1/2)$$

or, via integration by parts,

$$P_{FD} = \int_0^\infty db\, b^{N-3/2} \exp(-b) \left[1 - \sum_{i=0}^{N-1} [bC_0^2/\lambda_C^2]^i \exp(-bC_0^2/\lambda_C^2)/i! \right] / \Gamma(N-1/2)$$

$$= 1 - \sum_{i=0}^{N-1} \frac{\Gamma(N+i-1/2)}{\Gamma(N-1/2)\,i!} \frac{[C_0^2/\lambda_C^2]^i}{[1+C_0^2/\lambda_C^2]^{N+i-1/2}} \tag{5B.7}$$

The similar expression for P_{DMT} results when C replaces C_0.

Chapter 6

Definitions of Track Life Stages
(Track Initiation, Confirmation, Deletion, and Quality)

6.1 INTRODUCTION

Track status is typically defined in terms of three stages of track life: tentative, confirmed, and deleted. A tentative track is usually initiated on any observation that is not used to update an existing track or found to correlate with a previously established clutter point. For the airborne radar tracking problem, an exception to this track initiation rule can occur for certain returns that do not update existing tracks, but are close to the estimated position of an existing track. Some systems may not use these returns for new track initiation because it is suspected that they result from jet engine modulation, or from a failure in the observation redundancy elimination logic.

Simple track confirmation rules are often defined on the basis of some number of correlating returns with the tentative track. In the case of radar systems in which target Doppler (range rate) is measured, one confirming observation may be sufficient, while other, more restrictive, rules (such as M correlating detections out of N attempts) may be required if no measured range rate is available. Sections 6.2 and 6.3 discuss more general approaches to track confirmation. Section 6.2 discusses relatively simple sequential techniques that are more effective, but only slightly more involved than the simplest M-out-of-N type rules. Section 6.4 discusses more involved batch techniques that require the simultaneous processing of several data scans.

Simple track deletion criteria are based on unsuccessful detection attempts, such as N_D consecutive misses. A more general approach involves definition of a track quality indicator, such as a score function or an estimate of the probability of track validity. Section 6.5 introduces the concept of a score function and gives several that are easily computed. Then, Section 6.6 outlines how simple track deletion criteria can be defined.

The techniques discussed in this chapter are oriented toward nearest-neighbor (NN) correlation. The all-neighbors approach will be discussed in Chapter 10.

6.2   TRACK CONFIRMATION USING SEQUENTIAL ANALYSIS

Drawing from References [1, 2, 3], this section will summarize the method of sequential analysis and show how the resulting key relationships can be applied to the problem of track confirmation. The simplest form of this technique, the sequential probability ratio test (SPRT), is used to choose between two hypotheses, H_0 and H_1. For this application, the hypotheses are defined as:

H_0 = no true target present so returns are from false alarms or clutter;
H_1 = a true target is present.

Then, using the SPRT, every time data are received the three alternatives are to (1) accept H_0, (2) accept H_1, or (3) defer decision until more data are received.

Assume that an initial detection has occurred and that it must be determined whether this detection was from a true target. Then, given k subsequent scans with a particular sequence of m detections, the likelihood function for hypothesis H_1 (true target present) is

$$P_{1k} = P_D^m (1-P_D)^{k-m} \tag{6.1}$$

Similarly, for the false target hypothesis (H_0), the likelihood function is

$$P_{0k} = P_F^m (1-P_F)^{k-m} \tag{6.2}$$

where P_D and P_F are the probabilities of detection for true and false targets, respectively.

6.2.1   Definition of Test Statistic

The SPRT forms the likelihood ratio ($U_k = P_{1k}/P_{0k}$) of the two hypotheses and compares that ratio with two thresholds (C_1 and C_2). Then, the following decision logic is applied:

1. $U_k \leqq C_1$, accept H_0
2. $U_k \geqq C_2$, accept H_1 $\tag{6.3}$
3. $C_1 < U_k < C_2$, continue testing

The thresholds C_1 and C_2 are computed from the relationships:

$$C_2 = \frac{1-\beta}{\alpha}, \quad C_1 = \frac{\beta}{1-\alpha} \tag{6.4}$$

where α and β are predetermined allowable error probabilities defined as:

α = probability of accepting H_1 when H_0 is true;
β = probability of accepting H_0 when H_1 is true.

The relationships given by (6.4) do not exactly ensure the predetermined error probabilities, but the approximations are close [1].

Taking the logarithms, a convenient form for sequential calculations is derived. Using (6.1) and (6.2),

$$\ln(U_k) = \ln(P_{1k}/P_{0k}) = m \ln \left[\frac{P_D/(1 - P_D)}{P_F/(1 - P_F)} \right] + k \ln \left[\frac{(1 - P_D)}{(1 - P_F)} \right] \quad (6.5)$$

Define

$$a_1 \stackrel{\triangle}{=} \ln \left[\frac{P_D/(1 - P_D)}{P_F/(1 - P_F)} \right], \quad a_2 \stackrel{\triangle}{=} \ln \left[\frac{1 - P_F}{1 - P_D} \right]$$

Also, define a test statistic $ST(k)$:

$$ST(k) \stackrel{\triangle}{=} m\, a_1 \quad (6.6)$$

so that (6.5) can be rewritten

$$\ln(U_k) = ST(k) - k\, a_2$$

Referring back to (6.3), we accept H_0 if

$$\ln(U_k) = ST(k) - k\, a_2 \leqq \ln C_1$$

Similarly, we accept H_1 if

$$\ln(U_k) = ST(k) - k\, a_2 \geqq \ln C_2$$

Thus, an upper, $T_U(k)$, and a lower, $T_L(k)$, threshold can be defined

$$T_U(k) = \ln C_2 + k\, a_2, \quad T_L(k) = \ln C_1 + k\, a_2 \quad (6.7)$$

so that the decision logic of (6.3) becomes

1. $ST(k) \leqq T_L(k)$, accept H_0 (no target);
2. $ST(k) \geqq T_U(k)$, accept H_1 (true target present); $\quad$ (6.8)
3. $T_L(k) < ST(k) < T_U(k)$, continue testing.

The thresholds $T_L(k)$ and $T_U(k)$ are parallel lines that increase on each scan by the positive (since it must be assumed that $P_D > P_F$) amount a_2. The test statistic $ST(k)$ increases by amount a_1 each time a detection is received and remains unchanged if no detection is received. Then, whenever the statistic $ST(k)$ penetrates either of the lines $T_U(k)$ and $T_L(k)$, a decision is made.

6.2.2   Track Confirmation Example Using the SPRT

Consider an example with $P_D = 0.5$ and $P_F = 1/8 = 0.125$, and with the error probabilities specified to be

α = false track probability = 0.01;
β = false rejection probability = 0.05.

Thus, for this example,

$$\ln C_2 = \ln \left(\frac{0.95}{0.01} \right) = 4.55, \quad \ln C_1 = \ln \left(\frac{0.05}{0.99} \right) = -2.99$$

$$a_1 = \ln 7 = 1.95, \quad a_2 = \ln \frac{0.875}{0.5} = 0.56$$

The test statistic and the thresholds become

$$T_L(k) = -2.99 + 0.56\, k, \quad ST(k) = 1.95\, m, \quad T_U(k) = 4.55 + 0.56\, k$$

Figure 6-1 presents the results of two Monte Carlo experiments for the simulated conditions of true and false targets. The experiment, which can easily be repeated by the reader, consisted of flipping a coin and declaring a detection for the true target if a head appeared. For the false target, a detection occurred if each of three tosses produced a head. Referring to Fig. 6-1, for these experiments the true target hypothesis (H_1) was accepted after five detections on nine looks, while the false target hypothesis (H_0) was chosen after only two detections occurred on 13 looks.

6.2.3   Expected Decision Time

Next, consider the expected length (K) of the SPRT. The expected number of samples, $E[K]$, required for a decision is given by the relationship [1]

$$E[K \mid \theta] = \frac{P(\theta) \ln C_2 + [1 - P(\theta)] \ln C_1}{E[z \mid \theta]} \tag{6.9}$$

In order to apply (6.9), define the parameter θ to be

$$\theta = \begin{cases} \theta_0, \text{ hypothesis } H_0 \text{ (false target) correct} \\ \theta_1, \text{ hypothesis } H_1 \text{ (true target) correct} \end{cases}$$

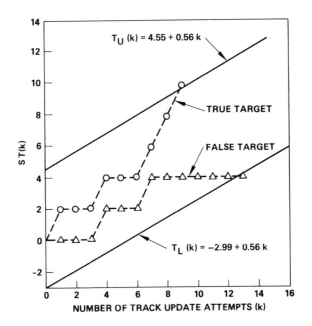

FIGURE 6–1. EXAMPLES OF SPRT APPLICATION
TO TRACK CONFIRMATION

Then, $P(\theta)$ is defined as the probability of accepting H_1 (rejecting H_0) given that θ is the true parameter. Thus,

$$P(\theta) = \begin{cases} P(\theta_0) = \alpha, \text{ hypothesis } H_0 \text{ correct} \\ P(\theta_1) = 1 - \beta, \text{ hypothesis } H_1 \text{ correct} \end{cases} \tag{6.10}$$

To complete specification of the terms in (6.9), we must define $E[z|\theta]$. This term is the expected increment to the quantity $\ln(U_k)$, given in (6.5), that will occur for each scan. For example, if a detection occurs on scan k the term $a_1 - a_2$ will be the contribution to $\ln(U_k)$ from that scan, while for no detection the contribution is $-a_2$. Thus,

$$E[z|\theta] = \begin{cases} E[z|\theta_0] = P_F a_1 - a_2, \; H_0 \text{ correct} \\ E[z|\theta_1] = P_D a_1 - a_2, \; H_1 \text{ correct} \end{cases} \tag{6.11}$$

Combining (6.9) through (6.11) gives the expected number of scans required for decision:

$$E[K] = \begin{cases} \dfrac{\alpha \ln C_2 + (1 - \alpha) \ln C_1}{P_F a_1 - a_2} & , H_0 \text{ correct} \\[3mm] \dfrac{(1 - \beta) \ln C_2 + \beta \ln C_1}{P_D a_1 - a_2} & , H_1 \text{ correct} \end{cases}$$

For the example given above,

$$E[K \mid \theta_0] = \frac{0.01(4.55) - 0.99(2.99)}{0.125(1.95) - 0.56} = 9.2$$

$$E[K \mid \theta_1] = \frac{0.95(4.55) - 0.05(2.99)}{0.5(1.95) - 0.56} = 10.1$$

The expected test length can be changed by varying the parameters α and β. Increasing these parameters will shorten the expected test length at the cost of increasing the error probabilities. For example, if α is increased from 0.01 to 0.1 (while maintaining $\beta = 0.05$), the expected test lengths become

$$E[K \mid \theta_0] = 7.5, \quad E[K \mid \theta_1] = 4.8$$

Thus, the expected time required to accept a valid target has been approximately halved but the probability of accepting a false target was increased from 0.01 to 0.1.

Define β_{FT} and V_s to be the false target density and the scan volume. Then, using the SPRT method developed above, the expected number of false tracks confirmed per scan is $\alpha \beta_{FT} V_s$. Thus, in determining the value of α, the trade-off to be considered is between the number of false targets confirmed and the time required to confirm a true target.

6.3 BAYESIAN TRACK CONFIRMATION

A relatively simple sequential technique for track promotion (confirmation) can be developed by applying Bayes' rule [4, 5]. This technique goes beyond the method discussed in the previous section because prior probabilities and track update residual information are readily included. Also, the same method will be applied to track deletion (Section 6.6).

Using Bayes' rule, the probability of a true track given the measurement data D is

$$P(T \mid D) = \frac{P(D \mid T) \, P_0(T)}{P(D)} \tag{6.12}$$

where $P(D|T)$ is the probability of receiving measurement data D given that a true target is present. Also, $P_0(T)$ is the *a priori* probability of a true target appearing within the scan volume. The term $P(D)$ is the probability of receiving the data D and is given by

$$P(D) = P(D|T)\, P_0(T) + P(D|F)\, P_0(F) \tag{6.13}$$

where $P(D|F)$ and $P_0(F)$ are defined for false targets in the same manner that $P(D|T)$ and $P_0(T)$ were defined for true targets.

Noting that $P_0(F) = 1 - P_0(T)$, combining (6.12) and (6.13), and dividing numerator and denominator by $P(D|F)$, gives

$$P(T|D) = \frac{L(D)\, P_0(T)}{L(D)\, P_0(T) + 1 - P_0(T)} \tag{6.14}$$

where $L(D)$ is the likelihood ratio for the data as defined

$$L(D) = \frac{P(D|T)}{P(D|F)}$$

Equation (6.14) can be placed in two convenient forms for recursive computation. First, defining L_k to be the likelihood ratio for the data received on the kth scan and $P(T|D_k)$ to be the probability of a true target given data through scan k, we have

$$P(T|D_k) = \frac{L_k\, P(T|D_{k-1})}{L_k\, P(T|D_{k-1}) + 1 - P(T|D_{k-1})} \tag{6.15}$$

An alternative representation is to maintain the form of (6.14), but to define $L(D)$ to be the likelihood associated with all scans of data. The data is assumed to be scan-to-scan independent. Thus, the likelihood function, $L(D)$, for all data (through scan K) is the product of the individual likelihoods (L_k) (for the data received on each scan), so that

$$L(D) = \prod_{k=1}^{K} L_k \tag{6.16}$$

Then, (6.14) can be used directly with $L(D)$ updated using (6.16) each time new data are received.

The true target hypothesis would be accepted whenever an acceptance probability threshold (P_A) is reached

$$P(T|D) \geqq P_A \tag{6.17}$$

Alternatively, combining (6.14) and (6.17) gives a condition in terms of the likelihood $L(D)$

$$L(D) \geqq \frac{P_A(1 - P_0)}{(1 - P_A)P_0} \tag{6.18}$$

Next, consider computation of L_k for the tracking problem. The likelihood L_k associated with data set D_k must be determined by first defining $P(D_k|T)$ and $P(D_k|F)$. Dropping subscript k, for a true target $P(D|T)$ is taken to be the product of the probability of detection P_D and the Gaussian likelihoood function defined in (4.11). Similarly, $P(D|F)$ is taken to be the probability of a false target return (P_F) times the likelihood function ($1/V_G$) associated with the assumed uniform distribution of false returns within the volume (V_G) of the gated region. Thus,

$$L_k = \frac{P_D\, e^{-\frac{d^2}{2}} \big/ [(2\pi)^{M/2} \sqrt{|S|}]}{P_F \left(\dfrac{1}{V_G}\right)} = \frac{P_D\, e^{-\frac{d^2}{2}}\, V_G}{P_F (2\pi)^{M/2} \sqrt{|S|}} \tag{6.19}$$

where d^2 is the normalized distance function and $|S|$ is the determinant of the residual covariance matrix.

Equation (6.19) can be simplified by noting that

$$P_F = \beta_{FT}\, V_G \tag{6.20}$$

where β_{FT} is the false target density. Thus, (6.19) becomes

$$L_k = \frac{P_D\, e^{-\frac{d^2}{2}}}{\beta_{FT}\, (2\pi)^{M/2} \sqrt{|S|}} \tag{6.21}$$

The initial true target probability can be defined in terms of the true new target density, β_{NT}, and β_{FT}, whereby we have

$$P_0(T) \triangleq P_0 = \frac{\beta_{NT}}{\beta_{NT} + \beta_{FT}} \tag{6.22}$$

Finally, in the case of a missed detection, we write

$$L_k = \frac{1 - P_D}{1 - P_F} \tag{6.23}$$

Equations (6.14) to (6.23) provide a convenient sequential confirmation scheme that can be adjusted to the environment. Also, the required length of the test can be adjusted through choice of P_A. Using the likelihood form of the test, defined by (6.18), it may be convenient to take logarithms, so that the test statistic becomes a sum of terms which are mostly constants.

6.4 BATCH PROCESSING TECHNIQUES FOR TRACK INITIATION AND CONFIRMATION

The sequential techniques discussed in the previous sections are appropriate for track confirmation in the presence of a relatively uncluttered background, such as for radar air-to-air tracking. However, in the presence of a heavy clutter background, such as for air-to-ground radar or infrared (IR) satellite surveillance, it may be necessary to use batch techniques. Using the batch processing approach, observations from several past scans of data are processed simultaneously to determine feasible target trajectories. Several techniques will be outlined below. These techniques are not too complex, but they assume essentially straight-line trajectories.

6.4.1 Pattern Matching Techniques

One batch processing technique for initial track formation is to apply coarse gating first in order to find sets of observations that form feasible tracks. Then, a curve fit to the points can be performed while the "goodness" of the track can be determined from the number of points included in the track and the deviations of the points from the curve fit. Alternatively, templates of admissable track trajectories can be overlaid onto the stored points comprising the track. If an acceptable number of points falls within the template, the track is accepted.

Figure 6-2 shows a set of templates that were used for a two-dimensional measurement IR surveillance system track initiation scheme. For IR systems, the detection plane is typically divided into picture elements (pixels). In this system, tentative tracks were formed using coarse gating and a lowered threshold was used for the pixels within the gated region. The tentative track was continued until 14 points were accumulated, or until misses were

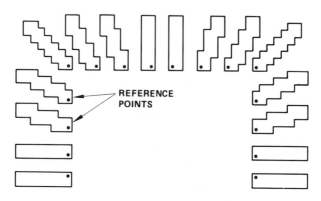

FIGURE 6-2. TEMPLATES COVERING
180 DEGREES OF TARGET TRAILS

recorded on two consecutive frames. After 14 points were accumulated, the template test was applied (with the initial point as the reference) and the track was confirmed if 12 of the 14 points fell within any of the templates shown in Fig. 6-2. Results indicated that the template test eliminated better than 99 percent of the false tentative tracks which were formed on false detections.

Reference [6] describes a similar approach in which an observation is compared with observations from previous scans to see if a probable track can be formed. This is done by examining all observations that fall within an angle and range window. The observations within this coarse gating window are then plotted on a range-*versus*-scan-time scale and compared with a set of constant velocity profiles. Track confirmation is based on proximity to the velocity profiles and the number of points in the track. Results showed that when using this track confirmation scheme, the probability of false alarm P_{FA} could be set at about 10^{-3} as opposed to the 10^{-6} value required without the initiation scheme. Indications are that this can lead to an increase in sensitivity of 3 to 12 dB for true target returns [6].

Next, we summarize a technique that has been proposed by Rauch and Firschein [7, 8] for track assembly in IR surveillance systems. For this method, assume that the detection plane is divided into pixels, that target returns occupy one pixel, and that targets move approximately one pixel per frame. Then, for a given frame of data, a binary matrix is formed with an element for each pixel, so that a one is entered in the corresponding element of each pixel that received a detection. A zero is entered in the elements for pixels that received no detection.

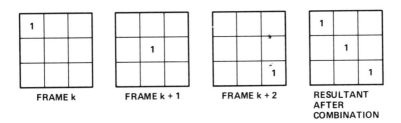

FIGURE 6-3. EXAMPLE OF COMBINING THREE FRAMES
OF DATA USING "OR" OPERATION

The next step is to form new binary matrices by combining the binary matrices from three consecutive frames of data. The combination technique is through the logical operation *OR*, so that a one is entered in a given element of the matrix if there was a one in that element for one or more of the original matrices. Figure 6-3 illustrates this operation and the result for a straight-line target. The assumption is that true target returns will form straight (or slightly curved) lines.

Consider a nine-pixel window formed by the combining operation discussed above with a one in the middle pixel. Figure 6-4 shows the types of patterns that will and will not be accepted as potential target tracks. Note that sharp turns are not accepted. Also, combinations with more than six non-zero elements in the nine-pixel window are dismissed (or given a low score as discussed in [8]) as being spatially correlated noise.

ACCEPTABLE

1	0	0
0	(1)	0
0	0	1

1	0	0
0	(1)	1
0	0	0

1	0	0
0	(1)	0
0	1	1

NOT ACCEPTABLE

1	0	1
0	1	0
0	0	0

1	1	0
0	1	0
0	0	0

1	0	1
0	1	1
1	1	1

FIGURE 6-4. EXAMPLES OF ACCEPTABLE AND
UNACCEPTABLE POTENTIAL TRACK PATTERNS

The next step is to set the value to zero for all elements that do not represent the middle element of an acceptable pattern. Thus, for the examples of Fig. 6-4, all elements except those circled would be set to zero. The non-zero elements may be assigned a score [8], but a value of one will be used here. Finally, an additional time constraint recommended in [7] is that a detection for the pixel in the center of the nine-pixel window must have occurred during the middle frame. Otherwise, regardless of the pattern, the corresponding matrix element is set to zero.

Consider seven frames of data. Then, the operation described above would form five matrices (A_i, $i = 1, 2, \ldots, 5$) such that each A_i has the combined elements from frames i, $i + 1$ and $i + 2$. Next, three matrices ($B_j, j = 1, 2, 3$) are formed such that B_j combines matrices A_j, A_{j+1}, and A_{j+2} in the same manner. Finally, a matrix C_1 is formed from B_1, B_2, and B_3. The desired results are that each non-zero element of C_1 represents a target track and that uncorrelated or stationary false returns will be eliminated.

The process described above will be illustrated with a simple example. Figure 6-5 shows a nine-by-eight pattern of pixels with elements representing the frames on which detections were assumed to occur. For example, $D5$ represents a detection on frame 5. Seven frames of data are considered and, for simplicity of representation, it is assumed that each pixel receives only one detection during the seven frames. The entries in rows 2 through 4 represent true target returns (denoted by * in Fig. 6-5) plus several extraneous returns, while those in rows 6 through 8 are all false returns. Also, for simplicity of representation, the pattern of the false returns is taken to move towards the right with time.

	1	2	3	4	5	6	7	8
1								
2	D1*		D3	D4	D6		D7*	
3		D2*	D3*			D6*		
4				D4*	D5*			
5								
6	D1			D4	D7	D6	D7	
7		D2	D3		D5			
8		D2		D4	D5			
9								

* DENOTES TARGET RETURNS

FIGURE 6-5. HYPOTHETICAL DETECTION MATRIX

Figure 6-6 illustrates how the combination process occurs as matrices A_i, B_j, and C_1 are formed. We apply the time constraint that a track is valid only if the middle point is from the middle time frame. Only those columns with non-zero elements are shown. The example was chosen (for simplicity of representation) so that each matrix had only three non-zero columns. Of course, this would not generally be the case. Each level of processing eliminates one point from each end of the target track, so that after three levels of processing only a single point representing the target return on the fourth frame remains. Thus, in order to reconstruct the track, a logic must be developed to save and later recall the other six associated points.

Referring to Fig. 6-6, the elements of the B matrices are formed from the circled elements of the A matrices. Then, the circled elements of the B matrices are identified as the center elements of the resulting patterns that conform to the acceptable patterns, such as shown in Fig. 6-4. Finally, the C matrix is formed from the circled elements of the B matrices.

Note that the link among the false returns is broken in matrix B_2 where the only ① entry represents the true target track. In general, the probability of a false track surviving three levels of processing is quite small. Reference [7] computes the probability of a seven-point false track occurring to be $972P_F^7$. This value represents the probability of a false track emerging at each frame for each pixel. Thus, the expected number (N_{FT}) of false tracks created each frame for N_P pixels is

$$E[N_{FT}] = 972 \, N_P \, P_F^7 \qquad (6.24)$$

Taking the typical values of 10^6 for the number (N_P) and 0.03 for P_F gives

$$E[N_{FT}] = 972 \times 10^6 \times (0.03)^7 = 0.02$$

Thus, the process efficiently limits the number of false tracks formed. This computation, using (6.24), did not include the time constraint that tracks should not be formed unless the middle point is from the middle time frame. Reference [7] indicates a significant further reduction in false track probability if this constraint can be maintained. References [7] and [8] also discuss implementation techniques, extensions to faster and slower moving targets, and a more complex scoring procedure.

6.4.2 The Hough Transform Approach

A transform technique proposed by Smith and Winter [9,10] uses a version of the Hough transform [11]. This method is based on the fact that, as illustrated in Fig. 6-7, all points (x_i, y_i) along a straight line can be

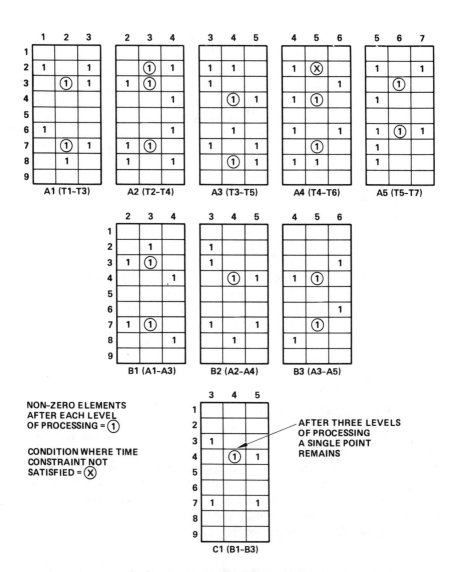

FIGURE 6-6. PROCESSING STEPS FOR EXAMPLE
OF FIGURE 6-5

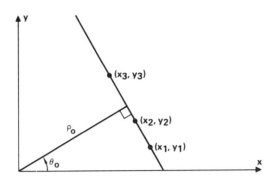

FIGURE 6-7. NORMAL PARAMETRIC REPRESENTATION
OF A STRAIGHT LINE x COS θ_0 + y SIN θ_0 = P_0

represented in the form

$$x_i \cos \theta_o + y_i \sin \theta_o = \rho_o \qquad (6.25)$$

As shown in Fig. 6-7, θ_o is the angle of the normal with the x axis and ρ_o is the perpendicular distance of the line from the origin. Thus, all points (x_i, y_i) along the line can be mapped into a single point (ρ_o, θ_o) in the $\rho - \theta$ parameter space.

Each point (x, y) in the $x - y$ plane can be mapped into a curve in the $\theta - \rho$ plane defined by the general relationship

$$x \cos \theta + y \sin \theta = \rho$$

Because each point in the $x - y$ plane defines a curve in the $\theta - \rho$ plane, a family of curves can be generated in the $\theta - \rho$ plane using various points in the $x - y$ plane. The family of curves generated by a set of points from the straight line defined by (6.25) will intersect at the point (θ_o, ρ_o). Thus, a group of points in the $x - y$ plane that all lead to a common point (θ_o, ρ_o) in the $\theta - \rho$ plane can be identified as a straight line. This leads to the proposed procedure (outlined next) for identifying straight-line target trajectories against a heavy clutter background.

The angle (θ) is restricted to values between zero and π radians, so that ρ can generally be positive or negative, with the restriction that

$$|\rho| \leq \sqrt{x_{max}^2 + y_{max}^2}$$

where x_{max} and y_{max} are the width and height of the picture (or image). A two-dimensional histogram (or set of accumulators) will be formed using parameter spacings $\Delta\theta$ and $\Delta\rho$. Then, thresholding is used to determine target presence within any of the $\Delta\theta - \Delta\rho$ bins.

The total number of increments in the θ parameter is

$$N_\theta = \frac{\pi}{\Delta \theta}$$

and the center points of the histogram bins are defined as

$$\theta_1 = \frac{\Delta \theta}{2} , \theta_2 = \frac{3\Delta \theta}{2} , \ldots, \theta_{N_\theta} = \left(N_\theta - \frac{1}{2} \right) \Delta \theta$$

A similar quantization of values for ρ would be defined. Reference [12] discusses how this quantization should be chosen to yield an equal number of expected background returns from extraneous sources for each quantization interval.

The histogram bin values are accumulated using the points in the detection plane where a threshold crossing occurs. Each point will contribute to the histogram values for N_θ bins, but for random points the contributions will be spread over the bins. On the other hand, points on a straight line will contribute mostly to the same or adjacent bins. Thus, after accumulation, the number of points within each bin will be compared with a threshold and a track declared if the threshold is exceeded.

As an example of how the process works, consider the line $x + 2y = 3$. This line can be put in the normal form:

$$x \cos 63.4° + y \sin 63.4° = 1.34$$

Assume that the histogram is formed using $N_\theta = 10$, so that $\Delta \theta = 18$ degrees $= 0.314$ radian. In practice, a much larger N_θ (Reference [9] uses $\Delta \theta = 0.033$ rad) would be required, but the value 10 will suffice for illustration. Using four points along the line, Table 6-1 gives the resulting values computed for ρ, which were associated with the ten values of θ_i. For a given (x, y), the ρ_i associated with each θ_i is computed using the formula:

$$\rho_i = x \cos \theta_i + y \sin \theta_i$$

Referring to Table 6-1, note that values of ρ close (or equal) to 1.34 appear under the θ value of 63 degrees. Thus, using the four points, the appropriate histogram (centered at 63 degrees in angle and containing the value of 1.34 in the parameters ρ) would have a count of four, while the other points are spread out. Each point on a true line, as well as each random point, will contribute to the background in the histogram. Thus, a thresholding process (outlined below) is required to distinguish bins containing contributions from true line points for those bins that contain only background.

TABLE 6-1
$\rho - \theta$ PARAMETER VALUES ASSOCIATED WITH 4 POINTS
ALONG LINE $x + 2y = 3$

					θ_i (deg)					
Point (x, y)	9	27	45	63	81	99	117	135	153	171
(3,0)	2.96	2.67	2.12	1.36	0.47	–0.47	–1.36	–2.12	–2.67	–2.96
(2,0.5)	2.05	2.01	1.77	1.35	0.81	0.18	–0.46	–1.06	–1.56	–1.90
(1,1)	1.14	1.34	1.41	1.34	1.14	0.83	0.44	0	–0.44	–0.83
(0,1.5)	0.23	0.68	1.06	1.34	1.48	1.48	1.34	1.06	0.68	0.23

Ideally, the bin quantization would be chosen such that the probability p of a background point falling within a given bin would be uniform ($p = 1/N_{TB}$), where N_{TB} is the total number of bins. However, as suggested in [12], if the uniform distribution cannot be assumed, an estimate, $\hat{p}$, of the probability that a background point will project into a given histogram bin can be obtained using a picture, or a simulated picture, which does not contain any straight lines (or other figures).

Next, consider a test picture and assume a total of N points. If there were no straight lines, the number of counts per bin would be described by the binomial distribution with parameters N and $\hat{p}$. Thus, the detection threshold can be based on the binomial distribution or, for the product $N\hat{p} \gtrsim 5$, the Gaussian approximation to the binomial.

When the number of counts within a histogram bin exceeds the threshold, a process of fitting a straight line to the data points involved is performed. First, extraneous points, which may have occurred due to noise or crossing tracks, are identified by examining the ordered (in time) list of points that contributed to histogram bin counts. Thus, points that lead to discontinuities in the time history of the target trajectory are removed. Second, points in adjoining histogram bins that satisfy a distance criterion are added. Third, the appropriate line parameter values (ρ_o, θ_o) are found using the N_L points assigned to the line and solving for the parameter values that minimize the total distance:

$$D^2 = \sum_{i=1}^{N_L} (\rho - x_i \cos \theta - y_i \sin \theta)^2$$

Finally, splicing of segments of the same line is performed. More details of the required operations are presented in [9, 10, 12, 13, 14].

The procedure described above has been for a straight line in the $x - y$ plane. The extensions to other types of curves (Reference [11] considers the extension to a circle) and to higher dimensional spaces are theoretically possible, but require more involved computations.

6.5 INDICATORS OF TRACK QUALITY (SCORE)

It is desirable that an easily computed statistic be available, so that the MTT system can assess its own performance as it goes along, and thus be able to make changes (such as in modeling target dynamics). Also, each track should have an associated indication of quality (or a score). Such a measure not only helps with decisions regarding data association, but also aids in the use of track information from an MTT system. For example, in an airborne radar tracking system, the ultimate goal is often weapon delivery, such as missile launch, and it would not be prudent to allocate limited resources, such as missiles, for other than high-quality tracks. On the other hand, it may be desirable to allocate more sensor resources, such as through increased sampling, if tracking quality is determined to be below expectations.

The mathematically preferable maximum-likelihood score function is defined as $-2 \ln [\text{Pr} (Z/Q)]$, where PR $[Z/Q]$ is the posterior probability (or likelihood function) of the data Z given the partitioning Q [15]. The partitioning Q refers to the particular assignment of observations to tracks and false alarms. This score function is essentially the same as that defined in the pioneering work of Sittler [16] and that which will be used later in Chapter 9. Note that this overall (for all tracks) score can be decomposed into a sum of contributions from each track. Thus, measures of quality for each track can be defined in terms of its present score, or the difference between the score and the maximum score that may have been obtained in the past.

Chapter 9 will present a complete discussion of how a maximum-likelihood score function is obtained and used. In this section, suboptimal, but more easily computed, indicators will be discussed.

6.5.1 Chi-Square Track Score

As previously discussed, the normalized distance function associated with a given observation-to-track pairing is defined

$$d^2 = \tilde{y}^T S^{-1} \tilde{y}$$

where $\tilde{y}$ is the residual vector and S is the residual covariance matrix. The measurement dimension is taken to be M. Then, if the observation-to-track pairing is correct, and if the filter's models for target dynamics and measurement noise are reasonably accurate, the quantity d^2 should have the chi-square distribution with M degrees of freedom ($d^2 \sim \chi_M^2$).

A cumulative chi-square score C_i can be defined for track i and normalized by the number (N_i) of track updates included in this score [17]:

$$C_i = \frac{1}{N_i} \sum_{n=1}^{N_i} d_n^2 \tag{6.26}$$

The quantity $N_i C_i$ has the $\chi_{MN_i}^2$ distribution with mean and standard deviation of C_i given by

$$E[C_i] = M, \qquad \sigma_{C_i} = \sqrt{\frac{2M}{N_i}}$$

Thus, a quality threshold can be established using the $\chi_{MN_i}^2$ distribution. Alternatively, using the Gaussian approximation (valid for $MN_i \gtrsim 10$) a threshold can be set at the value $M + \alpha \sigma_{C_i}$ with $\alpha \gtrsim 3$. In either case (using $\chi_{MN_i}^2$ or Gaussian distributions), when C_i exceeds threshold, it indicates either incorrect data assignment or an incorrect filter model. Similarly, if C_i is too small ($C_i < M_i - \alpha \sigma_{C_i}$), the indication is that the filter model is too pessimistic (the assumed target dynamics or the assumed measurement noise variance is too large).

As N_i increases, the statistic C_i, defined in (6.26), may become too heavily weighted toward old data, and thus may no longer be responsive to recent track degradation. One solution to this problem is to use a sliding window with a fixed N_i so that only the last N_i residuals are included in the sum. Another alternative is to keep a weighted sum of past normalized distances:

$$C_i' = \sum_{n=1}^{N_i} a_n d_n^2 \tag{6.27}$$

where the index n goes from the most recent ($n = 1$) to the initial ($n = N_i$) observation included in the sum. Thus, the choice of weighting coefficients would be

$$a_1 = 1, \qquad a_n > a_{n+1}$$

and a fixed number of non-zero a_n would be used. Alternatively, a recursive relationship could be used so that, for scan k,

$$C_i'(k) = d_k^2 + \alpha \, C_i'(k-1) \tag{6.27a}$$

giving, for $n \geq 2$,

$$a_n = \alpha^{n-1}, \quad \alpha < 1$$

Using either (6.27) or (6.27a), the quantity C_i' is a weighted sum of χ_M^2 variables. A practical approximation to a weighted sum of χ^2 variables has been found and is discussed in Appendix 6A. Using this method, the distribution for C_i' is approximately the same as the distribution for the quantity $A\chi_{\nu_T}^2$

$$C_i' \cong A\chi_{\nu_T}^2$$

where

$$A = \frac{\displaystyle\sum_{n=1}^{N_i} a_n^2}{\displaystyle\sum_{n=1}^{N_i} a_n}, \quad \nu_T = M \frac{\left[\displaystyle\sum_{n=1}^{N_i} a_n\right]^2}{\displaystyle\sum_{n=1}^{N_i} a_n^2}$$

Thus, the weighted sum of χ^2 variables (C_i') is approximated by the product of a constant times another χ^2 variable with ν_T degrees of freedom. Then, the same thresholding techniques discussed for C_i are applicable.

6.5.2 A Score Function Including Clutter Points

We next discuss a score function that has been proposed by Alspach and Lobbia [17] to include the contribution from points determined to be false alarms (or clutter points). This score function (SF), including tracks and clutter points, is

$$SF = \frac{1}{N_o}\left[\sum_{i=1}^{N_T} N_i\, C_i + N_c\, S_c\right] \tag{6.28}$$

where N_o and N_T are the total numbers of observations and tracks, respectively. Also, N_c and S_c are the number of clutter points and the score associated with clutter, respectively. Note that the goal will be to minimize SF, as opposed to maximizing the score function, which will be defined in Chapter 9. However, this difference is merely due to an arbitrary choice of signs and, as shown below and in Appendix 6B, SF is essentially an approximate form of the score function developed in Chapter 9.

The expected value of the score defined by (6.28) has an absolute minimum when the correct number of points is assigned to tracks. Then, the expected score value increases linearly as true track reports are assigned to clutter. Also, the score function curve is concave and monotonically increasing as clutter points are assigned to tracks [17].

In order to use (6.28) it is necessary to define S_c. Reference [17] indicates that S_c can be chosen experimentally until the proper sensitivity is achieved. Anticipating results from Chapter 9, Appendix 6B indicates that an appropriate value for S_c can also be chosen from the relationship:

$$S_c = 2 \ln \left[\frac{P_D}{1 - P_D} \right] - 2 \ln \left[\left(\frac{\pi}{2} \right)^{\frac{M}{2}} n_{TF} \right] \tag{6.29}$$

As previously defined in Chapter 4, n_{TF} is the expected number of false (clutter) returns within an M-dimensional box with sides of length two residual standard deviations. For example, taking $M = 2$, $P_D = 0.5$, and $n_{TF} = 0.03$ gives a value for S_c of approximately 6.

The expected value of SF is

$$E[SF] = M + \frac{N_c (S_c - M)}{N_o}$$

Thus, overall MTT system performance can be evaluated by comparing SF, as computed from (6.28), with its expected value. Then, if $SF > E[SF]$ an attempt may be made to reduce SF by extracting potential clutter points from tracks or by adding other observations to tracks. Then, the resultant score is re-evaluated. Alternatively, the filtering model may be re-examined.

6.6 TRACK DELETION

Degraded tracks must be deleted. One common form of degradation occurs as a result of missed data whereby the simplest track deletion criterion uses the number of consecutive missed observation attempts. A slightly more complex method, also considering only track update history, is to use the sequential techniques discussed in Section 6.2 for track termination. Exactly the same techniques described in that section would be used so that track deletion occurs whenever the statistic $ST(k)$ falls below the lower threshold $T_L(k)$. Also, whenever $ST(k)$ exceeded the upper threshold $T_U(k)$, the track would be considered to be reconfirmed and the test begun again.

The optimal gate G_o, defined in Chapter 4 and derived in Chapter 9, can be used for determining a track termination criterion. The gate is given by

$$G_o = 2 \ln \left[\frac{P_D}{(1 - P_D)\, \beta(2\pi)^{M/2} \sqrt{|S|}} \right]$$

As long as the observation-to-track normalized distance function d^2 satisfies the relationship $d^2 \leqq G_o$, the pairing is more likely than the alternative of declaring the observation in question to be from a new source. Thus, as long as $G_o > 0$, there is some hope that the given track can receive an update. However, if $G_o \leqq 0$ any return that is received will be more likely from a new source (new target or false alarm) than from the track in question. This principle is similar to that recognized by Maged [18] for defining critical parameters under which tracking is feasible.

If elliptical gates are already being calculated, a natural termination criterion is to delete a track whenever the computed gate G_o for that track becomes less than some minimum value G_{MIN}. The value of G_{MIN} could be taken from standard chi-square tables (using the measurement dimension M) to ensure that tracks are not deleted as long as a predetermined probability of track update exists.

Next, consider deletion criteria that include track update information. First, the track chi-square score function C_i (or C_i') defined in the previous section can be compared with a threshold to determine degradation and possible deletion. However, application of a Bayesian approach, such as defined in Section 6.3 for track confirmation, is more general because both residual and detection histories can readily be included in the statistics.

Using a Bayesian approach to track deletion, the likelihood function for all scans of data can be computed as the product of the individual likelihood functions, using (6.16). Also, the individual likelihood functions are computed either from (6.21) if detection occurs or from (6.23) if there is a missed observation. Then, the deletion criteria become

$$P(T/D) \leqq P_{DEL}$$

or

$$L(D) \leqq \frac{P_{DEL}\,(1 - P_0)}{(1 - P_{DEL})\, P_0}$$

where P_{DEL} is a probability of track validity below which the track is terminated.

Tests for confirmation (or reconfirmation) and for deletion would be performed simultaneously. Whenever the track is confirmed, the test begins again with an appropriate large value for P_0.

More comprehensive, but also more complex, track deletion criteria involve use of the score function that will be defined in Chapter 9. These tests will be presented there.

6.7 SUMMARY

This chapter has discussed some of the techniques that are used for track confirmation, deletion, and quality determination. The relatively simple track confirmation criteria defined in Sections 6.2 and 6.3 are most applicable for sequential processing in low clutter environments. These techniques are generally preferable to the very simple M-out-of-N type criteria that are often used for track confirmation.

Section 6.4 presents track confirmation techniques that may be appropriate when a heavy clutter background is present. These methods require processing several scans of data simultaneously and are probably most applicable for use in surveillance systems in which a large amount of data can be collected and then processed. Smith [19] presents a similar type of approach.

Several more complex approaches to initial track formation have also been proposed. Morefield [20] develops an integer programming method in which batch processing could be used to form tracks using all data from a selected number of scans. Chang and Youens [21] outline an iterative method for track initiation that uses two passes through the data. Finally, dynamic programming techniques have been proposed for track initiation and maintenance [22, 23].

It is desirable that an estimate of the efficiency of the tracking system be available to the user. Also, this estimate can be used for an automatic allocation of sensor resources, so that ambiguous tracking can potentially be improved by increasing the data rate. Thus, a score function, such as the ones discussed in Section 6.5 and the more complex one defined in Chapter 9, should be computed.

Track deletion criteria are often defined in terms of simple rules. For example, deletion may be defined to occur on N_D consecutive missed update attempts or after a certain time interval without update. These criteria are typically difficult to define accurately because of variations in P_D and in the sampling interval. Also, the deletion criterion should include the quality (in terms of the residual errors) of the track updates that have occurred. Finally, deletion should also be based upon the likelihood of a correlating return being received (thus, salvaging the track). Section 6.6 has discussed several approaches that go beyond the simplest deletion rules but which are not too computationally involved. Again, use of the score function from Chapter 9 is more general, but also requires more computation.

REFERENCES

1. Hoel, P.G., *Introduction to Mathematical Statistics*, New York: John Wiley and Sons, 1971.
2. Holmes, J.E., "Development of Algorithms for the Formation and Updating of Tracks," *Proceedings of IEE 1977 International Radar Conference*, London, Oct. 25–28, 1977, pp. 81–85.
3. Fleskes, W., and G. Van Keuk, "Adaptive Control and Tracking with the ELRA Phased Array Radar Experimental System," *Proceedings of the 1980 IEEE International Radar Conference*, Arlington, VA, April 28–30, 1980, pp. 8–13.
4. Casner, P.G., and R.J. Prengaman, "Integration and Automation of Multiple Colocated Radars," *Proceedings of the IEE 1977 International Radar Conference*, London, Oct. 25–28, 1977, pp. 145–149.
5. Bath, W.G., *et. al.*, "False Alarm Control in Automated Radar Surveillance Systems," *Proceedings of the IEE 1982 International Radar Conference*, London, Oct. 18–20, 1982, pp. 71–75.
6. Prengaman, R.J., R.E. Thurber, and W.G. Bath, "A Retrospective Detection Algorithm for Extraction of Weak Targets in Clutter and Interference Environments," *Proceedings of the IEE 1982 International Radar Conference*, London, Oct. 18–20, 1982, pp. 341–345.
7. Rauch, H.E., and O. Firschein, "Track Assembly from Two-Dimensional Images of Binary Data," *Proceedings of the 1980 IEEE Conference on Decision and Control*, Albuquerque, NM, Dec. 10–12, 1980, pp. 813–819.
8. Firschein, O., H.E. Rauch, and W.G. Eppler, "Track Assembly and Background Suppression Using an Array Processor and Neighborhood Coding," *SPIE*, Vol. 241, Real-Time Signal Processing III (1980), pp. 258–266.
9. Smith, M.C., and E.M. Winter, "On the Detection of Target Trajectories in a Multi-Target Environment," *Proceedings of the 1978 IEEE Conference on Decision and Control*, San Diego, CA, Jan. 10–12, 1979, pp. 1189–1194.
10. Smith, M.C., "Feature Space Transform for Multitarget Detection," *Proceedings of the 1980 IEEE Conference on Decision and Control*, Albuquerque, NM, Dec. 10–12, 1980, pp. 835–836.
11. Duda, R.O., and P.E. Hart, "Use of the Hough Transform to Detect Lines and Curves in Pictures," *Communications of the ACM*, Vol. 15, Jan. 1972, pp. 11–15.

12. Cohen, M., and G.T. Toussaint, "On the Detection of Structures in Noisy Pictures," *Pattern Recognition*, Vol. 9, 1977, pp. 95–98.

13. O'Gorman, F., and M.B. Clowes, "Finding Picture Edges Through Collinearity of Feature Points," *IEEE Transactions on Computers*, C-25, April 1976, pp. 449–456.

14. Dudani, S.A., and A.L. Luk, "Locating Straight-Line Edge Segments on Outdoor Scenes," *Proceedings of the IEEE Pattern Recognition and Image Processing Conference*, 1977, pp. 367–377.

15. Goodman, I.R., "A Scoring Procedure for the Multiple Target Correlation and Tracking Problem," *Proceedings of the 1980 IEEE Conference on Decision and Control*, Albuquerque, NM, Dec. 10–12, 1980, pp. 829–834.

16. Sittler, R.W., "An Optimal Data Association Problem in Surveillance Theory," *IEEE Transactions on Military Electronics*, MIL-8, April 1964, pp. 125–139.

17. Alspach, D.L., and R.N. Lobbia, "A Score for Correct Data Association in Multi-Target Tracking," *Proceedings of the 1979 IEEE Conference on Decision and Control*, Fort Lauderdale, FL, Dec. 12–14, 1979, pp. 389–393.

18. Maged, Y.A., "Critical Probabilities for Optimum Tracking System," *Proceedings of the 1980 IEEE International Radar Conference*, Arlington, VA, April 28–30, 1980, pp. 330–335.

19. Smith, P.L., "Reduction of Sea Surveillance Data Using Binary Matrices," *IEEE Transactions on Systems, Man, and Cybernetics*, SMC-6, Aug. 1976, pp. 531–538.

20. Morefield, C.L., "Applications of 0-1 Integer Programming to Multi-Target Tracking Problems," *IEEE Transactions on Automatic Control*, AC-22, June 1977, pp. 302–312.

21. Chang, C.B., and L.C. Youens, "An Algorithm for Multiple Target Tracking and Data Correlation," M.I.T. Lincoln Laboratory Report TR-643, June 13, 1984.

22. Wishner, R.P., *et al.*, "Advanced Techniques for Multi-Target Track Formation," Advanced Information and Decisions Systems Report No. 1005, AD-B057823, April 1981.

23. Barniv, Y., "Dynamic Programming Solution for Detecting Dim Moving Targets," *IEEE Transactions on Aerospace and Electronic Systems*, AES-21, Jan. 1985, pp. 144–156.

Appendix 6A

Approximate Distribution for a Weighted Sum of Chi-Square Variables

Consider the weighted sum of N independent chi-square variables:

$$y = \sum_{n=1}^{N} a_n \chi^2_{\nu_n}$$

where $\chi^2_{\nu_n}$ are chi-square variables with ν_n degrees of freedom and a_n are weighting coefficients. The proposed approximation is

$$\hat{y} = A \chi^2_{\nu_T}$$

where $\chi^2_{\nu_T}$ is a chi-squared variable with ν_T degrees of freedom and A is a weighting coefficient. The quantities A and ν_T are computed by matching the mean and standard deviation of y and $\hat{y}$:

$$E(y) = \sum_{n=1}^{N} a_n \nu_n = E(\hat{y}) = A \nu_T \tag{6A.1}$$

$$\sigma^2_y = 2 \sum_{n=1}^{N} a_n^2 \nu_n = \sigma^2_{\hat{y}} = 2A^2 \nu_T \tag{6A.2}$$

Solving (6A.1) and (6A.2) yields

$$A = \frac{\displaystyle\sum_{n=1}^{N} a_n^2 \nu_n}{\displaystyle\sum_{n=1}^{N} a_n \nu_n}$$

$$\tag{6A.3}$$

$$\nu_T = \frac{\displaystyle\sum_{n=1}^{N} a_n \nu_n}{A} = \frac{\left[\displaystyle\sum_{n=1}^{N} a_n \nu_n\right]^2}{\displaystyle\sum_{n=1}^{N} a_n^2 \nu_n}$$

In the special case where all v_n are the same ($v_n = v$ for all n), (6A.3) reduces to

$$A = \frac{\displaystyle\sum_{n=1}^{N} a_n^2}{\displaystyle\sum_{n=1}^{N} a_n}, \quad v_T = v \frac{\left[\displaystyle\sum_{n=1}^{N} a_n\right]^2}{\displaystyle\sum_{n=1}^{N} a_n^2}$$

The practical validity of this approximation has been tested using Monte Carlo simulation and the Kolmogorof-Smirnov test.

Appendix 6B

Score Associated With Clutter Point Designation

Chapter 9 derives a score function that includes all the aspects of tracking. Consider two alternatives for a given observation. The first is to assign the observation to a given track and the second is to declare the observation to be clutter (and, thus, to declare a nondetection for the track). The contributions from these two alternatives to the score are shown in Chapter 9 to be

$$\text{Score Contribution} = \begin{cases} \ln\left[\dfrac{P_D}{(2\pi)^{M/2}\sqrt{|S|}}\right] - \dfrac{d^2}{2}, & \text{observation included in track} \\[4mm] \ln\beta_{FT} + \ln(1 - P_D), & \text{observation declared to be clutter} \end{cases} \quad (6B.1)$$

where β_{FT} = false target (clutter) density.

The score function considered in this chapter [1] uses the term d^2, but leaves the score (S_c) associated with assigning a point to clutter undefined. However, by comparing the terms in (6B.1), it can be seen that if d^2 is assigned to the score for a track update, the equivalent score associated with assigning a point to clutter is

$$S_c = 2 \ln \left[\frac{P_D}{(1 - P_D)\, \beta_{FT}\, (2\pi)^{M/2}\, \sqrt{|S|}} \right] \qquad (6B.2)$$

Assuming independence of the residual errors gives

$$\beta_{FT} \sqrt{|S|} = \beta_{FT}\, (\sigma_{r1}\ \sigma_{r2}\ \dots\ \sigma_{rM}) = \frac{n_{TF}}{2^M} \qquad (6B.3)$$

where the σ_{ri} are the residual standard deviations and n_{TF} is as defined in Chapter 4. Thus, combining Equations (6B.2) and (6B.3), gives

$$S_c = 2 \ln \left[\frac{P_D}{1 - P_D} \right] - 2 \ln \left[\left(\frac{\pi}{2} \right)^{\frac{M}{2}} n_{TF} \right] \qquad (6B.4)$$

The term S_c is, in effect, the addition to the score function that occurs when an observation is assigned to clutter rather than to a given target track. The quantity n_{TF} is actually a variable, varying with the residual covariance matrix, S. The probability of detection, P_D, also varies. However, because the goal is to define a simple measure of tracking quality, approximations using typical expected values should be made.

REFERENCE

1.   Alspach, D.L., and R.N. Lobbia, "A Score for Correct Data Association in Multi-Target Tracking," *Proceedings of the 1979 IEEE Conference on Decision and Control*, Fort Lauderdale, FL, Dec. 12–14, 1979, pp. 389–393.

Chapter 7

Analytic Techniques for System Evaluation

7.1 INTRODUCTION

MTT system design typically requires the development of a detailed Monte Carlo type simulation, which includes all system elements, and a model of the target geometry. Chapter 8 will outline the development of such a simulation. However, it is usually convenient (and is an aid to the initial design process) to separately evaluate the elements, using less elaborate techniques, before they are all included in the detailed simulation for final validation. This chapter discusses analytic techniques for use in design and preliminary system evaluation.

This chapter begins with a discussion of covariance analysis for use in design and evaluation of the tracking filters. Next, expressions are derived for use in the preliminary determination of observation-to-track correlation performance. These expressions are designed to consider a single established track and one or more potential correlating observations. Finally, Markov chain techniques are developed for use in determining target track maintenance and false track statistics. Examples will be given to illustrate application of the methods.

7.2 COVARIANCE ANALYSIS

Covariance analysis is a very convenient tool for the evaluation of tracking filter performance. As one application of covariance analysis, it is possible to evaluate the effects of mismatch between the Kalman filter model and the true target maneuver model. For example, the effects of reducing the state model from three to two states are evaluated below. Also, the effects of varying the sampling interval and the relative performance of various fixed-gain filters, as compared with a Kalman filter, can be readily computed using covariance analysis.

7.2.1 Covariance Analysis for Tracking System Evaluation

The use of covariance analysis is illustrated by the following example.

Assume the target state evolves according to the state equation:

$$x(k + 1) = \Phi x(k) + q(k) \tag{7.1}$$

Also, following the notation of Chapter 2, assume a filtering and prediction method (not necessarily Kalman) described by the equations:

$$\hat{x}(k|k) = \hat{x}(k|k - 1) + K(k) [y(k) - H \hat{x}(k|k - 1)]$$

$$\hat{x}(k + 1|k) = \Phi\hat{x}(k|k)$$

Taking the measurement to be

$$y(k) = H x(k) + v(k)$$

gives

$$\hat{x}(k + 1|k) = \Phi\hat{x}(k|k) = \Phi[I - K(k)H] \hat{x}(k|k - 1) + \Phi K(k) v(k)$$
$$+ \Phi K(k) Hx(k) \tag{7.2}$$

Defining the one step prediction error vector as

$$\tilde{x}(k + 1) = x(k + 1) - \hat{x}(k + 1|k)$$

and combining (7.1) and (7.2) gives

$$\tilde{x}(k + 1) = \Phi[I - K(k)H] \tilde{x}(k) - \Phi K(k) v(k) + q(k) \tag{7.3}$$

The error covariance matrix is defined

$$P_e(k) \overset{\Delta}{=} E[\tilde{x}(k) \tilde{x}^T(k)] \tag{7.4}$$

Equations (7.3) and (7.4) lead to a convenient recursion relationship for the error covariance:

$$P_e(k + 1) = \Phi_p(k) P_e(k) \Phi_p^T(k) + \Phi K(k) R_c K^T(k) \Phi^T + Q \tag{7.5}$$

where the following relationships and definitions have been used:

$$\Phi_p \overset{\Delta}{=} \Phi[I - K(k)H]$$

$$E[\tilde{x}(k) q^T(k)] \equiv 0, \ E[\tilde{x}(k) v^T(k)] \equiv 0,$$

$$E[q(k) q^T (k)] \overset{\Delta}{=} Q = \text{process noise covariance matrix}$$

$$E[v(k) v^T (k)] \overset{\Delta}{=} R_c = \text{measurement noise covariance matrix}$$

For the case in which the Kalman filter is used and the Kalman filter model matches the target state model of (7.1), the Kalman covariance matrix P is identical to the error covariance matrix P_e. However, for any type of mismatch, the gain $K(k)$ will differ from that which would have resulted from an optimal Kalman filter that used (7.1) as its state model. These mismatch conditions occur, for example, for a reduced-state Kalman filter, for a fixed-coefficient filter, or for cases where there is mismatch between truth and the assumed models.

Covariance analysis cannot be used directly in the case of a Kalman filter and probabilistic input data (potential missing data). This is because the Kalman filter gains adjust to the input data sequence and the number of permutations of detections and misses grows exponentially. Thus, it is not feasible to include an averaging over the random detection sequence directly in the covariance equation. However, if the gain is constant ($K(k) = K$), the covariance propagation of (7.5) extends directly to the case of nonunity probability of detection (P_D)

$$P_e(k + 1) = P_D[\Phi_p\, P_e(k)\, \Phi_p^T + \Phi K\, R_c\, K^T \Phi^T] + (1 - P_D)\, \Phi P_e(k)\, \Phi^T + Q$$

When the gains adapt to a variable detection sequence (potential missed data), Monte Carlo methods must be used. For this approach, a large number of covariance runs are made, with differing measurement sequences. Then, the covariance values are averaged over the Monte Carlo runs. By using this combined covariance and Monte Carlo approach, covariance analysis is effectively being used to average over measurement noise and target maneuver effects, while Monte Carlo averaging is done over varying detection histories. More discussion of the Monte Carlo method is given in the next chapter.

As an example of the use of covariance analysis, consider the angle tracking filter derived in Chapter 3, which is described by the state equation:

$$\begin{bmatrix} \theta(k+1) \\ v_p(k+1) \\ a_p(k+1) \end{bmatrix} = \begin{bmatrix} 1 & T\,C_R/R & T^2/2R \\ 0 & \rho_R & T(C_R - \beta T/2) \\ 0 & 0 & \rho_m \end{bmatrix} \begin{bmatrix} \theta(k) \\ v_p(k) \\ a_p(k) \end{bmatrix}$$

$$+ \begin{bmatrix} 0 \\ 0 \\ \sqrt{1 - \rho_m^2}\, \sigma_m\, r(k) \end{bmatrix} \tag{7.6}$$

where

$$C_R = 1 - v_R T/2R, \qquad \rho_R = e^{-v_R T/R}, \qquad v_R = \dot{R}$$

$$\rho_m = e^{-\beta T}, \qquad r(k) \sim N(0,1), \qquad \beta = \frac{1}{\tau_m}$$

Also, v_p and a_p are the velocity and acceleration components perpendicular to the line-of-sight, as defined in Chapter 3. The state equation given by (7.6) can represent tracking of the stabilized azimuth angle ($\theta = \eta$) defining target motion in the horizontal plane or tracking of the stabilized elevation angle ($\theta = \epsilon$).

The state model of (7.6) provides the transition matrix Φ and random forcing function q. Since the angle is measured, the measurement noise covariance matrix becomes the scalar observation variance $\sigma_{\theta_o}^2$.

7.2.2   Studies of Sensitivity to Maneuver Model and Sampling Interval

Covariance analysis will first be used to examine tracking for the case of mismatch between the filter model and the actual system. The results will be used to determine the sensitivity to mismatches in the filter model. The filter is assumed to use the same form of state model, the Singer model discussed in Chapter 2, that describes the actual system. However, the target acceleration (maneuver) standard deviation used in the filter (σ_{mf}) will be mismatched from the target maneuver standard deviation (σ_m) assumed valid for the actual system.

Probabilistic detection will be modeled by using a constant probability of detection ($P_D = 0.7$). Typical radar detection probabilities are range-dependent, but for simplicity a constant value of P_D is used here and for other examples in this book. Tracking was assumed to begin at 30 nmi with a closing rate of 2000 ft/s. Finally, the angular measurement error standard deviation (σ_{θ_o}) was chosen to be 0.01 rad (10 mrad) and the maneuver time constant, τ_m, was chosen to be 10 s for both the filter and the system model.

Since non-unity probability of detection ($P_D < 1$) was used, it was necessary to use Monte Carlo averaging over the detection sequence. Results are averaged over 200 Monte Carlo runs. Figure 7-1 gives results for the four combinations considering σ_m and σ_{mf} to be 1 g and 2 g. For this figure, the sampling interval was 3.0 s.

Referring to Fig. 7-1, the largest prediction-error standard deviation occurs when the actual system-maneuver standard deviation (σ_m) is 2 g while the filter value (σ_{mf}) is 1 g. A significant reduction of this error occurs when σ_{mf} is increased to 2 g to match σ_m, but the prediction error is still much larger than when σ_m is 1 g. Considering the case of σ_m equal to 1 g, the use of too large a filter maneuver term ($\sigma_{mf} = 2 g$) leads to relatively small degradation. Thus, the conclusion is that performance is rather insensitive to errors in the filter acceleration model but that in the presence of uncertainty it is best to ensure that $\sigma_{mf} \gtrsim \sigma_m$.

Next, consider the relative effectiveness of adaptively varying the sampling interval with the target maneuver capability. Figure 7-2 indicates how performance improves if the sampling interval is chosen according to the relationship:

$$T^2 \sigma_m = \text{const} \tag{7.7}$$

For the case of $\sigma_m = 2\,g$, Fig. 7-2 shows how angular prediction error varies with mismatch in σ_{mf} and with decreasing T by a factor of $\sqrt{2}$. Evidently, decreasing the sampling interval is more effective than eliminating the mismatch in target maneuver model. Reducing T to 2.12 s effectively reduces the prediction error, even if the incorrect filter model ($\sigma_{mf} = 1\,g$) is used.

Next, Table 7-1 summarizes the results of a study to determine the sensitivity to target maneuver model when both the filter acceleration value (σ_{mf}) and the sampling interval are adjusted. For σ_{mf} of $1\,g$ the sampling interval was 3.0 s and for other values of σ_{mf}, as expressed in units of g, and consistent with (7.7),

$$T = 3.0 \sqrt{1\,g / \sigma_{mf}}$$

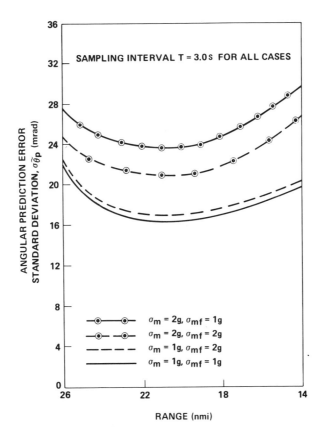

FIGURE 7-1. ANGULAR PREDICTION ERROR AS A FUNCTION OF MANEUVER MODEL MISMATCH

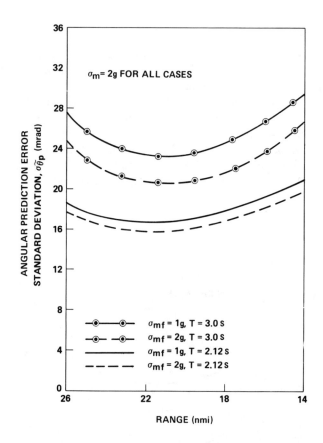

**FIGURE 7-2. ANGULAR PREDICTION ERROR AS A FUNCTION
OF FILTER MANEUVER MODEL AND SAMPLING INTERVAL**

Results given in Table 7-1 are the standard deviation of the angular prediction error $(\sigma_{\tilde{\theta}_p})$ when the target is at 20 nmi.

The results given in Table 7-1 show that performance is not too sensitive to mismatches of the order of 0.5 g between the actual and the assumed target acceleration capability. As long as the correct filter acceleration is used and T is chosen according to (7.7), the prediction error remains essentially constant at about 16.3 mrad. Then, a few milliradians of error are introduced for each 0.5 g that the true target acceleration standard deviation (σ_m) exceeds the filter assumed value (σ_{mf}).

The results of Table 7-1 again show the relative importance of the sampling interval, T. For example, the minimum prediction error shown, 13.3 mrad, occurs when σ_{mf} is 2.5 g and σ_m is 1 g. Thus, even though the value for σ_{mf} is too large, the relatively short sampling interval, 1.9 s, compensates for the mismatch.

TABLE 7-1
ANGULAR PREDICTION ERROR (σ_{θ_p}) AS A FUNCTION
OF ACTUAL AND ASSUMED TARGET MANEUVER
MODEL AND SAMPLING INTERVAL
(PREDICTION ERROR STANDARD DEVIATION
IN mrad AT R = 20 nmi)

Filter Maneuver Model	*Sampling Interval*	*Actual Target Maneuver Model Standard Deviation (σ_m) in g*			
σ_{mf} (g)	$T(s)$	1.0	1.5	2.0	2.5
1.0	3.0	16.4*	20.1	24.0	28.5
1.5	2.45	14.2	16.2	18.4	21.0
2.0	2.12	13.7	15.0	16.3	18.3
2.5	1.9	13.3	14.2	15.2	16.3

*Results presented in terms of mrad (1 mrad = 0.001 rad)

7.2.3 Covariance Analysis of Reduced State Filters

Next, we examine the effects of reducing the number of states in the Kalman angle filter. In particular, the third state, acceleration, will be removed. Thus, the process noise (or forcing) covariance matrix Q of the resulting two-state filter must be chosen to compensate for the missing acceleration state. Covariance analysis is then used to determine the degradation (as compared with the full three-state filter) associated with the simplified two-state filter. Note that the covariance analysis is performed using the three-state covariance matrix equations, while the gain, for use in the covariance equations, is computed using a reduced-state filter.

Upon elimination of the acceleration state, the two remaining states are angle (θ) and perpendicular (cross line-of-sight) velocity (v_p). Thus, a two-state Kalman filter is used and the transition and process noise covariance matrices are chosen to be

$$\Phi_f = \begin{bmatrix} 1 & T\,C_R/R \\ 0 & \rho_R \end{bmatrix}, \quad Q_f = C_Q\,\sigma_{mf}^2 \begin{bmatrix} \dfrac{T^3}{3R^2} & \dfrac{T^2}{2R} \\ \dfrac{T^2}{2R} & T \end{bmatrix}$$

The filter transition matrix, Φ_f, is a two-by-two submatrix of the full transition matrix defined in (7.6) and Q_f is based upon the approximation discussed in Chapter 2. The subscript f has been added to the transition and the process noise covariance matrices used by the filter to distinguish these quantities from those used for the actual system model.

The form of Q_f is an approximation and the constant C_Q is a tuning factor used to adjust the magnitude of the matrix. For the limiting case where $\tau_m \ll T$, the Q_f matrix is exact and, from (2.18), the value of C_Q is $2\tau_m$. However, this is not the normal case (usually $\tau_m \gtrsim T$) and was not the case for the example results to be shown. Thus, C_Q was taken to be a parameter chosen in an *ad hoc* (experimental) manner in order to optimize performance for the two-state filter.

For this covariance study, σ_m and σ_{mf} were both taken to be 1 g. After some experimentation, the value of C_Q was taken to be 10. This value optimized performance over the range of sampling intervals (0.5 to 3.0 s) examined.

Figure 7-3 compares the angular prediction error standard deviation obtained, using covariance analysis, for the two- and three-state filters. Again, tracking was assumed to begin at 30 nmi and results were obtained using 200 Monte Carlo runs with a constant probability of detection, $P_D = 0.7$. The angular measurement noise standard deviation was again taken to be 10 mrad. Clearly, for the three sampling intervals and over the range interval considered, the performance of the two filters is nearly indistinguishable.

Angular prediction errors were found to increase rapidly at ranges shorter than those for the results given in Fig. 7-3. However, results again indicated essentially no degradation associated with the reduced-state filter. Thus, when computational considerations are also included, the covariance study indicates that the use of two-state filters is preferable for this application.

7.3 TECHNIQUES FOR ESTIMATING CORRELATION PERFORMANCE

Most MTT system designs are ultimately verified by examining statistics derived using detailed Monte Carlo simulation. However for a preliminary design, the probability of correct correlation (P_{CC}), the probability of false correlation (P_{FC}), and the probability of correct decision (P_{CD}) are useful. As shown next, these quantities can be readily computed and thus used to determine feasibility of design. A nearest-neighbor rule for observation-to-track association will be assumed. For this rule, the observation within the gate (defined next) that is closest to the predicted target position is associated with the track.

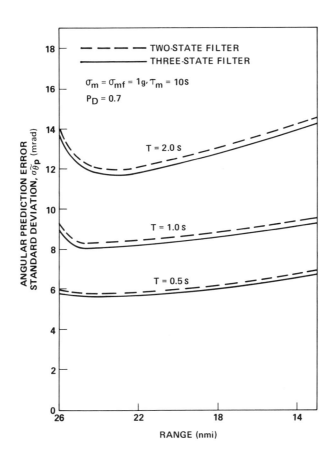

FIGURE 7-3. COMPARATIVE ANGULAR TRACKING
FOR TWO AND THREE STATE FILTERS

7.3.1 Gate Definition

For the example to follow, an ellipsoidal gate is assumed. By using the expressions developed in Appendix 4A, similar results could be derived using rectangular gates. Assume that the optimal gate defined in Chapter 4 is used:

$$G = 2 \ln \left[\frac{P_D}{(1 - P_D) \, \beta (2\pi)^{M/2} \sqrt{|S|}} \right] \qquad (7.8)$$

where

P_D = probability of detection

β = new source density = $P_{FA}/V_M + \overline{N}_E/V_S$ (7.9)

V_M = measurement volume

V_S = scan volume

$\overline{N}_E$ = expected number of new targets within the scan volume

P_{FA} = probability of false alarm (or clutter) within measurement volume

M = measurement dimension

$|S|$ = determinant of residual covariance matrix

Then, the gate is satisfied if the normalized distance (d^2) satisfies

$$d^2 = \tilde{y}^T S^{-1} \tilde{y} \leqq G \tag{7.10}$$

where $\tilde{y}$ is the M-dimensional residual vector.

The gating relationship of (7.10) defines a constant likelihood ellipsoid. Then, as discussed in Chapter 4, the probability $P_G(M)$ that a valid observation falls within the gate can be computed and is given in Table 4-1 for values of $M = 1$ to 6.

7.3.2 Derivation of Expressions for Evaluating Correlation Performance

The probability of correct correlation (P_{CC}) is given by

$$P_{CC} = P_D P_{CC/D} \tag{7.11}$$

where, as derived in Appendix 4A, $P_{CC/D}$ is the probability of correct correlation given that a detection occurred. This is defined to be the probability that the true return is inside the gate and that no false return has smaller normalized distance. The probability of correct decision (P_{CD}) is P_{CC} plus the joint probability that no target detection occurs and that no correlation occurs given that there is no detection. Thus,

$$P_{CD} = P_{CC} + (1 - P_D) P_{NE} \tag{7.12}$$

where, as also derived in Appendix 4A,

    P_{NE} = probability that no extraneous sources fall within the gate (so that no correlation occurs). P_{NE} is given by (4A.10).

Next, define

    P_E = probability that an extraneous source is detected closer to the predicted position than is the true return. This probability is also conditioned on the true return being within the gate.

The probability of correct correlation given a detection $(P_{CC/D})$ is the product of the probability that the true observation falls within the gate (P_G)

and the probability that no extraneous return is closer:

$$P_{CC/D} = P_G(1 - P_E)$$

We can then solve for P_E:

$$P_E = 1 - \frac{P_{CC/D}}{P_G} \tag{7.13}$$

Finally, the probability of false correlation (P_{FC}) is the sum of two terms that represent the probability of false correlation given that the true observation is within the gate and that it is not. Thus,

$$P_{FC} = P_D P_G P_E + (1 - P_D P_G)(1 - P_{NE})$$
$$= P_D(P_G - P_{CC/D}) + (1 - P_D P_G)(1 - P_{NE}) \tag{7.14}$$

Equations (7.11), (7.12), and (7.14) provide convenient expressions for use in preliminary system evaluation. The required quantities P_G, $P_{CC/D}$, and P_{NE} can be computed using the methods presented in Chapter 4 and P_E is given by (7.13). Note that these expressions are related to P_D and P_{FA} through G and β defined in (7.8) and (7.9). Thus, as illustrated in the next example, assume a relationship between P_D and P_{FA}, which will involve a threshold setting as discussed in Chapter 5. Then, the correlation probabilities can be computed as a function of threshold setting and the expected number of new targets ($\overline{N}_E$).

7.3.3 Examples of Correlation Performance Computation

First, a simple example will be used to illustrate the methods previously discussed. For this example, consider various threshold settings (defining $P_D - P_{FA}$ pairs) with the idea that the appropriate setting is to be determined from an examination of the resulting correlation statistics. For simplicity, assume a two-dimensional (x, y) measurement, so that, using Table 4-1 for $M = 2$, we obtain

$$P_G = 1 - e^{-\frac{G}{2}} \tag{7.15}$$

Next, also for simplicity, define the basic measurement volume unit to be a pixel with length and width each equal to unity. P_{FA} is defined with respect to the pixel and a negligible number of expected new targets ($\overline{N}_E \cong 0$) is assumed. This could correspond to the tracking of an isolated aircraft or missile target by an IR surveillance system. Thus, because the basic measurement volume (V_M) is a pixel of unit volume, $\beta = P_{FA}$ from (7.9). Also, assume x and y residual errors to be uncorrelated and with standard deviations σ_x^- and σ_y^- so that $\sqrt{|S|} = \sigma_x^- \sigma_y^-$.

With the system as defined above and using (4A.9), (4A.10) and (4.10), we have

$$P_{CC/D} = P_G - \frac{\pi}{2} P_{FA}\, \sigma_x^- \sigma_y^- \left[4 - e^{-\frac{G}{2}} (2G + 4) \right]$$

(7.16)

$$V_G = \pi\, \sigma_x^- \sigma_y^-\, G, \quad P_{NE} = \exp(-P_{FA} V_G)$$

Also, from (7.8), the gate is given by

$$G = 2 \ln \left[\frac{P_D}{(1 - P_D)\, 2\pi\, P_{FA}\, \sigma_x^- \sigma_y^-} \right]$$

(7.17)

Finally, for a given threshold setting, a convenient approximate relationship between P_D and P_{FA}, used also in (5.5), is [1]

$$P_D = (P_{FA})^{\frac{1}{1 + SNR}}$$

(7.18)

Table 7-2 summarizes the computations given by (7.14) through (7.18) and the resulting P_{CC}, P_{FC}, and P_{CD} as a function of the threshold setting (with resulting P_D and P_{FA}). For case 1, $\sigma_x^- = \sigma_y^- = 10$ and $SNR = 24$ (or in decibels, 13.8 dB) is chosen. Case 2 considers a lower SNR value, 14, while case 3 increases the residual error standard deviations, so that

$$\sigma_x^- = \sigma_y^- = 10 \sqrt{10} = 31.6$$

Referring to Table 7-2, the results for cases 1 and 2 are similar except that P_D and P_{CC} are decreased when SNR is smaller. The effect of reducing SNR is to decrease the gate somewhat so that P_{FC} and P_{CD} remain about the same for a given P_{FA}. Conversely, for a case not shown in Table 7-2, when SNR was increased to 100 while σ_x^- and σ_y^- were maintained at 10, P_{CC} increased, but improvements in P_{FC} and P_{CD} were minimal. However, increasing σ_x^- and σ_y^- to 31.6 leads to a requirement that P_{FA} be decreased in order to maintain the same values for P_{FC}. For example, the setting for $P_{FA} = 10^{-3}$ is no longer considered because G becomes negative. Increasing target position uncertainty leads to a considerable decrease in gate size (G).

The first general conclusion from the data of Table 7-2 is that the threshold setting must increase (leading to lower P_{FA}) as residual error increases. This was also shown in Fig. 5-2. Thus, the threshold should be raised after a period of target extrapolation. This is in contrast to an intuitive approach that might consider lowering the threshold to ensure target detection and thus compensate for the lack of target data during extrapolation.

Results show that the gate varies with SNR so that P_{FC} and P_{CD} remain about the same. For example, for a case not shown in Table 7-2, raising SNR

TABLE 7-2
CORRELATION STATISTICS AS FUNCTION OF THRESHOLD SETTING

Case	P_{FA}	P_D	G	P_G	$P_{CC/D}$	P_{NE}	P_{CC}	P_{FC}	P_{CD}
1. $SNR = 24$	10^{-3}	0.76	3.2	0.80	0.50	0.36	0.38	0.48	0.47
	10^{-4}	0.69	7.15	0.97	0.92	0.80	0.63	0.10	0.88
$\sigma_x = \sigma_y = 10$	10^{-5}	0.63	11.2	0.996	0.99	0.97	0.63	0.017	0.98
	10^{-6}	0.58	15.4	1.0	0.999	0.995	0.58	0.002	0.997
2. $SNR = 14$	10^{-3}	0.63	2.0	0.63	0.47	0.53	0.29	0.38	0.49
	10^{-4}	0.54	5.9	0.95	0.90	0.83	0.49	0.11	0.87
$\sigma_x = \sigma_y = 10$	10^{-5}	0.46	9.9	0.99	0.99	0.97	0.46	0.019	0.98
	10^{-6}	0.40	13.9	1.0	0.998	0.996	0.40	0.003	0.997
3. $SNR = 24$	10^{-4}	0.69	2.6	0.72	0.49	0.45	0.34	0.43	0.48
	10^{-5}	0.63	6.6	0.96	0.91	0.81	0.57	0.11	0.87
$\sigma_x = \sigma_y = 31.6$	10^{-6}	0.58	10.8	0.995	0.99	0.97	0.57	0.017	0.98
	10^{-7}	0.52	14.9	1.0	0.998	0.995	0.52	0.003	0.997

to 100 while maintaining P_{FA} at 10^{-5} and the residual standard deviations at 31.6 led only to minor improvements in P_{FC} and P_{CD}, which became 0.08 and 0.91, respectively, (compared with the values 0.11 and 0.87 found for $SNR=24$). However, G and P_{CC} increased to 9.8 and 0.83, respectively (compared with 6.6 and 0.57 for $SNR=24$).

The results of this study indicate that a slight decrease in the threshold, increasing P_{FA} as shown in Fig. 5-2, may be appropriate for lower SNR, but little degradation would be expected if the threshold setting is not made a function of SNR. Thus, to maintain $P_{FC}<0.02$, a threshold setting that gives $P_{FA} \gtrsim 10^{-5}$ seems appropriate when the residual standard deviation is 10. However, as the residual standard deviation increases by factor $\sqrt{10}$ the P_{FA} should be decreased to about 10^{-6}. This has the effect of maintaining a constant value for the factor, $P_{FA}\,\sigma_x^-\,\sigma_y^-$, that arises in the computations of G, P_{NE}, and $P_{CC/D}$.

The above methods can be extended to other applications. As an example, for an IR surveillance problem it was required to determine whether a low SNR target could be reacquired after a period of extrapolation. Once reacquisition began, the target could be illuminated for up to 30 scans. The problem was to calculate the probability that a correct correlation would occur before a false correlation and before 30 scans had elapsed. Kalman filtering was used, and the target maneuver capability was assumed to be small. The gating and other calculations were as described above.

In order to compute the correlation probabilities for this example, we define $CP_{CC}(k)$ and $CP_{FC}(k)$ to be the cumulative probabilities of correct correlation and false correlation at scan k. Then, these cumulative probabilities can be computed using the recursion relationships:

$$CP_{CC}(k + 1) = CP_{CC}(k) + [1 - P_T(k)]\,P_{CC}(k + 1)$$

$$CP_{FC}(k + 1) = CP_{FC}(k) + [1 - P_T(k)]\,P_{FC}(k + 1)$$

where the probability of receiving at least one correlating observation (correct or false) at or before scan k is given by

$$P_T(k) = CP_{CC}(k) + CP_{FC}(k)$$

Figure 7-4 shows the values for $CP_{CC}(k)$ that were computed for three threshold settings. The setting that gave $P_D=0.074$ and $P_{FA}=4\times10^{-5}$ was found to maximize CP_{CC}. However, for this low SNR target the probability of reacquisition ($CP_{CC}(30)$) is still less than 80 percent. This led to the conclusion that the extrapolation period (before reacquisition began) was too long; in order for this system to successfully maintain tracks, the revisit time had to be decreased.

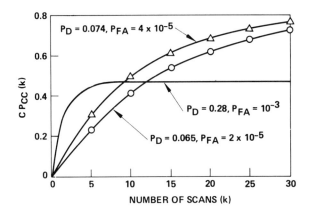

FIGURE 7-4. CUMULATIVE PROBABILITY OF SUCCESSFUL TRACK UPDATE

7.4 TRACK CONFIRMATION AND RETENTION STATISTICS US-ING MARKOV CHAIN TECHNIQUES

In the first published paper on MTT, Wax [2] recognized the applicability of Markov chain techniques for examining track birth and death statistics. The Markov chain approach is very useful for deriving a variety of statistics associated with track life. This section will develop some useful applications and the next section will outline extensions.

7.4.1 General Development for Track Confirmation and Deletion

Many track initiation and deletion processes are conveniently represented by the Markov chain relationship:

$$P(k + 1) = \Phi(k, k + 1) P(k) \tag{7.19}$$

Here, P is a vector of probabilities (P_i) associated with being in various discrete states (S_i) and Φ is the transition matrix. The transition matrix $\Phi(k, k + 1)$ will be a known function of the probability of detection, P_D. Thus, given an initial condition vector $P(1)$, succeeding values of $P(k + 1)$ can be calculated given $P(k)$. The process is illustrated by a simple example.

For a first application, consider the cumulative probability of track confirmation assuming the (2/3) confirmation criterion defined as two detections out of three consecutive looks. Letting 1 represent a detection and 0 a nondetection, the appropriate states are defined as

$S_1 = 0$ 0 = two consecutive misses

$S_2 = 0$ 1 = miss followed by a detection

$S_3 = 1$ 0 = detection followed by a miss

S_4 = state of having achieved confirmation (the $2/3$ confirmation criterion has been achieved)

Equation (7.20) shows how the general Markov relationship of (7.19) is used to represent this process:

$$\mathbf{P}(k+1) = \begin{bmatrix} P_1(k+1) \\ P_2(k+1) \\ P_3(k+1) \\ P_4(k+1) \end{bmatrix} = \begin{bmatrix} Q_D & 0 & Q_D & 0 \\ P_D & 0 & 0 & 0 \\ 0 & Q_D & 0 & 0 \\ 0 & P_D & P_D & 1 \end{bmatrix} \begin{bmatrix} P_1(k) \\ P_2(k) \\ P_3(k) \\ P_4(k) \end{bmatrix} \tag{7.20}$$

Referred to (7.20), a constant value of P_D (and $Q_D = 1 - P_D$) is indicated, but, in general, the detection probability would (usually through range) be a function of time ($P_D = P_D(k+1)$). An alternative representation is through the state diagram shown in Fig. 7-5. Using this representation, state transitions are indicated with arrows and the transition probabilities are given next to the arrows.

S1   = NO TRACK STATE
S2, S3 = TENTATIVE TRACK STATES
S4   = CONFIRMED TRACK STATE
Q_D = $1 - P_D$

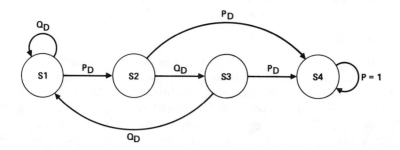

FIGURE 7-5. STATE DIAGRAM FOR TRACK CONFIRMATION
(NO WAIT STATE)

The Markov representation may be thought of as a representation of the manner in which probability transitions (or flows) between states. This is illustrated by examining the relationship for the probability of being in the cumulative confirmed state. From (7.20), we write

$$P_4(k + 1) = P_4(k) + P_D[P_2(k) + P_3(k)] \tag{7.21}$$

Equation (7.21) shows the manner in which probability enters state S_4. Also, referring to (7.20), we see that because the first three elements of the fourth column are zero, there is no flux of probability out of state S_4. Thus, S_4 is an absorbing state that is not left once it is entered. Similarly, the system stays in state S_1 or enters S_1 from S_3 with probability Q_D, while the probability of leaving state S_1, by going to S_2, is P_D.

Next, consider the cumulative probability of track deletion for a previously confirmed track. Given N_D consecutive nondetections as the deletion criterion, the appropriate states are

$$S_1 = 1 \qquad = \text{detection just received}$$
$$S_2 = 1 \quad 0 \qquad = \text{one nondetection}$$
$$S_3 = 1 \quad 0 \quad 0 \quad = \text{two consecutive nondetections}$$
$$\vdots$$
$$S_{N_D+1} = 1 \quad 0 \quad 0 \quad \ldots \quad 0 \quad \text{Cumulative state of having obtained}$$
$$N_D \text{ consecutive nondetections}$$

The Markov chain representation for this process is

$$
\begin{bmatrix}
P_1(k+1) \\
P_2(k+1) \\
P_3(k+1) \\
\vdots \\
P_{N_D}(k+1) \\
P_{N_D+1}(k+1)
\end{bmatrix}
=
\begin{bmatrix}
P_D & P_D & \ldots & P_D & 0 \\
Q_D & 0 & \ldots & 0 & 0 \\
0 & Q_D & \ldots & 0 & 0 \\
\vdots & \vdots & & \vdots & \ddots \\
0 & 0 & \ldots & 0 & 0 \\
0 & 0 & & Q_D & 1
\end{bmatrix}
\begin{bmatrix}
P_1(k) \\
P_2(k) \\
P_3(k) \\
\vdots \\
P_{N_D}(k) \\
P_{N_D+1}(k)
\end{bmatrix}
\tag{7.22}
$$

Equations (7.20) and (7.22) give examples of tracking processes that are easily placed in the form of Markov chains to allow relatively simple recursive calculations. A quick test to determine if the process has been correctly formulated can be made by checking to ensure that the sum of all elements in each column of the transition matrix adds up to unity. An initialization (such as $P_1(1) = 1$, $P_2(1) = P_3(1) = \ldots = 0$) of the probability vector, **P**, is required. Another convenient check of the formulation and programming is that the sum of all elements of **P** add to unity at all times.

An important measure of track retention performance is the probability of having a track that will not later be deleted. This is the cumulative probability of track confirmation without later deletion, and its calculation proceeds directly by making a minor extension to the Markov chains described above. This criterion is used because it incorporates both search and track update capability into a comprehensive measure of tracking performance.

The process of computing the probability of track without later deletion consists of two steps. Assume a closing target with range decreasing with time (increasing scan number). Then, first consider all ranges at which a track may become confirmed, and by iterating (7.22) compute the probability that, once confirmed at a given range, the track will be maintained until the end of the encounter. The purpose of this first step is to compute and store probabilities of track maintenance as a function of confirmation range.

The second step computes, as a function of range (scan number), the probability that track confirmation occurs at that range and multiplies this probability times the probability of maintenance given confirmation (computed from the previous step). This product represents the probability that a confirmed track that will not later be deleted emerges at a given range (scan). Keeping a running sum of these probabilities gives the probability of having a confirmed track that will not later be deleted. Implementation is described below.

Assuming the previously defined confirmation and deletion criteria, define the state variables:

S_1 = No track, at least two consecutive nondetections

$S_2 = 0$ 1 = tentative track, an observation just received

$S_3 = 1$ 0 = tentative track, an observation followed by a nondetection

S_4 = new track, just confirmed

S_5 = track with a detection just received

S_6 = track in which the last look produced a miss

S_7 = track with two consecutive nondetections

.
.
.

S_{N_D+4} = track with $N_D - 1$ consecutive nondetections

The above process is defined by the Markov chain:

$$
\begin{bmatrix}
P_1 (k + 1) \\
P_2 (k + 1) \\
P_3 (k + 1) \\
P_4 (k + 1) \\
P_5 (k + 1) \\
P_6 (k + 1) \\
P_7 (k + 1) \\
\vdots \\
P_{N_D + 4} (k + 1)
\end{bmatrix}
$$

$$
=
\begin{bmatrix}
Q_D & 0 & Q_D & 0 & \ldots & & & & 0 & Q_D \\
P_D & 0 & 0 & 0 & \ldots & & & & & \\
0 & Q_D & 0 & 0 & \ldots & & & & & \\
0 & P_D & P_D & 0 & \ldots & & & & & \\
0 & 0 & 0 & P_D & P_D & P_D & P_D & \ldots & P_D & P_D \\
0 & 0 & 0 & Q_D & Q_D & 0 & 0 & \ldots & 0 & 0 \\
0 & 0 & 0 & 0 & 0 & Q_D & 0 & \ldots & 0 & 0 \\
\vdots & \vdots & \vdots & & & & & & \vdots & \vdots \\
\vdots & \vdots & \vdots & & & & & & \vdots & \vdots \\
0 & 0 & 0 & & & & & & Q_D & 0
\end{bmatrix}
\begin{bmatrix}
P_1 (k) \\
P_2 (k) \\
P_3 (k) \\
P_3 (k) \\
P_5 (k) \\
P_6 (k) \\
P_7 (k) \\
\vdots \\
P_{N_D + 3} (k) \\
P_{N_D + 4} (k)
\end{bmatrix}
$$

$$(7.23)$$

Note that the transition is made from state $S_{N_D + 4}$ to state S_1 upon deletion. Also, the state S_4 is entered from either state S_2 or S_3 whenever a track becomes confirmed.

The process given by (7.23) can be solved at any scan time (k) for the probability, $P_4(k)$, of just having confirmed a track. This is multiplied by the probability of not later deleting a track confirmed at scan k (calculated by iteration of (7.22)) to determine the probability of having just confirmed a track at scan k that will not later be deleted. Summing these probabilities over k gives the cumulative probability of having a confirmed track that will not later be deleted.

To summarize the above application, assume a closing (decreasing range) target that first enters the sensor field of view at some initial range and that is to be tracked until some minimum range. Given the initial range and the closing rate, the target separation range can be computed as a function of time. For each scan (k) there is a corresponding range separation interval and an appropriate probability of detection, $P_D(k)$. In order to compute (as a function of range separation) the probability of having a confirmed track that will not later be deleted, a preliminary calculation is made (using (7.22)) at each range interval to determine the cumulative probability of track deletion for tracks confirmed at that range. Then, at each range the probability (P_4) of being in state S_4 is multiplied by one minus the appropriate cumulative track deletion probability, and the sum of these factors is accumulated.

The Markov chains just described are basically for TWS systems in which search and track update are performed simultaneously, and thus at the same rate. The extension to a system, such as the radar electronically scanned antenna (ESA), in which search and track update can be performed at different rates is direct if "wait states" are introduced. The wait state is merely an intermediate state in which no action occurs, but that serves to delay the next time an action does occur. Application of the wait state is illustrated by the example which follows.

Assume that we wish to model a system (such as the ESA) in which track update can occur at a faster rate (for example, double) than search. The agile beam capabilities of the ESA allow adaptive sampling to be used, so that track update illumination can be chosen to occur at a faster rate than search. Further assume that this faster update rate capability is used by performing a special update illumination on a tentative track, after receiving the initial detection, during the middle of the search scan. Again consider the cumulative probability of track confirmation using the (2/3) criterion, but with the faster update of tentative tracks. Then, the basic time interval in which the process is iterated is halved from that considered in the previous example, and a wait state is introduced. The wait state simulates the condition where the search scan requires two multiples of the basic time interval. Introducing the wait state causes the transition from the state of no track to the tentative track state to take two basic time intervals.

Figure 7-6 and Eq. (7.24) describe the process. Note that S_2 (with probability P_2) is the wait state. Finally, upon a missed detection, the transition is from S_4 to the wait state S_2. This simulates the situation where there will be a delay of a full scan interval before another tentative track can be initiated on a target whose track was just deleted.

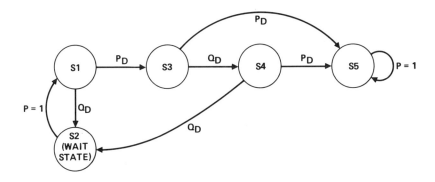

FIGURE 7-6. STATE DIAGRAM FOR TRACK CONFIRMATION (INCLUDING WAIT STATE)

$$
\begin{bmatrix}
P_1\,(k+1) \\
P_2\,(k+1) \\
P_3\,(k+1) \\
P_4\,(k+1) \\
P_5\,(k+1)
\end{bmatrix}
=
\begin{bmatrix}
0 & 1 & 0 & 0 & 0 \\
Q_D & 0 & 0 & Q_D & 0 \\
P_D & 0 & 0 & 0 & 0 \\
0 & 0 & Q_D & 0 & 0 \\
0 & 0 & P_D & P_D & 1
\end{bmatrix}
\begin{bmatrix}
P_1\,(k) \\
P_2\,(k) \\
P_3\,(k) \\
P_4\,(k) \\
P_5\,(k)
\end{bmatrix}
\qquad (7.24)
$$

7.4.2 Examples of Markov Chain Application

We first present results of a study conducted to examine the increase in tracking range associated with using a lowered threshold for track update illumination. The lower threshold setting was determined by examining the probability of false correlation (P_{FC}) defined in the previous section. This examination determined that P_{FA} could be significantly increased for those range, range rate detection cells within the target track gate. Thus, a corresponding increased P_D was also achieved in the region of the expected target return.

Figure 7-7 shows comparative probabilities of having a track that will not be later deleted. Results are presented in terms of the normalized range (R/R_o) where R_o is the range at which signal and noise power are equal. A system with a constant threshold setting and the one with a lowered threshold setting for track update are compared. The constant threshold setting was chosen so that the required false alarm rate was maintained during search. The (2/4) track confirmation criterion and the seven consecutive miss

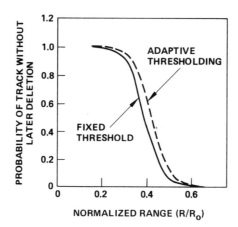

FIGURE 7-7. COMPARATIVE TRACKING RANGE FOR
ADAPTIVE AND FIXED THRESHOLDING

($N_D = 7$) deletion criterion were used. As is also indicated in Chapter 5, the results showed that adaptive thresholding achieved a rather small increase in tracking range as measured by the criterion of having a confirmed track without later deletion.

The second example is drawn from the design of an electronically scanned antenna (ESA) MTT system. The basic sampling interval was defined to be T and it was assumed that targets were illuminated at time intervals which were multiples of T. A nominal value for T was 1.25 s and it was assumed that the entire search volume was scanned every $4T$ s. The adaptive sampling method is summarized by the following rules:

1. Track illumination occurs every T seconds for all tentative tracks and for confirmed tracks after two or more consecutive misses;
2. Confirmed tracks with either one consecutive update or one consecutive miss are next illuminated after interval $2T$;
3. Confirmed tracks with two or more consecutive successful updates are illuminated at an interval $4T$.

Figure 7-8 gives the Markov chain representation for the above process, again assuming the (2/4) and $N_D = 7$ confirmation and deletion criteria. A number of wait states have been introduced. Also, note that the probability of detection in search (P_{DS}) may differ from the value of P_D associated with track update.

One purpose of the study was to determine the relative merits of two techniques for track illumination. These techniques involved using different times on target (TOT). Of course, P_D increases with increased TOT so that

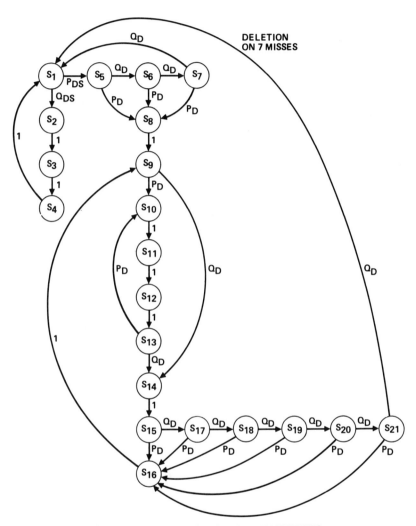

$S_2, S_3, S_4, S_8, S_{10}, S_{11}, S_{12}, S_{14}, S_{16}$ = WAIT STATES

FIGURE 7-8. MARKOV CHAIN REPRESENTATION
OF ESA ADAPTIVE SAMPLING SCHEDULE

performance for existing tracks should improve. However, as TOT increases, the amount of time between completions of search also increases, so that new targets entering the scan volume are illuminated less frequently. It is, thus, of interest to determine the degradation in new track detection as a function of the increased resources spent illuminating existing tracks.

The Markov chain technique can be extended to compute the expected illumination time required by a given track during its lifetime. At any particular scan, the expected time devoted to illumination of a given track is the product of the illumination time and the sum of the probabilities of being in the states (S_5, S_6, S_7, S_9, S_{13}, S_{15}, S_{17}, S_{18}, S_{19}, S_{20}, and S_{21}) that call for track illumination. Also, because a sequential detection scheme was used (Chapter 12), the expected time required by a search illumination, occurring in state S_1, is computed and added to the expected track illumination time in order to compute the total required time. Thus, the expected time that a given target requires can be computed for each scan, and the average time over the encounter is found by averaging the times for each scan.

Table 7-3 gives comparative results for the two systems. The second system used an illumination time on target (TOT) that was 3.7 times the TOT used by the first system. The increased TOT was used by the second system in order to employ techniques (to be discussed in Chapter 12) for enhancing detection performance. It was assumed that the time required for search illumination was the same for both systems. Table 7-3 gives the normalized ranges (T_{50} and T_{90}) at which there were 50 and 90 percent probabilities of having a confirmed track that would not be later deleted. This table also gives the expected illumination time required for each target per every 5 s ($4T$) scan interval. The system with longer TOT significantly increases tracking range. Although the ratio of the TOT values is nearly four, the expected illumination time is only doubled when the larger TOT is used; the increased P_D leads to fewer repeated update attempts necessary after unsuccessful looks.

TABLE 7-3
COMPARATIVE TRACKING PERFORMANCE FOR TWO
POTENTIAL ESA DETECTION METHODS

Detection Method	Tracking Ranges		Expected Illumination Time (*per* 5 s *Scan*)
	T_{50}^*	T_{90}^*	
1	1.0	1.0	0.10
2	1.26	1.28	0.21

$^*T_X$ = Range at which the probability of track without later deletion is X percent. Results are normalized with respect to the first detection method.

Next, consider the effect of increasing the time spent for track illumination upon the search detection performance. Here, the statistics R_{50} and R_{90}, which are defined as the ranges at which there are 50 and 90 percent probability of at least one target detection, are examined. Consider the degradation of detection performance for new targets when there are ten targets in track. Further assume that the additional time required for track illumination is reflected by increases in the time required to complete a scan. For the shorter TOT, the ten targets lead to an increase of one second (10 times 0.1 s from Table 7-3) in the time required to complete a scan. Similarly, the longer TOT leads to approximately a two-second increase in scan interval. Thus, the required scan intervals are now six and seven seconds for the two methods.

Table 7-4 shows normalized R_{50} and R_{90} for scan intervals of 5, 6, and 7 seconds. Note the relatively small degradation in search performance associated with the improved tracking even when there are assumed to be ten existing target tracks. Similar results will be shown in Chapter 12 where an approach for determining the allocation of an ESA between existing target tracks and search is presented. Thus, the general conclusion is that much can be gained by allocation of antenna resources for updating existing tracks without a significant loss in detection performance for new targets.

TABLE 7-4
COMPARATIVE SEARCH DETECTION PERFORMANCE

Search Time Interval (s)		Normalized Detection Ranges	
		R_{50}	R_{90}
5.0	(No Existing Tracks)	1.0	1.0
6.0	(10 Existing Tracks with 0.1 s Average Illumination Time)	0.987	0.971
7.0	(10 Existing Tracks with 0.2 s Average Illumination Time)	0.962	0.95

7.5   EXTENSIONS OF MARKOV CHAIN TECHNIQUES

Markov chains can be used to examine a number of more complex processes. First, consider a confirmation process that uses a score function, L. The score function is a measure of track quality. For simplicity, we assume a constant increase in the score function for each detection and a constant decrease for each miss. Thus, we define

$$L = L_{IN} + NDET \cdot \overline{G}_D - NMISS \cdot \overline{L}_M$$

where

$NDET, NMISS$ = number of detections and misses in the track
$\overline{G}_D$ = incremental average gain in L due to a detection
$\overline{L}_M$ = incremental average loss in L due to a nondetection
L_{IN} = initial value

The quantities L_{IN}, $\overline{G}_D$, and $\overline{L}_M$ can be chosen in an *ad hoc* manner (by experimentation), or by using the methods discussed in Chapters 6 and 9. A more refined version of the score function will be defined probabilistically in Chapter 9.

The next step is to define a Markov chain using two indices. The first, no track, state is defined to be S_{11} and the other states, S_{IJ}, are related to the detections and misses through the indices:

$$I = NDET + 1, \quad J = NMISS + 1$$

where $NDET$ and $NMISS$ are the number of detections and misses included in the track. The number of states can generally grow indefinitely for this formulation. However, the number of states can be limited by declaring a track to be confirmed if it persists for some maximum number of scans without deletion.

We define P_{IJ} to be the probability of being in state S_{IJ}, with initial conditions:

$$P_{11}(1) = 1, \quad P_{IJ}(1) = 0 \text{ for } I \geqq 2 \text{ or } J \geqq 2$$

Then, the Markov chain can be updated with the simple equations:

$$P_{11}(k + 1) = (1 - P_D) P_{11}(k) + P_{DEL}(k + 1)$$
$$P_{I + 1, J}(k + 1) = P_D \cdot P_{IJ}(k)$$
$$P_{I, J + 1}(k + 1) = (1 - P_D) \cdot P_{IJ}(k)$$

where P_{DEL} is the sum of the probabilities from all states that, at scan $k + 1$, satisfy the deletion criterion discussed next.

Define deletion to occur when L falls below the threshold L_{TD}. Thus, for those I, J satisfying the relationship:

$$(I - 1) \, \overline{G}_D - (J - 1) \, \overline{L}_M < L_{TD} - L_{IN}$$

the no track probability is incremented by P_{IJ}, $P_{11} = P_{11} + P_{IJ}$, and P_{IJ} is set to zero. Similarly, define L_C to be the confirmation threshold, S_{TC} to be the state representing the condition that a confirmed track has been achieved, and P_{TC} to be the probability associated with state S_{TC}. Then, to determine the cumulative probability of track confirmation, for all I, J satisfying the relationship:

$$(I - 1) \, \overline{G}_D - (J - 1) \, \overline{L}_M > L_C - L_{IN}$$

increment P_{TC} by P_{IJ} and set P_{IJ} to zero.

As in the example to be presented below, the false track confirmation rate can be calculated from the steady-state flux of probability into the state S_{TC}. Ideally, the entire confirmed track deletion process should be represented in order that the probability (P_{TC}) associated with state S_{TC} eventually be returned to the probability (P_{11}) of being in state S_{11}. However, for the example discussed below an approximation was used that simply incremented P_{11} by P_{TC} ($P_{11} = P_{11} + P_{TC}$) and then set P_{TC} to zero after each iteration. This approximation only increases the rate of new false track confirmation by a negligible amount for applications (such as the one examined) where the false track confirmation rate is small.

This Markov technique is convenient for analyzing complex track confirmation processes such as may be used for an IR satellite surveillance system designed to detect missile launch. A very low rate of false track confirmation per detection element (pixel) is typically required for this application. This is because the large number of pixels and the high sampling rate provide many opportunities for false track confirmation. Also, the nature of this problem is such that it is very important to minimize false track confirmation.

Figure 7-9 shows the probability of track confirmation against a missile target as a function of time after the target becomes visible. These results are shown for two false track confirmation rates. The rates resulted from multiplying the very small ($\gtrsim 10^{-13}$) steady state probabilities of transition into the state S_{TC} by the large number of opportunities (many samples from many pixels). Varying false track confirmation rates were achieved by varying the thresholds L_{TD} and L_C.

7.5.1 Extension to Include Correlation Accuracy

Markov chain techniques may also be applied to obtain preliminary performance for problems involving effects such as miscorrelation. For example, the probabilities of false correlation (P_{FC}) and of a valid observation falling outside the gate ($1 - P_G$) can be included in a Markov chain to determine the probability of track loss. A technique that has been applied to this problem is discussed next and a similar application is outlined by Stigter [3].

Define the probability state vector to consist of component subvectors, so that

$$S = \begin{bmatrix} S_C \\ S_{JC} \\ S_{GT} \\ S_{DT} \end{bmatrix}$$

where

S_C = subvector containing the states associated with confirmation

S_{JC} = state representing a newly confirmed track

S_{GT} = subvector containing the states associated with a good (as defined below) track

S_{DT} = subvector containing the states associated with a degraded (as defined below) track

A good track is defined to be a track where the target is still within the gate and where a miscorrelation that will eventually lead to track deletion has not occurred. A degraded track is defined to be a track where the correct target return will never again correlate with the track. This condition can

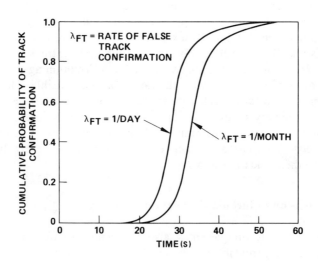

FIGURE 7-9. TRUE TARGET TRACK CONFIRMATION FOR
TWO FALSE TRACK CONFIRMATION RATES

occur in two ways. First, the target may be outside the gate now and for all subsequent observations. Second, a miscorrelation may have occurred so that the correct return will never again be associated with the track. Thus, a degraded track is also defined as a track that can only be continued on a false alarm.

It is convenient to represent the Markov process using the partitioned matrix formulation:

$$
\begin{bmatrix}
\mathbf{S}_C(k+1) \\
\mathbf{S}_{JC}(k+1) \\
\mathbf{S}_{GT}(k+1) \\
\mathbf{S}_{DT}(k+1)
\end{bmatrix}
=
\begin{bmatrix}
\Phi_{C\text{-}C} & 0 & \Phi_{C\text{-}GT} & \Phi_{C\text{-}DT} \\
\Phi_{JC\text{-}C} & 0 & 0 & 0 \\
0 & \Phi_{GT\text{-}JC} & \Phi_{GT\text{-}GT} & 0 \\
0 & \Phi_{DT\text{-}JC} & \Phi_{DT\text{-}GT} & \Phi_{DT\text{-}DT}
\end{bmatrix}
\begin{bmatrix}
\mathbf{S}_C(k) \\
\mathbf{S}_{JC}(k) \\
\mathbf{S}_{GT}(k) \\
\mathbf{S}_{DT}(k)
\end{bmatrix}
$$

The dimensions of the submatrices are determined by the number of states in the subvectors. For example, $\Phi_{C\text{-}GT}$ will have the number of rows equal to the number of states in $\mathbf{S}_C$ and the number of columns equal to the number of states in $\mathbf{S}_{GT}$.

For the application considered, it was assumed that any correlating observation received during confirmation was from the true target. This assumption was justified because of the high threshold setting and resulting low probability of false alarm (P_{FA}) during confirmation. As discussed below, the effects of miscorrelation were considered for confirmed tracks. However, because of the low P_{FA} and the large gate chosen during confirmation, it was assumed that before confirmation occurred all true target detections were correctly correlated.

The basic elements involved in the transition submatrices were P_{CC}, P_G, and other terms derived from the quantities discussed in Section 7.3. These terms are defined to be

P_{NC} = joint probability that the target is within the gate, and that no correlating observation is received = $(1 - P_D) P_G P_{NE}$

P_{FC1} = joint probability that a true return will be received within the gate, but that a false alarm will be closer = $P_D P_G P_E$

P_{FC2} = probability that there will be no true target return within the gate, and that there will be at least one false alarm within the gate = $(1 - P_D P_G)(1 - P_{NE})$

Using the above expressions, the probability that a track becomes degraded because of a false correlation becomes

$$P_{DG} \overset{\triangle}{=} k_1 P_{FC1} + k_2 P_{FC2} \tag{7.25}$$

where k_1, k_2 are factors to be discussed next.

Non-unity k_1 and k_2 ($k_1 < 1, k_2 < 1$) were chosen because experience with simulation results indicated that miscorrelation does not always lead to track degradation and subsequent loss. Thus, the form of (7.25) was chosen to represent one of the transition probabilities from good to degraded track status.

Similarly, the transition from good to degraded track status can also occur when the target goes outside the gate. Simulation experience indicated that for this application a target would rarely reappear in the gate once it had left. Thus, an additional factor ($k_3 \leqq 1$) is multiplied by ($1 - P_G$) to form the second transition probability from good to degraded status.

A choice of parameter values that led to correspondence between Monte Carlo simulation and Markov chain results for an IR surveillance problem with aircraft targets in a high false alarm (clutter) background was

$$k_1 = 0.5, \quad k_2 = 0.67, \quad k_3 = 0.9$$

Choice of these parameter values reflects the fact that false correlation (P_{FC1}) because of a nearer return is less likely to lead to degraded track than false correlation (P_{FC2}) without the target return present. Also, the probability that a degraded track will result when the target reaches the outside of the gate is large ($\cong 0.9$).

Given the probabilities discussed above, the elements of the transition submatrices were defined and results were compared with Monte Carlo simulation. Figure 7-10 shows the cumulative probability of track deletion.

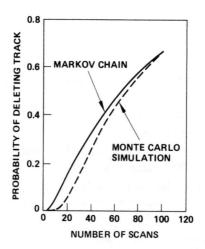

FIGURE 7-10. COMPARATIVE TRACK DELETION PREDICTION

The approximate Markov method deletes more tracks initially but the correspondence is fairly close overall. The true system Monte Carlo simulation deletes fewer tracks initially because of the very accurate initial estimates from a detailed acquisition process, which was not modelled in the approximate Markov representation.

Once a Markov chain representation has been defined, other interesting results can be derived using the properties of Markov chains. First, if the process can be propagated to a steady state condition, the proportion of time spent in each state can be found. Also, using methods presented in Kemeny and Snell [4], the mean passage time matrix M can be computed from the matrix relationship:

$$M = (I - Z + E\,Zdg)\,D$$

where

$$Z = (I - \Phi^T + A)^{-1}$$

A = matrix with rows $\alpha = (\alpha_1, \alpha_2, \ldots, \alpha_r)$

α_i = steady-state probability of process being in state i

Zdg = results from Z by setting off-diagonal entries equal to zero

D is the diagonal matrix defined so that $d_{ij} = \begin{cases} 1/\alpha_i, & i = j \\ 0, & i \neq j \end{cases}$

E is defined as a matrix with all entries 1

The elements (m_{ij}) of the mean passage time matrix are the mean times for the transition from state i to state j to occur. Of particular interest is the mean transition time $(\overline{T}_D)$ from the state (S_{JC}) where a track has been confirmed back to the first state (S_{1C}) of the confirmation process. This is the mean track segment length (from confirmation to deletion). Also of interest is the mean transition time $(\overline{T}_C)$ from S_{1C} to S_{JC}. This is the mean time required for track confirmation.

The proportional time (P_T) for which a confirmed track exists on a given target can be found in two ways. First, it can be computed by summing over the probabilities of being in states other than those in S_C. Alternatively, it can be computed from

$$P_T = \frac{\overline{T}_D}{\overline{T}_C + \overline{T}_D}$$

Computation of P_T by the two methods described above is a convenient check of the method and of the computer program. However, the probability of having a valid track is probably a more important statistic. This is computed by summing over the probabilities of being in the state S_{JC} and of being in those states contained in S_{GT}.

The results shown in Table 7-5 give the comparative track lengths, as computed using the methods described above, for an IR surveillance system designed for aircraft targets. These results are given as a function of the increasing signal-to-noise ratio (SNR) for two threshold setting strategies. The first strategy maintained the threshold chosen for the lowest SNR (2.5) case, while the second strategy adapted threshold to SNR. Results for this application clearly indicate the potential advantages associated with adaptive thresholding. The low threshold setting required in order that the low SNR target produce detections also leads to many false alarms and resultant track degradation. For larger SNR the adaptively chosen threshold could be raised so that fewer false alarms occur, thus improving track maintenance. Finally, note that the Markov chain method allowed predictions for the high SNR conditions where Monte Carlo simulation would be too expensive due to the long track lengths involved.

TABLE 7-5
COMPARATIVE MEAN TRACK SEGMENT LENGTHS

	Threshold Setting	
SNR	Fixed	Adaptive
2.5	95	95
3.0	168	225
3.5	259	588
4.0	353	1912
4.5	416	5622

7.6 SUMMARY

This chapter has discussed three methods for system evaluation that do not require detailed Monte Carlo simulation. These methods are useful in preliminary design and analysis. The first method, covariance analysis, is useful in filter design. For the example presented, the use of covariance analysis leads to the important conclusion that, for the application considered, the use of two-state filtering leads to essentially the same accuracy as does use of a three-state filter. This conclusion could lead to significant reductions in computational requirements.

The probabilities of correct correlation (P_{CC}), false correlation (P_{FC}), and correct decision (P_{CD}) are important measures of predicted system performance. These quantities can be used to determine system feasibility and to aid in determining design parameters such as threshold setting, as discussed in the example.

Finally, Markov chain techniques are very convenient for estimating statistics related to track life for valid targets. These techniques can also be used to estimate statistics, such as the formation rate and density, related to false tracks. Several examples, taken from airborne radar and IR satellite surveillance MTT systems, illustrate the variety of interesting statistics that can be examined using the Markov chain method.

The analytic methods discussed in this chapter cannot be used to completely evaluate the effects of such complex processes as target evasive maneuvers, complex and correlated measurement noise and clutter processes, and miscorrelation between closely spaced target tracks. Thus, before a system can actually be implemented, it is usually necessary to evaluate performance through the Monte Carlo simulation techniques discussed in the next chapter.

REFERENCES

1. DiFranco, J.V., and W.L. Rubin, *Radar Detection*, Dedham,MA: Artech House, 1980.
2. Wax, N., "Signal-to-Noise Improvement and the Statistics of Track Populations," *Journal of Applied Physics*, Vol. 26, May 1955, pp. 586–595.
3. Stigter, L., "Experience with Automatic Tracking Systems of the Royal Netherlands Navy," *AGARD Conference Proceedings No. 252, Strategies for Automatic Track Initiation*, Monterey, CA, Oct. 1978, pp. 16-1 to 16-7.
4. Kemeny, J.G., and J.L. Snell, *Finite Markov Chains*, Princeton, NJ: Van Nostrand, 1960.

Chapter 8

Design of a Detailed Multiple-Target
Tracking Simulation*

8.1 INTRODUCTION

The purpose of this chapter is to provide the tools and the framework that can be used to design a detailed Monte Carlo MTT simulation. The previous chapter discussed ways to obtain preliminary estimates of system performance. However, when evaluating a complex problem containing many random elements, such as an MTT system, it is often necessary to use Monte Carlo methods.

Briefly, the Monte Carlo approach is to examine the statistics of a random process by performing a large number of computer experiments and then compiling statistical results. The random processes are replaced by random number generators and nonrandom elements are simulated exactly. This chapter begins with some preliminaries concerning the generation and use of random numbers and the application to random variables associated with radar. Then, following [1,2], an outline is given concerning the analysis and statistical interpretation of the simulation output data.

The final sections outline a procedure that uses modular design for developing an MTT simulation. Topics include a suggested approach for documentation and checkout, choice of evaluation statistics, and techniques for presenting results. A typical detailed design is illustrated using a simulation that has been developed for a radar TWS system.

8.2 GENERATION AND USE OF RANDOM NUMBERS

This section outlines methods for obtaining samples from commonly used probability densities. The process of random number generation usually begins by obtaining numbers from the uniform density. Computer systems typically allow the user convenient access to a subroutine that will generate uniform random numbers over the interval (0,1). Some discussion (for example, [3]) has indicated potential problems associated with nonrandom

---

*This chapter was coauthored by Mr. S.P. Ickovic.

properties, such as periodicities, that may occur for certain of these uniform random number generators. However, experience with MTT simulations has shown that problems which at first may seem to be the result of "bad" uniform random numbers are later typically found to be attributable to faulty system design or to programming errors.

Perhaps the complexity of most MTT simulations and the resultant irregular manner in which random number generators are called tends to mask inherent periodicities or similar problems. However, to be safe, some care should be exercised in the choice of a uniform number generator. For example, Reference [3] recommends the URAND subroutine, in preference to the RANDU subroutine that is also commonly used.

8.2.1 Conversion of Uniform to Other Random Numbers

Convenient transformations exist for the conversion of uniform random numbers to numbers from other probability distributions. Define u to be a random number from the uniform distribution over the interval $(0,1)$. Also, define x to be a number having the probability density $f(x)$, such that

$$\int_{-\infty}^{\infty} f(x)\,dx = 1$$

Then, a number from distribution $f(x)$ can (in theory) be generated using the relationship:

$$u = \int_{-\infty}^{x} f(z)\,dz = F(x) \tag{8.1}$$

and solving for x in terms of u.

Equation (8.1) is convenient for generating numbers from probability densities that have closed form integrals. For example, consider the exponential probability density:

$$f(s) = \frac{1}{\bar{s}}\, e^{-s/\bar{s}}, \quad s \geqq 0$$

Then, a uniform random number u is conveniently converted to an exponential variable through the transformation:

$$u = \int_{0}^{s} \frac{1}{\bar{s}}\, e^{-z/\bar{s}}\, dz = 1 - e^{-s/\bar{s}}$$

Thus,

$$s = -\bar{s}\,\ln(1-u) = -\bar{s}\,\ln u' \tag{8.2}$$

Note that $u' \triangleq 1-u$, used in (8.2), just defines another uniform random number that can be generated and used directly.

An MTT simulation will always require the generation of random measurement errors. Also, it is frequently desirable to generate random target accelerations. Both measurement error and target maneuver statistics are typically modeled through use of Gaussian random numbers.

Numbers from the Gaussian (or normal) probability density cannot be generated directly using (8.1). Box and Muller [4] present a method which generates a pair of Gaussian variables (r_1, r_2) from a pair of independent uniform variables (u_1, u_2). The transformation is

$$r_1 = \sqrt{-2 \ln u_1} \cos (2\pi u_2)$$

$$r_2 = \sqrt{-2 \ln u_1} \sin (2\pi u_2)$$

(8.3)

The resultant r_1 and r_2 are independent Gaussian variables with zero mean and unit standard deviation. The transformation from the zero-mean, unit standard deviation Gaussian, r, to a generalized Gaussian x with mean μ_x and standard deviation σ_x is

$$x = \mu_x + \sigma_x r$$

Reference [5] presents a faster, but less direct, way of generating Gaussian variables. This method should be considered for use in those cases where the generation of random numbers consumes an appreciable portion of the Monte Carlo simulation run time.

The techniques outlined in this section should suffice for generating the required random numbers for most MTT simulations. This is particularly true because many other important distributions, such as the chi-square, are derived from the Gaussian. A more detailed discussion of the generation of random numbers from other distributions is given in the book by Fishman [6], and Appendix 8A presents a general technique that can be used for essentially any distribution of practical interest for MTT. More detail on the generation of random variables specific to the airborne radar MTT system detection process is given in Section 8.3

8.2.2 Generation of Time-Correlated Random Processes

It is often necessary to include the time-correlation properties of certain random variables. For example, a Gaussian measurement noise process may be correlated from one measurement frame to the next. There is no general solution to the problem of generating random numbers with arbitrary time-correlation properties while maintaining a specified probability distribution. However, there are simple algorithms for generating time-correlated random variables for the most important random processes that require modeling in a radar detection and tracking simulation. These will be described below.

Probably the most important time-correlated random process to be modeled is the first-order Gaussian-Markov process. This process, used to model random target acceleration and correlated (colored) noise processes, is defined for quantity x by the recursive relationship

$$x(k+1) = \rho_x(k) + \sqrt{1-\rho_x^2}\, \sigma_x r(k) \tag{8.4}$$

where $\rho_x(T)$ is the autocorrelation coefficient defined by

$$\rho_x(T) \triangleq \frac{E\{[x(t)-\bar{x}][x(t+T)-\bar{x}]\}}{\sigma_x^2} \triangleq \frac{R_x(T)}{\sigma_x^2} = e^{-\beta T} \tag{8.5}$$

T = sampling interval
β = $1/\tau$
τ = process correlation time constant
$\bar{x}, \sigma_x$ = process mean, standard deviation
$r(k)$ = zero mean, Gaussian process with unit standard deviation
$R_x(T)$ = autocorrelation function

The spectral density of the first-order Markov process defined by (8.4) and (8.5), from [7], is

$$S_x(\omega) = \frac{2\beta}{\beta^2 + \omega^2} \tag{8.6}$$

Because the autocorrelation function and the spectral density are Fourier transform pairs, the first-order Gaussian-Markov process can be defined by either (8.5) or (8.6). The spectral representation of (8.6) is sometimes most suitable for fitting to experimentally derived data. Then, after determining τ (or equivalently β) and σ_x, the process can be conveniently simulated using (8.4). The initial value, $x(1)$, is generated as a zero-mean Gaussian with standard deviation σ_x.

Next, consider a time-correlated variable that has the exponential probability density:

$$f(s) = \frac{1}{\bar{s}} e^{-s/\bar{s}} , \quad s \geq 0$$

The time-correlated exponential random variable is very useful because the exponential probability density is commonly used to describe target radar cross section (or amplitude) scintillation [8]. Also, experimental data [8,9] indicate the spectral density of target amplitude scintillation to be well approximated by a spectral density of the form given in (8.6). Reference [10] also states that the spectrum of the radar cross section variation process can generally be fitted to the "Markoffian" form of (8.6). Finally, the radar cross section scintillation process can typically be correlated over several sampling intervals [11]. Thus, a technique will be developed next for application whenever a time-correlated cross section (or amplitude) scintillation process is included in the MTT simulation.

An exponentially distributed random variable, s, can be expressed in terms of two zero-mean Gaussian variables (x, y), with common standard deviation σ, using the relationship

$$s = x^2 + y^2 \tag{8.7}$$

Thus,

$$E[s] = \bar{s} = 2\sigma^2$$

Also, as developed in Appendix 8B, we have

$$E[s^2] = E\{[x^2 + y^2]^2\} = 8\sigma^4$$

so that

$$\sigma_s^2 \triangleq E[s^2] - \bar{s}^2 = 4\sigma^4 \tag{8.8}$$

Appendix 8B shows that the autocorrelation function for s is given by

$$R_s(T) \triangleq E[s(t+T)\,s(t)] = 4\sigma^4 [1 + e^{-2\beta T}]$$

Then, using (8.7) and (8.8), we obtain

$$\rho_s(T) \triangleq \frac{E\{[s(t) - \bar{s}][s(t+T) - \bar{s}]\}}{\sigma_s^2} = e^{-2\beta T} \tag{8.9}$$

Comparing (8.5) and (8.9), the exponential process, s, and the Gaussian processes, x and y, have the same form of correlation coefficient and thus the same form of spectral density as given by (8.6). However, the correlation time of the exponential process is now half that of the Gaussian process:

$$\rho_s = e^{-\beta_s T}, \quad \beta_s = \frac{1}{\tau_s} = 2\beta = \frac{2}{\tau}, \quad \tau_s = \frac{\tau}{2}$$

To summarize, a time-correlated exponential process with correlation coefficient $\rho_s = e^{-T/\tau_s}$ can be formed using two independent, time-correlated Gaussian processes generated using (8.3) and (8.4) and the transformation of (8.7). However, the correlation time constant of the Gaussian process should be twice the value of the desired time constant for the exponential process.

8.3 MODELING THE RADAR DETECTION PROCESS*

This section outlines how the random variables usually required in the detection model of a radar MTT simulation can be generated. More detailed

*The authors wish to acknowledge the contributions of Ms. S.I. Lobell to this section.

discussions of radar detection processes are given in [8, 9, 10, 12] and other radar textbooks. In order for a detection to be declared, the envelope of the returning signal amplitude plus noise must exceed a predetermined threshold. Models for the process are discussed below.

8.3.1   Simplified Radar Target Signal Model

For a single target, a standard model for the returning signal-plus-noise process is a sine wave with amplitude A plus a narrowband Gaussian random noise process [12], which can be written

$$y(t) = A \cos(\omega_c t + \psi) + x(t)$$
$$= [A \cos \psi + x_c(t)] \cos \omega_c t - [A \sin \psi + x_s(t)] \sin \omega_c t$$
$$= V(t) \cos[\omega_c t + \phi(t)]$$

where

$V(t) =$ envelope of signal plus noise

The narrowband noise process has been represented as

$$x(t) = x_c(t) \cos \omega_c t - x_s(t) \sin \omega_c t$$

with variances

$$\sigma_{x_c}^2 = \sigma_{x_s}^2 = \sigma_n^2 = \text{noise variance}$$

With no loss of generality the phase angle ψ can be taken to be zero, so that when a single signal is present the envelope is

$$V = \sqrt{(A + x_c)^2 + x_s^2} \tag{8.10}$$

When two signals are present the expression for V is

$$V = \sqrt{(A_1 + A_2 \cos \psi_2 + x_c)^2 + (A_2 \sin \psi_2 + x_s)^2}$$

where

A_1, A_2 =signal amplitudes
ψ_2 =phase angle for second signal. The phase angle distribution can be taken to be uniform over the interval $(0, 2\pi)$

The signal amplitude (A) and the noise variance (σ_n^2) can be related to the signal-to-noise ratio (SNR) by

$$\frac{A}{\sigma_n} = \sqrt{2 SNR}$$

Normalizing to unit noise variance ($\sigma_n^2 = 1$) and using the relationship

$$SNR = (R_o / R)^4$$

gives

$$A = \sqrt{2}(R_o / R)^2 \tag{8.11}$$

The quantity R_o is the range at which SNR is unity. It is expressed in terms of several radar parameters including the radar antenna gain G, the target cross section σ, and other (for our purposes) fixed quantities, so that

$$R_o^2 = CG \sqrt{\sigma}$$

where C is a constant containing radar parameters such as transmitter power, reception losses, *et cetera*. The radar cross section varies with the scintillation variable s, such that

$$\sigma = \frac{s \bar{\sigma}}{\bar{s}}$$

where $\bar{\sigma}$ is the mean cross section and $\bar{s}$ is the mean value of s. The quantity $\bar{s}$ can be defined to be unity by taking the standard deviation for x and y of (8.7) to be

$$\sigma_x = \sigma_y = 1 / \sqrt{2}$$

The antenna gain G is decreased from its maximum value, G_{max}, by the factors l_e and E_r associated with eclipsing and target off-boresight angle, respectively, so that

$$G = d_e E_r G_{max}$$

Thus,

$$R_o^2 = C d_e E_r \sqrt{(s / \bar{s}) \bar{\sigma}} \; G_{max} = d_e E_r \sqrt{(s / \bar{s})} \; R_o^2 (NOM) \tag{8.12}$$

where

d_e = variable associated with the eclipsing factor. Eclipsing results because all or part of the target return can arrive at a time when the radar system is not receiving

E_r = antenna attenuation factor associated with the target being off-boresight

G_{max} = maximum effective antenna gain that could be used if there were no eclipsing and the target were exactly on boresight

s = scintillation variable with mean value $\bar{s}$

$R_o(NOM)$ = nominal value for R_o that would be applicable without scintillation, eclipsing, or target off-boresight angle

8.3.2   Simulating the Detection Process

There are two methods for simulating the detection process. The first is to compute a curve for the probability of detection, $P_D(SNR)$, as a function of $SNR = (R_o/R)^4$. Taking R_o to be constant, the result is a probability of detection that can be expressed as a function of range, $P_D(R)$. Then, for any given range, a uniform random number (u) is generated and detection is declared if $u \leqq P_D(R)$. The second technique is actually to generate the amplitude of the signal return and compare it with the threshold so as to determine if detection occurs. These techniques are outlined below.

The probability of detection (P_D) calculation requires the probability density [12] for V (given A and normalizing to $\sigma_n^2 = 1$):

$$f(V|A) = V \exp[-(V^2 + A^2)/2] \, I_0(AV) \qquad (8.13)$$

where

$I_0(Z)$ = modified Bessel function of zero order and argument Z and
from above

$$A^2 = 2\,SNR$$

Then, the probability of detection as a function of A and threshold V_T is

$$P_D(A) = \int_{V_T}^{\infty} f(V|A) \, dV \qquad (8.14)$$

The integral defined by (8.13) and (8.14) must be evaluated according to numerical techniques. Then, P_D can be computed as a function of $SNR = (R_o/R)^4$ and stored by the use of tables or simple curve fits. The quantity R_o is the range at which signal and noise power are equal. It can be defined [8,9,10] in terms of standard radar parameters, Eq. (8.12). Then, once R_o is specified, P_D, for a given range R, can be calculated from predetermined curve fits or tables. In general, the effects of scintillation, eclipsing, and off-boresight angle must also be included. This can be most conveniently done by computing curves that are averaged over scintillation and eclipsing and by including off-boresight angle directly as will be discussed next.

Relatively simple expressions can normally be used for the attenuation factor, E_r, due to target off-boresight angle. For example, a $\sin x / x$ type of attenuation may be used, or as Barton [10] suggests:

$$E_r = \cos^2(1.14\,\Delta)$$

where Δ is the normalized angle off-boresight, relative to the half-power beamwidth. Then, during the course of a simulation, the true off-boresight angle to the target can be computed and the correct attenuation factor used in the computation of P_D. Referring to (8.12), E_r less than unity has the effect of decreasing R_o so that P_D can again be readily found from table or curve fit, given R and the effective value of R_o (modified by E_r).

The cross section scintillation variable, s, is typically taken to have the exponential distribution, but the Rayleigh and log-normal distributions may also be considered [8]. Similarly, as defined below, the distribution for the eclipsing variable, d_e, can be determined from the radar receiver timing characteristics. Thus, using numerical integration, a value for P_D can be computed, for any given SNR, by averaging over these quantities.

The modeling of scintillation has been discussed previously and the eclipsing variable will be defined next, with more detail given in [8]. An eclipsing model will be developed for the attenuation of a single returning radar pulse. The eclipse cycle is determined by the transmitting, receiving, and dead-time duty factors (d_T, d_R, d_D) of the radar. The eclipse cycle determines the percentage of the transmitted pulsewidth actually received. Target eclipsing occurs when part or all of the received signal reaches the radar when the system is not receiving (i.e., transmitting or switching between transmitting and receiving). Because the eclipse cycle repeats as a function of target range, a normalized eclipse function is defined where the received signal has equal probability of falling anywhere within the cycle. The normalized eclipse cycle is illustrated in Fig. 8-1.

To determine the regions of the normalized eclipse cycle, we first define

d_T = proportion of time that the radar is transmitting;

d_R = proportion of time that the radar is receiving;

d_D = proportion of dead time (radar neither transmitting nor receiving).

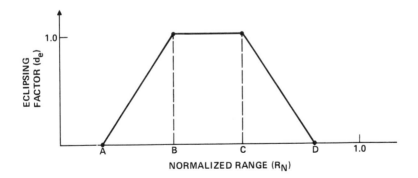

FIGURE 8-1. NORMALIZED ECLIPSE CYCLE

Then, the regions in Fig. 8-1 are defined:

$$A = \frac{d_D}{2}$$

$$B = A + min\,(d_T, d_R)$$

$$C = A + max\,(d_T, d_R)$$

$$D = 1 - \frac{d_D}{2}$$

The equation describing the eclipse function is

$$d_e(R_N) = \begin{cases} 0 & ,\ R_N < A \\[2mm] \dfrac{R_N - A}{B - A} & ,\ A \leqq R_N < B \\[2mm] 1 & ,\ B \leqq R_N < C \\[2mm] \dfrac{D - R_N}{D - C} & ,\ C \leqq R_N < D \\[2mm] 0 & ,\ D \leqq R_N \leqq 1 \end{cases} \qquad (8.15)$$

where

R_N = fractional part of R/R_e
R_e = eclipse cycle repetition range $= c/(2\,PRF)$
c = speed of light
PRF = radar pulse repetition frequency

In the case where the transmit time exceeds the receive time $(d_T > d_R)$ the eclipse function, d_e, is actually scaled by the factor d_R/d_T. This can, however, be interpreted as a decrease in SNR by the factor $(d_R/d_T)^2$. Then, an effective value for the signal-to-noise ratio can be defined:

$$SNR' = (d_R/d_T)^2\,SNR$$

where SNR is the signal-to-noise ratio, assuming the entire transmitted pulse can be received. Thus, this effect can also be modeled through use of a modified R_o.

The most accurate approximation to the actual detection process is to use a P_D curve that is averaged over the scintillation and eclipsing effects. Thus, first averaging over eclipsing:

$$\overline{P_D(SNR)} = \int_0^1 P_D(d_e^2(u)\,SNR)\,f(u)\,du \qquad (8.16)$$

where u has replaced R_N of (8.15), $d_e(u)$ is as defined in (8.15), and u has uniform distribution over zero to unity:

$$u \sim U(0,1)$$

Combining (8.15) and (8.16), and simplifying, leads to

$$\overline{P_D(SNR)} = 2d_{T/R} \int_0^1 P_D(u^2 SNR) \, du + |d_T - d_R| \, P_D(SNR) \quad (8.17a)$$

where

$$d_{T/R} = min \, (d_T, d_R)$$

Finally, assuming exponential distribution for eclipsing with $\bar{s} = 1$, the final P_D, averaged over eclipsing and scintillation becomes

$$\left\langle \overline{P_D(SNR)} \right\rangle = \int_0^\infty e^{-s} \, \overline{P_D(s \cdot SNR)} \, ds \quad (8.17b)$$

The use of (8.17) is applicable for the computation of a P_D curve that is averaged over the random effects of scintillation and eclipsing. As discussed previously, the exact attenuation due to off-boresight angle would be included in SNR. However, it is often desirable to simulate the time-correlation properties of the scintillation and eclipsing variables. For example, experimental results [11] have shown that the target cross section can be reduced for extended periods during a target "fade." Thus, an alternative more exact simulation method generates s and d_e using the models described above and then computes conditional values of P_D.

Including the scintillation and eclipsing variables (s and d_e) and the off-boresight correction, the modified value of R_o becomes

$$R_o = \sqrt{E_r d_e} \, (s/\bar{s})^{1/4} \, R_o(NOM)$$

Thus, the detection process can be modeled using the SNR value, $(R_o/R)^4$, to compute P_D (with a curve that has not been averaged over scintillation and eclipsing) and comparing P_D with a uniform random number. Alternatively, the transformation from R_o to A can be made through (8.11). Then, using A and two zero-mean, unit standard deviation Gaussians (x_c, x_s), the envelope can be computed from (8.10) and compared with the threshold V_T to determine if detection occurs. The required relationship for detection is

$$V = \sqrt{(A + x_c)^2 + x_s^2} \geqq V_T$$

The threshold (V_T) is chosen so that the required probability of false alarm (P_{FA}) is maintained.

8.4 MONTE CARLO SIMULATION DESIGN AND INTERPRETATION OF RESULTS

In this section, following [1, 2], we outline the most basic principles of interpreting Monte Carlo simulation data that are valid for all types of system analysis. The next section discusses issues related specifically to MTT.

8.4.1   Establishing Confidence Intervals

The primary outputs of a Monte Carlo simulation for MTT are estimates of such quantities as the mean tracking error, the probability of having established a valid track, *et cetera*. It is important to be able to place confidence intervals on these estimates such that the intervals will include the actual values of the quantities being estimated with a known degree of uncertainty.

Consider an estimate $(\hat{x})$ of the parameter x. Then, the confidence interval is defined by placing upper and lower limits so that

$$\Pr\left[f_L(\alpha, \hat{x}) \leqq x \leqq f_U(\alpha, \hat{x})\right] = 1 - \alpha \tag{8.18}$$

where α is the allowable probability of error. Thus, based upon simulation results, with estimate $\hat{x}$, the claim could be made that the true value of x is within the limits $f_L(\alpha, \hat{x})$ and $f_U(\alpha, \hat{x})$ with probability $1 - \alpha$. For any given parameter x and estimate $\hat{x}$ the relationship is either true or not. However, assuming the confidence intervals are set properly, if we perform many Monte Carlo experiments and estimate many parameters, we will find, in the long run, the proportion of true quantities that fall within our confidence intervals to be $1 - \alpha$. Next, we will outline how the confidence limits are formed for typical estimated quantities.

Some of the most basic outputs derived from a Monte Carlo simulation are estimates of the probabilities of occurrence for various events (such as false correlation). The unbiased estimate $(\hat{p})$ for the probability (p) of occurrence of an event that occurred n times in N opportunities is

$$\hat{p} = \frac{n}{N}$$

The standard deviation of the error on the estimate $\hat{p}$ is given by

$$\sigma_{\hat{p}} = \sqrt{\frac{p(1-p)}{N}} \tag{8.19}$$

Assume enough samples such that $n > 5$ for $\hat{p} \leqq 1/2$ or $N - n > 5$ for $\hat{p} > 1/2$. Then, the estimate $\hat{p}$ will have Gaussian distribution with mean p and we can replace p in (8.19) by $\hat{p}$ so that [1]:

$$\sigma_p \cong \sqrt{\frac{\hat{p}(1-\hat{p})}{N}}$$

Thus, the confidence limits of (8.18) are defined through the relationship:

$$\Pr\left[z_{1-\alpha/2} \leqq \frac{p-\hat{p}}{\sigma_{\hat{p}}} \leqq z_{\alpha/2}\right] = 1-\alpha$$

or

$$\Pr\left[\hat{p} + \sigma_{\hat{p}}\, z_{1-\alpha/2} \leqq p \leqq \hat{p} + \sigma_{\hat{p}}\, z_{\alpha/2}\right] = 1-\alpha \qquad (8.20)$$

Note that the quantities $z_{1-\alpha/2}$ and $z_{\alpha/2}$ define confidence limits such that a zero-mean unit standard deviation Gaussian will exceed $z_{1-\alpha/2}$ and $z_{\alpha/2}$ with probabilities $1-\alpha/2$ and $\alpha/2$, respectively. Thus, the extent of the confidence interval is $(1-\alpha/2)-\alpha/2 = 1-\alpha$.

The confidence limits can be formed from standard tables such as provided by [1, 2]. For example, for $\alpha = 0.05$, we have

$$z_{1-\alpha/2} = z_{0.975} = -1.96, \quad z_{\alpha/2} = z_{0.025} = 1.96$$

If, for illustration, a Monte Carlo simulation containing 100 runs gives premature track deletion in 10 runs, the estimated probability of track deletion is

$$\hat{p}_{DEL} = 10/100 = 0.1$$

Thus,

$$\sigma_{\hat{p}} = \sqrt{\frac{(0.9)(0.1)}{100}} = 0.03$$

and the 95 percent confidence limits for the true deletion probability are $0.1 \pm (1.96)(0.03) \cong (0.04, 0.16)$.

Two other important parameters are the mean and variance of such quantities as tracking error. Again assuming N independent observations and considering quantity x, the unbiased estimates $(\bar{x}, s_x^2)$ of the mean (μ_x) and variance (σ_x^2) for the process are

$$\bar{x} = \frac{1}{N} \sum_{i=1}^{N} x_i$$

and

$$s_x^2 = \frac{1}{N-1} \sum_{i=1}^{N} (x_i - \bar{x})^2 = \frac{1}{N-1} \sum_{i=1}^{N} x_i^2 - \frac{N}{N-1} \bar{x}^2$$

The $1-\alpha$ confidence intervals for the true mean, μ_x, and variance, σ_x^2, are given by [2]

$$\bar{x} - \frac{st_{\nu:\alpha/2}}{\sqrt{N}} \leqq \mu_x \leqq \bar{x} + \frac{st_{\nu:\alpha/2}}{\sqrt{N}}$$

and

$$\frac{(N-1)s^2}{\chi^2_{\nu:\alpha/2}} \leqq \sigma_x^2 \leqq \frac{(N-1)s^2}{\chi^2_{\nu:1-\alpha/2}}$$

The quantity $\nu = N-1$ is the number of degrees of freedom and $t_{\nu:\alpha/2}$ and $\chi^2_{\nu:\alpha/2}$ are the appropriate confidence values for the student t and chi-square variables with ν degrees of freedom. For example, for $N = 25$ ($\nu = 24$) and $\alpha = 0.05$, we have

$$\frac{t_{24:0.025}}{\sqrt{25}} = \frac{2.064}{5} = 0.41$$

and

$$\frac{N-1}{\chi^2_{24:0.025}} = \frac{24}{39.36} = 0.61, \qquad \frac{N-1}{\chi^2_{24:0.975}} = \frac{24}{12.4} = 1.94$$

Then, if the estimated mean and standard deviation for the range tracking error are 50 and 100, respectively, the 95 percent confidence limits are

$$50 - 0.41(100) \leqq \mu_x \leqq 50 + 0.41(100)$$
$$9 \leqq \mu_x \leqq 91$$
$$\sqrt{0.61}(100) \leqq \sigma_x \leqq \sqrt{1.94}(100)$$
$$78 \leqq \sigma_x \leqq 139$$

8.4.2 Comparing Results for Two Methods

Assume that we performed two Monte Carlo experiments with N_1 and N_2 runs, respectively, where N_1 and N_2 are both at least 50. Further assume that the purpose of this study was to compare performance, as measured by parameter x, for two methods. The measured quantities were the sample means ($\bar{x}_1, \bar{x}_2$) and sample variances ($s_{x_1}^2, s_{x_2}^2$).

Assume that we wish to test the hypothesis that $\mu_{x_1} > \mu_{x_2}$. For example, x might be tracking error, and method 2 might be using an improved (we hope) tracking filter. Define $dx = x_1 - x_2$. Then, under the hypothesis that x_1 and x_2 have the same mean, dx will have Gaussian distribution with

$$\mu_{dx} = 0, \quad \sigma_{dx} = \sqrt{\frac{\sigma_{x_1}^2}{N_1} + \frac{\sigma_{x_2}^2}{N_2}}$$

The true variances ($\sigma_{x_1}^2, \sigma_{x_2}^2$) are usually not known, but, following[1], a valid approximation when N_1 and N_2 are at least 50 is to replace the true variances with the sample values, so that

$$\sigma_{dx} \cong \sqrt{\frac{s_{x_1}^2}{N_1} + \frac{s_{x_2}^2}{N_2}}$$

The hypothesis that the mean of x_1 exceeds the mean of x_2 will be accepted, if

$$\frac{\bar{x}_1 - \bar{x}_2}{\sigma_{dx}} \geqq z_\alpha$$

where z_α is the $(1 - \alpha)$ confidence value for the Gaussian distribution. Note that this is a one-tailed test (we are only testing if $\mu_{x_1} > \mu_{x_2}$) so that for $\alpha = 0.05$, we have $z_{0.05} = 1.645$. If we only wish to test whether the mean values are significantly different, the test becomes

$$z_{1-\alpha/2} \leqq \frac{\overline{x}_1 - \overline{x}_2}{\sigma_{dx}} \leqq z_{\alpha/2}$$

where, for $\alpha = 0.05$, $z_{0.975} = -1.96$, $z_{0.025} = 1.96$.

The above test can be extended to a test of the relative probability of event occurrence (such as the probability of having a confirmed track) by replacing x_1 and x_2 by the probabilities p_1 and p_2. The equation for the standard deviation of the difference in estimated probabilities is

$$\sigma_{dp} = \sqrt{\frac{\hat{p}_1(1-\hat{p}_1)}{N_1} + \frac{\hat{p}_2(1-\hat{p}_2)}{N_2}}$$

Finally, it is often of interest to compare the variances of two processes. A typical example is the comparison of the tracking error variances for two filtering methods. Again assume N_1 and N_2 samples and define:

$$\nu_1 = N_1 - 1, \quad \nu_2 = N_2 - 1$$

Then, the ratio of the sample variances is described by the relationship:

$$\frac{s_{x_1}^2 / \sigma_{x_1}^2}{s_{x_2}^2 / \sigma_{x_2}^2} = F_{\nu_1, \nu_2}$$

where F_{ν_1, ν_2} is the F variable with degrees of freedom ν_1 and ν_2. Assume that we wish to test the hypothesis that method two leads to smaller variance $(\sigma_{x_2}^2 < \sigma_{x_1}^2)$ *versus* the hypothesis that the variances are equal $(\sigma_{x_2}^2 = \sigma_{x_1}^2)$. Then, we will accept the smaller variance hypothesis with confidence $1 - \alpha$, if

$$\frac{s_{x_1}^2}{s_{x_2}^2} \geqq F_{\nu_1, \nu_2 : \alpha}$$

Similarly, if there is no reason to believe that either method should be better, the hypothesis that the variances are equal will be accepted, if

$$F_{\nu_1, \nu_2 : 1 - \alpha/2} \leqq \frac{s_{x_1}^2}{s_{x_2}^2} \leqq F_{\nu_1, \nu_2 : \alpha/2}$$

For example, taking $\alpha = 0.05$ and ν_1 and ν_2 to be 50 gives

$$F_{50,50:0.975} = 0.57, \qquad F_{50,50:0.025} = 1.75$$

8.4.3   Simulation Design

A great deal of study has gone into the development of methods for efficiently performing Monte Carlo simulation. These methods are detailed in [13,14]. The application of these methods to a problem with the complexity of MTT appears, however, still to be an open area for research.

One basic principle for efficient MTT Monte Carlo simulation is to maintain the same conditions, as much as possible, when the comparative performance of two methods is being evaluated. Thus, it would be desirable to maintain the same detection sequence and the same random measurement errors during the comparison of two correlation methods. However, this requires special effort because the order of the random number sequences readily changes as, for example, differing numbers of tracks are maintained by the different correlation methods so that different target illumination sequences occur.

One crucially important feature is to ensure repeatability so that any given run (or runs) of a Monte Carlo simulation can be repeated with more detailed printout. This ensures that interesting, or anomalous, results can be examined in more detail without repeating the entire Monte Carlo experiment (for all runs). This can be accomplished by printing out the random number seeds (the first uniform number used) at the beginning of each run. Then, the run can be conveniently repeated for more detailed examination by initiating the simulation with the appropriate random number seed.

8.5   SELECTION OF EVALUATION STATISTICS

First, it is extremely helpful in the interpretation of results to plot time histories of the true target positions, the observations, and the resulting tracks that are formed. The plot will give either angle or range as a function of time. Figures 1-5 and 1-6 show representative plots for targets that were separated in angle.

In addition to track plots, there are three main categories of statistics that should be compiled in summary tables and, whenever possible, plotted as functions of time. The three categories, discussed below, are track maintenance, correlation, and kinematic estimation accuracy.

8.5.1 Track Maintenance Statistics

The three most important track maintenance statistics are the probabilities of having an initiated track, a confirmed track, and a confirmed track that will not later be deleted. For example, Fig. 8-2 shows the probabilities of having at least N confirmed tracks for a particular geometry with four closely spaced targets. Ideally, we would like to have exactly $N = 4$ confirmed tracks at all times. However, for the particular system being evaluated, confirmation of the fourth track is delayed. Later in the run, spurious tracks are maintained as a result of miscorrelation and the associated poor tracking performance (similar to the condition illustrated in Fig. 1-5). Finally, for the same case, Fig. 8-3 shows the probability of having N confirmed tracks that will not later be deleted. Comparing Figs. 8-2 and 8-3 indicates that a substantial number of tracks were confirmed and then were later deleted.

Another pair of interesting track maintenance statistics are the expected number of tracks and the number of targets in track. For the latter statistic, a track is assigned to the target which produced the last observation included in the track. Ideally, both of these numbers should equal the number of true targets. However, divergences from the ideal are shown, for example, as

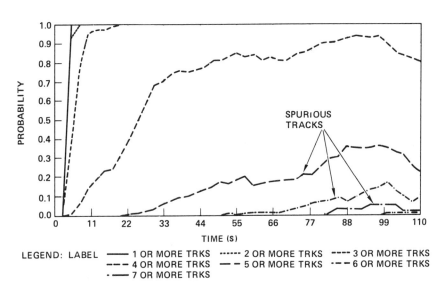

LEGEND: LABEL ⸻ 1 OR MORE TRKS ⸱⸱⸱⸱⸱⸱ 2 OR MORE TRKS ⸺⸺ 3 OR MORE TRKS
⸺ ⸺ 4 OR MORE TRKS ⸺ ⸻ 5 OR MORE TRKS ⸱⸺ 6 OR MORE TRKS
⸱ ⸻ 7 OR MORE TRKS

FIGURE 8-2. PROBABILITIES OF AT LEAST N CONFIRMED TRACKS FOR A
PARTICULAR CLOSELY SPACED FOUR TARGET ENCOUNTER

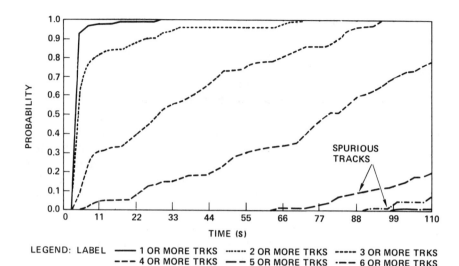

LEGEND: LABEL ——— 1 OR MORE TRKS ······· 2 OR MORE TRKS ----- 3 OR MORE TRKS
              --- 4 OR MORE TRKS —— 5 OR MORE TRKS ·—— 6 OR MORE TRKS
              ·——— 7 OR MORE TRKS

FIGURE 8-3. PROBABILITIES OF AT LEAST N CONFIRMED TRACKS
WITHOUT LATER DELETION

multiple tracks are formed on the same target. Figure 8-4 shows these statistics for the same four-target case that produced Figs. 8-2 and 8-3. Note that during most of the encounter more than four tracks are expected, but the expected number of targets in track is less than 3.5

Expected track length and the average length of the tracks remaining at the end of each Monte Carlo run are important statistics. Finally, track deletion statistics of interest are the average time required to delete a track on a target that leaves the scan volume and the number of premature track deletions that occur when the target in track is still present.

8.5.2 Correlation Statistics

As previously discussed (Chapter 7), probably the most important correlation statistics are the probability of correct correlation (P_{CC}), the probability of false correlation (P_{FC}), the probability of correct decision (P_{CD}), and the probability that the gate will include a true target observation (P_G). As shown in Fig. 4-6, the expected number of false correlations per scan also provides a useful plot. Another interesting statistic is track depth. Following [15], track depth is defined for a given track as the number of observations which we can go back from the most recent observation before the actual target identity of an observation changes, or before the first observation of the track is reached.

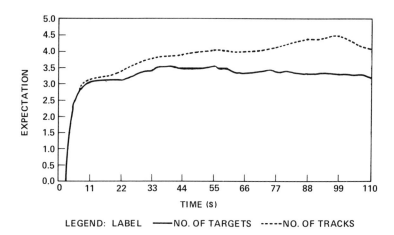

LEGEND: LABEL ———NO. OF TARGETS -----NO. OF TRACKS

FIGURE 8-4. EXPECTED NUMBER OF TRACKS AND NUMBER OF TARGETS TRACKED

8.5.3 Kinematic Statistics

The usual kinematic statistics are the means and standard deviations of the tracking errors for such measures of position and velocity as range, range rate, angle,· and target velocity components. However, problems can arise in the compilation of the statistics in the presence of false correlation. Either a track-oriented or a target-oriented approach can be used. Using either approach, statistics must be compiled based upon the last observation received for a given track. Using the track-oriented approach, the errors are compiled for a given track by comparing the track's estimates with the true quantities associated with the target that produced the last observation assigned to the track.

Using the target-oriented approach is somewhat more complicated. Here, we can use the track that includes the last observation generated by the target. However, a provision may also be made not to use a track that has a more recent update with an observation from another target. Also, special logic must be used to account for the condition where tracks are dropped so that there is no longer a track on a given target.

8.5.4 Other Statistics

In addition to the statistics discussed previously, it may be desirable to compile statistics related to computational requirements. For example, the number of tracks (and hypotheses if multiple hypothesis tracking is used) formed, or, when using an electronically scanned antenna (ESA) system, the number of required track updates may be of interest. Finally, for conditions where the input measurement process is so complex that a well-defined statistical model is not available, it may be desirable to compile statistics on the input observations. This may be useful, for example, for the evaluation of an observation redundancy elimination logic such as described in Chapter 5.

8.5.5   A Single Measure of Effectiveness

Using a variety of statistics may lead to contradictory conclusions. For example, one method may have smaller tracking errors and prematurely delete fewer tracks, while another competing method may have a closer match between the expected number of targets and the true number of targets. Thus, based upon [15], the following general measure of effectiveness (MOE) is presented.

An effectiveness measure is computed at each scan (k), such that

$$\text{MOE}(k) = \frac{1}{N_o} \sum_{j=1}^{N_o} s_j(k)$$

where $s_j(k)$ is an effectiveness score contributed from object j. The quantity N_o is the total number of objects present, and includes true targets and false alarms that may have been generated on scan k. A true target is only considered if it is within the scan volume and if it either generates an observation on scan k, or if it has previously generated an observation. Finally, to evaluate tracking and correlation performance, a rule is defined such that a target corresponds to an existing track only if the last observation generated (on a scan prior to k) by the target is included in that track and if that observation is the last observation in the track. Otherwise, the target belongs to no track and any correlation with observations from that target are taken to be false. Thus, using this rule, the condition where multiple tracks are formed on the same target is penalized.

Table 8-1 presents representative effectiveness values that may be assigned to various correlation events for an observation. The values range from zero (for incorrect correlation) to unity. The highest values (1.0) are assigned to correct correlation with a confirmed track and to the correct recognition of a new source. Correct establishment of a new track and correlation with an existing tentative track lead to intermediate score values (between zero and unity) if the target has been previously detected. The reasoning for this last rule is that an ideal system would have previously established a confirmed track and thus, for an ideal system, the observation in question would be correlated with a confirmed track.

Next, consider scoring for targets that have produced observations on previous scans but that produce no observation on scan k. First, define a

TABLE 8-1
OBSERVATION SCORING (VALUES FOR $s_j(k)$)

	Description of Observation		
Correlation Result	False Alarm or Initial Target Detection	Observation from Target without Existing Track*	Observation from Target with Existing Track
New (Tentative) Track Formed	1.0	0.3	0
Correct Correlation with Tentative Track	Not Applicable (N/A)	N/A	0.6
Correct Correlation with Confirmed Track	N/A	N/A	1.0
Incorrect Correlation	0	0	0

*A previous detection has been received from the target in question.

normalized distance (d_n^2), which includes the position coordinates (and possibly velocity), and which is normalized with respect to the Kalman filter covariance matrix. For example, considering angle (η, ϵ) and range (R), we obtain

$$d_n^2 = \frac{(\delta\eta)^2}{P_\eta(1,1)} + \frac{(\delta\epsilon)^2}{P_\epsilon(1,1)} + \frac{(\delta R)^2}{P_R(1,1)}$$

where the $\delta x (x = \eta, \epsilon, R)$ are the differences between the true and predicted target quantities and the $P_x(1,1)$ are the corresponding Kalman filtering covariance values. Then, the following scoring procedure is proposed for targets that do not produce an observation on scan k:

$$s_j(k) = \begin{cases} 1.0, & \text{confirmed track on target } j \text{ and } d_n^2 \leq d_{min}^2 \\ 0.5, & \text{confirmed track } (d_n^2 > d_{min}^2) \text{ or tentative track on target } j \\ 0, & \text{no track on target } j \end{cases}$$

An appropriate value would be chosen for d^2_{min} based upon the chi-square distribution.

The values for MOE(k) could be plotted directly or averaged over appropriate time intervals. Finally, note that the proposed intermediate scoring values (between 0 and 1.0) were chosen arbitrarily and other values could be used.

8.6 SIMULATION DEVELOPMENT

This section outlines the steps involved in the actual development, documentation, and verification of a detailed Monte Carlo MTT simulation. The recommended approach is based upon the development of several TWS simulations for major airborne radar tracking systems. However, the general methods are applicable to any detailed MTT simulation.

Development of an MTT simulation typically takes about one year. Once developed, the simulation may be used for many years. It is important to remember that numerous modifications and changes in personnel involved with the simulation are to be expected. In addition, a high degree of credibility in the analysis resulting from use of the simulation requires a thorough testing of the simulation, a clear understanding of how all functions are modeled, and how these functions influence the results obtained. Thus, emphasis on modular design and extensive documentation are worthwhile (and probably necessary) investments in time. Attempts to shortcut these processes may lead to temporary gains in development time, but in the long run such would be costly.

In order to complete any large development in a reasonable period of time, it is necessary to divide the task into smaller tasks, which can be handled independently by different people. This can lead to difficulties when the pieces are later collected to form the whole. Minimization of this type of problem requires good communication between the members of the development team and good coordination of the team. This is probably best handled through the use of a coordination focal point — the team leader. It is also the team leader's job to see that all procedures set forth for the development are complied with and to understand the design and development of the various parts of the simulation. This understanding is necessary for the coordination of the various interfaces between modules and as a check on the clarity of the documentation.

A convenient breakdown for a Monte Carlo radar TWS simulation is shown in Fig. 8-5. Here, each box represents an entire function which is performed independently from the other functions. Each box may be thought of as having a required set of inputs and outputs, but knowledge of how the outputs are generated from the inputs is not needed to complete the other boxes. This "black box" approach helps ensure that the module will be

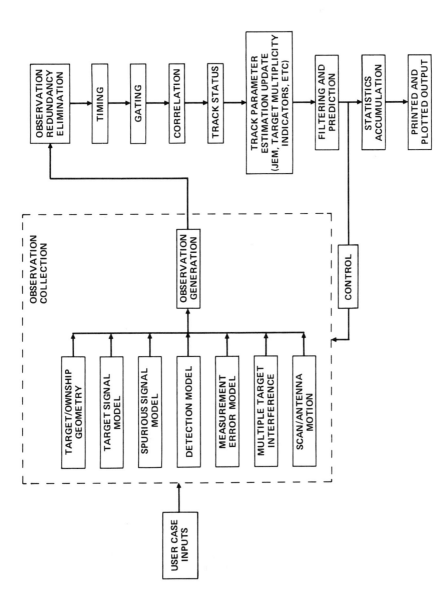

FIGURE 8-5. TRACK-WHILE-SCAN (TWS) SIMULATION OVERVIEW

isolated ("stand alone") in a way that will make it easy to modify each function or replace it in the future. In addition, various versions of the modules (each containing different algorithms to accomplish the module's functions) may be used in trade-off analysis studies without the need to modify the surrounding boxes. Finally, using this approach, various system simulations can be created from a single library of such modules.

The ease of modification and flexibility of use of each module is enhanced by breaking down each high-level module into a module driver and several subroutines (one such breakdown of the track initiation/deletion function is shown in Fig. 8-6). However, distributing development of the subroutines among too many individuals can create so many interface points that the integration of the entire simulation becomes difficult. Although proposed methods for defining a structured program differ considerably, the following is generally accepted by many interested in software design and serves as an example of a technique used with success.

Guidelines

At the initiation of the development, some ground rules (programming standards and practices) should be set forth as a guide to how the development will proceed and to ensure a reliable product at completion.

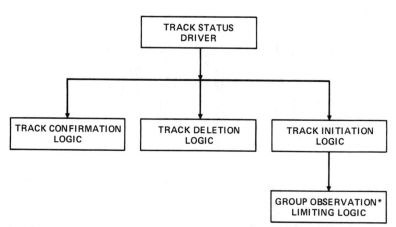

*THIS LOGIC INHIBITS TRACK INITIATION ON A GROUP OF OBSERVATIONS THAT HAVE THE CHARACTERISTICS OF JET ENGINE MODULATION (JEM)

FIGURE 8-6. SUBROUTINE PARTITIONING OF TRACK STATUS MODULE

Language

An appropriate choice of programming language is essential. The most important feature of the language is the availability of structured programming controls. Without these controls, the clarity of code and ease of future modification will be limited. A language that insists on adherence to structured programming techniques (e.g., if-then-else, go-to-less/top down flow control) and does not afford many pathways around those techniques is best. Otherwise, the guidelines should require strict adherence to the structured programming facilities of the language.

If possible, a single language (and a restricted programming style) should be used in writing the modules. This will make it easy for program developers to switch between modules when making future additions or attempting to understand or correct program logic. Additional convenient features to look for in a languarge are: (1) open naming of variables (large number of letters per name); (2) the ability to reference associated data items as a group or individually; (3) special tools for handling arrays (pointer and link lists) and arithmetic computations; (4) free format for commenting and coding; and (5) ease of input/output (I/O) between routines and between the simulation and the user. The latter is especially important in debugging or detailed reviewing of specific occurrences of particular interest in a Monte Carlo iteration and for easy changing of test cases for simulation execution. Other features of interest might be the ability to change the dimensions of arrays at compilation or at execution time, the ability to include identical blocks of code or data easily in all modules, and the ability to restrict variables as to input or output use only. Finally, if a change in the computer on which the simulation will reside is possible during its life, consideration should be given to a language which is transportable (that is, available on many machines).

Module Design

Before actually programming any functions, a flow of the process should be developed as a guide for the coding. This flow should be documented in an easy to read form (avoiding use of variable names and describing the process in terms of the ideas involved) that mimics the programming language. It will later serve as both a high-level description of the process and as a valuable aid in quickly understanding the process, which will enable the reader to avoid becoming bogged down in the minute details that often obscure the larger picture.

Programming Style

Having chosen a language with the necessary capabilities, a set of rules governing the use of the language should be proposed to reduce the potential for error. For example, the restriction of all communication between modules to the argument list of the call will ensure a well controlled and easily followed interface. Some global common for the entire simulation might be useful for data such as physical constants which should be the same wherever they appear in the simulation. Requirements for alphabetizing and identifying all arguments as to input or output and for defining all arguments and local variables of each routine as to type, size, and function insure against misuse of the variables.

Comments should precede each small block of code (several lines involved in a process) with additional comments to the side of those procedures that are not immediately clear otherwise. Also, each routine might be preceded by a general description of the purpose and function of the routine, noting any important features of the routine. Routines should be held to small size for ease in reading and maintenance, with subroutines used for all definable functions larger than a predetermined number of lines of code.

Debugging and Detailed Analysis

The option to list inputs and outputs of each module and its routines, specified at run time, should be included so as to debug the modules properly as well as understand what each function is doing under the unusual conditions which sometimes arise in one Monte Carlo iteration or another. Also, the general ability to follow the gross functioning of the processing (accomplished by listing such items as observed signal data, observation-to-track association data, and track filtering data), and the ability to repeat any Monte Carlo run in a series (accomplished by making the initial random number seed of each Monte Carlo run available) are necessary. These capabilities are required so that the designer may fully understand, and thus potentially improve upon, algorithm performance.

Testing

Testing is the next important part in the development procedure, and it serves to generate a great deal of the future credibility of the simulation. Once a module is developed, an extensive test plan should be formulated and documented. This test should consider the module in isolation and exercise all logic branches, so that the details of the processing may be thoroughly verified in a way which would be difficult within the larger simulation. The test documentation also serves as a demonstration of what the module is expected to do and helps to clarify the functioning of the module further to someone unfamiliar with the code. A test driver for the stand-alone module is written to execute the test plan. The test driver is then saved to allow for further detailed investigation of the function in an environment that is isolated from the larger system. The test driver will also serve as an example of how the module interface is to be handled.

Modification of Routines

As routines in the simulation are modified over time to add capabilities, to improve algorithms, *et cetera*, a history of the nature of the changes made to each routine should become a part of the general description of the routine. In addition, the name of the routine should incorporate an identifier for the version of the routine (e.g., ALPHA02 for version 2 subroutine alpha). The above provisions help to ensure that the latest version of a module is being used and help to trace the capabilities used in older versions of the simulation when making comparisons between recent and past simulation results. Finally, very specific (non-general) processes should be isolated (as in module drivers) wherever possible for ease of future modification.

Elements of a Typical Simulation

An MTT simulation is statistical in nature because the real world processes that influence the performance of any design are random. As noted earlier in this chapter, when using Monte Carlo simulation, a single test encounter is repeated numerous times with independent random real-world processes simulated during each iteration (or Monte Carlo run). The analysis and testing is then done by reviewing statistical output as discussed in Section 8.4. Thus, simulation elements are required for modeling of the MTT environment, for the actual MTT processing algorithms, and for the accumulation and display of the resulting statistics.

Figure 8-5 shows a block diagram of a typical radar TWS simulation. It consists of blocks commonly found in an air-to-air radar mechanically scanned antenna (MSA) TWS system. This system uses the sequential nearest-neighbor correlation logic.

We will illustrate the principles of simulation design by outlining the contents of the blocks shown in Fig. 8-5. Run time considerations will determine the actual level of modeling for any function. Finally, it should be noted that in order to avoid a too detailed representation, only the major interactions between elements are shown in Fig. 8-5.

A. *User Inputs*:
These give the user the ability to specify a given test environment and radar capabilities at the time of execution. This allows tests of a proposed algorithm to be made under various conditions without repeated recompilation of the large simulation. Some examples of the inputs specified at the time of a given run are: (1) target encounter geometry; (2) the radar processing capabilities (i.e., power, eclipsing, scan rates); (3) a selection of algorithms to be used in the processing (i.e., different filter types); (4) a selection of output statistics of interest; and (5) a selection of any detailed processing or debugging required. There are so many options here that they are more conveniently read from a data set than entered for each run from the keyboard.

B. *Target/Own-ship Motion and Dynamics*:
This is an example of a module that should be designed as general as is feasible because the types of encounter geometries that will be of interest can vary greatly. It may be convenient to develop a file of standard test geometries, which can be readily accessed for repeated comparative studies. However, the provision should also be allowed for the system designer to be able to specify new encounter conditions in a flexible manner.

C. *Signal Model*:
This is a model of various effects influencing the returned radar target signal power. Effects may include scintillation and eclipsing (Section 8.3), target aspect changes, PRF mode, beam shape losses, *et cetera*.

D. *Spurious Signals*:
A model of corrupting signals (JEM, ECM) and false alarms.

E. *Detection*:
A model of the capability of the radar to detect signals of varying strengths (Sections 8.2 and 8.3).

F. *Measurement Error Generation*:
A model of how accurately the system measures the target parameters of interest (such as range, range rate, and angle). This module generates the outputs of the signal processing function of the radar.

G. *Multiple Target Interference*:
A model of the capability of the system to resolve closely spaced targets. Unresolved targets are combined into a single detection.

H. *Scan Volume/Antenna Motion*:
A model of how the antenna scans through a search volume in space. This determines what targets will be illuminated.

I. *Observation Redundancy Elimination Processing*:
A model of how detections at various points in the scanned volume are

processed to determine if they are due to single or multiple target sources. This may occur throughout the scan, or, if insufficient data are available at the time of observation, this process may take place at the end of the scan (Chapter 5).

J. *Timing:*
A module that accounts for the time taken by the various radar functions and processing. Delays in making data available may be handled here or in the modules requiring the data.

K. *Gating:*
Process that determines allowable pairing of observations with tracks (Chapter 4).

L. *Data Association/Correlation:*
Final pairing of observations and tracks (Chapter 4).

M. *Track Status:*
Logic for starting a new track, confirming that a previously initiated track history is valid, and dropping a track when it is no longer valid (Chapter 6).

N. *Track Parameter Update:*
Update of track quality parameters, such as confidence indicators that the track is from the target skin return, rather than from JEM, or that the track represents a single target (Chapter 5).

O. *Track Filtering and Prediction:*
Filtering and future position prediction for the track histories (Chapter 2).

P. *Outputs:*
This is the accumulation and presentation to the user of the data by which system performance can be evaluated (Section 8.4).

Q. *Control:*
Various control functions allowing the radar to respond to changes in the environment as indicated by the track history data (such as switch PRFs, change the scan volume, or change the detection thresholds).

Items C through H (describing signal generation, processing, and antenna motion) are given as input to an observation generator. This portion of the simulation may be modeled in extensive detail, potentially requiring a great deal of execution time and expense, or performance data on the processing involved may be compiled into a form allowing the use of high-level, simplified (fast running) models in order to simulate the radar detection outputs. The decision as to which approach to use depends on the perceived importance of the process to the ultimate tracking system performance.

Items J and Q, the timing and control functions, should be given special attention as they involve some implicit assumptions critical to a model of real-world run time processing. In the real-world radar system, all processing is performed simultaneously with data collection. The results of the processing are often not available until some time has passed. For instance, Fig. 8-7 indicates a time line for the collection and processing of data used to control the scan volume of the antenna. Note that the data collected during the first collection (or scan) period can be used to control the scan of the third collection period at the earliest.

The sequence of events shown in Fig. 8-7 can be described as follows. During Period 1 data are collected and processed for detections. All detections which occurred during Period 1 are processed during Period 2 to eliminate redundant target detections. Next, the observations are assigned to the tracks and updated track state predictions are obtained. These predictions are used to control the antenna (or to schedule other resources) for the coming period (Period 3). If the computations during Period 2 require more processing time than is available during this period, then Period 2 must be lengthened beyond the time required to collect the data, or the next controlled period will be Period 4. All during this cycle of computation, data are being collected for Period 2.

The simulation may require much buffering of data (saving old values for later use) to execute the proper timing delays. However, it is often possible to eliminate some data buffering by properly choosing the order of execution of the modules. For example, if the observation collection modules come first, the timing and control modules follow, and the tracking modules are last, buffering of some data can be avoided. Thus, referring to Fig. 8-5, although the output of the control function feeds directly into the observation processing function, the actual calculation of control function quantities may be performed elsewhere in the loop.

Simulation Output Data

The proper presentation of the data generated by the simulation is of utmost importance because these data form the basis of the decisions which will be made as a result of using the simulation. The types of statistics of interest may vary (a basic set was discussed in Section 8.4).

The most convenient form for review and analysis of statistical data is plotted output. Thus, access to a good plotting package is desirable. This package should be able to label all plots adequately and plot easily readable multiple curves on a single grid.

In addition to ensemble Monte Carlo statistics, regular summary output indicating track quality for each Monte Carlo iteration (along with the Monte Carlo starting seed) is a desirable option. By examining individual runs in

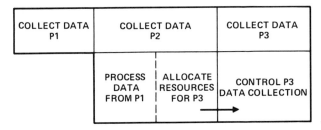

FIGURE 8-7. DATA COLLECTION AND PROCESSING TIME LINE

detail, the designer can determine the source of irregularities that appear in the ensemble statistics. Such output typically consists of a list of the tracks formed during each iteration, including track information such as the number of track drops, the number of track miscorrelations, the target originating the track, the time of track initiation, and the probability of updating the track and detecting the target for the entire iteration.

The collection of statistics to provide meaningful data for a multiple target/multiple track Monte Carlo simulation is not straightforward. A major complication is that various tracks will represent different targets on different iterations and even on the same iteration if a track drop and restart occurs. In addition, an active track may be assigned to different targets during its life. One resolution of this problem is to assign a key (e.g., target identifier) to each track when it is first initiated, and then to accumulate (in a single group) all data for tracks having the same key.

Another problem source is that various processes may lead to the same statistical representation so that interpretation of the results may be misleading unless a significant variety of output representations is provided. For example, a plot of the mean and standard deviation for all tracks on a given target may not distinguish whether many tracks had a short period of large tracking error or just a few tracks had long periods of large tracking error. As another example, if we want to know how often spurious tracks are generated, simply counting the number of tracks and comparing that number to the number of targets is insufficient (because some targets may not be tracked at all, while other targets may produce many spurious tracks).

Another deleterious effect on data interpretation of tracking error is the combining of tracks at various points in their histories into the same statistics point, thus obscuring the true track response over time. For example, a time history of the tracking error for a given target may, when averaged over many Monte Carlo runs, include statistics on tentative as well as confirmed tracks, and thus will not give valid statistics for either track state. In order to control this situation, restrictions on the data collection may be imposed. For example, the compilation of tracking statistics may be restricted to confirmed tracks.

Another situation to look out for is the accumulation of data by specific number, such as the probability of having a given number of tracks at a given time. The number changes with each Monte Carlo iteration and varies considerably from time to time, leading to a jumble of data (criss-crossed lines). An easy way to view such data is by having the lines represent "N or more" occurrences for each number of interest, or by showing the expected number of occurrences at each time.

Another situation to keep in mind is that a data processing period may require more time in one Monte Carlo than in another. It is, therefore, insufficient to accumulate statistics on a processing period basis because these may represent widely varying times (for example, collection of data on a scan basis when the scan time may vary). A solution for this problem is to collect statistics on a time-bin (window in time) by time-bin basis, making sure to show each event in all time bins covered by its duration. If a discrete count of events is desired, (such as number of track drops), care should be taken to show each event *at least* once, but *only* once. Finally, because the interpretation of data depends on sample size, the number of samples used to produce the statistics must be included along with the statistics.

REFERENCES

1. Hoel, P.G., *Introduction to Mathematical Statistics*, New York: John Wiley and Sons, 1971.
2. Bendat, J.S., and A.G. Piersal, *Random Data: Analysis and Measurement Procedures*, New York: Wiley-Interscience, 1971.
3. Forsythe, G.E., M.A. Malcolm, and C.B. Moler, *Computer Methods for Mathematical Computations*, Englewood Cliffs, NJ: Prentice-Hall, 1977.
4. Box, G.E.P., and M.E. Muller, "A Note on the Generation of Normal Deviates on Digital Computers," *Annals of Mathematical Statistics*, Vol. 29, 1958, pp. 610–611.
5. Marsaglia, G., M.D. MacLaren, and T.A. Bray, "A Fast Procedure for Generating Normal Random Variables," *Communications of the ACM*, Vol. 7, 1964, pp. 4–10.
6. Fishman, G.D., *Principles of Discrete Event Simulation*, New York: John Wiley and Sons, 1978.
7. Papoulis, A., *Probability, Random Variables and Stochastic Processes*, New York: McGraw-Hill, 1965.
8. Hovanessian, S.A., *Radar System Design and Analysis*, Dedham,

MA: Artech House, 1984.
9. Skolnik, M.I., *Radar Handbook*, New York: McGraw-Hill, 1970.
10. Barton, D.K., *Radar Systems Analysis*, Dedham, MA: Artech House, 1976.
11. Riggs, D.D., "Target Scintillation Fades and Their Impact on Tracking and Detection," *Proceedings of the 1975 IEEE International Radar Conference*, Arlington, VA, April 21–23, 1975, pp. 446–451.
12. Davenport, W.B., and W.L. Root, *Random Signals and Noise*, New York: McGraw-Hill, 1958.
13. Hammersley, J.M., and D.C. Handscomb, *Monte Carlo Methods*, London: Methuen, 1964.
14. Rubinstein, R.Y., *Simulation and the Monte Carlo Method*, New York: John Wiley and Sons, 1981.
15. Wiener, H.L., A.S. Distler, and J.H. Kullbach, "Operational and Implementation Problems of Multi-Target Correlator-Trackers," *Proceedings of the 1979 IEEE Conference on Decision and Control*, Fort Lauderdale, FL, Dec. 12–14, 1979, pp. 361–367.

Appendix 8A
A General Technique for Generating Random Numbers

This appendix defines a method that can be used to generate a random number from any bounded density function $f(x)$ with a finite range (b,c) First, choose numbers $a, b,$ and $c,$ such that

$$af(x) \leq 1 \text{ for all } x$$

and

$$f(x) \cong 0 \text{ for } x < b, x > c$$

Then, pairs of uniform numbers u_1 and u_2 are generated until the relationship

$$u_1 \leq af[b + (c-b) u_2] \tag{8A.1}$$

is satisfied. If (8A.1) is satisfied, the value $x = b + (c-b) u_2$ is chosen. Otherwise, another pair of uniform numbers is generated and the relationship of (8A.1) is checked again.

Appendix 8B
Derivation of the Correlation Properties of an Exponentially Distributed Random Variable

A process s with exponential distribution can be generated from two independent Gaussians (x,y) with zero mean and standard deviation σ through the relationship:

$$s = x^2 + y^2 \qquad (8B.1)$$

It follows that

$$E[s] = \bar{s} = E[x^2] + E[y^2] = 2\sigma^2$$

Also, using the property of Gaussian variables (x_1, x_2, x_3, x_4),

$$E(x_1 x_2 x_3 x_4) = E(x_1 x_2)\,E(x_3 x_4) + E(x_1 x_3)\,E(x_2 x_4) \\ + E(x_1 x_4)\,E(x_2 x_3) \qquad (8B.2)$$

gives

$$E[s^2] = E\{[x^2 + y^2]^2\} = E[x^4 + 2x^2 y^2 + y^4] = 8\sigma^4$$

so that

$$\sigma_s^2 = E[s^2] - \bar{s}^2 = 4\sigma^4$$

Next, consider the time correlation properties of s generated according to (8B.1) when x and y are first-order Gaussian-Markov processes with correlation coefficient $\rho(T) = e^{-\beta T}$. Assuming x and y are independent, we have

$$E[x^2(t)\,y^2(t+T)] = E[x^2(t+T)\,y^2(t)] = \sigma^4$$

Also,

$$E[x^2(t)\,x^2(t+T)] = E[y^2(t)\,y^2(t+T)]$$

Then the autocorrelation function for s is

$$R_s(T) = E[s(t)s(t+T)] = E\{[x^2(t) + y^2(t)][x^2(t+T) + y^2(t+T)]\} \\ = 2\sigma^4 + 2E[x^2(t)\,x^2(t+T)] \qquad (8B.3)$$

Again using (8B.2) and defining $R_x(T) \triangleq E[x(t)\,x(t+T)]$, we obtain

$$E[x^2(t)\,x^2(t+T)] = \sigma^4 + 2R_x^2(T) = \sigma^4[1 + 2\rho^2(T)]$$

Thus, (8B.3) becomes

$$R_s(T) = 4\sigma^4 [1 + \rho^2(T)] = 4\sigma^4 [1 + e^{-2\beta T}]$$

and

$$\rho_s(T) = \frac{E\{[s(t) - \bar{s}][s(t + T) - \bar{s}]\}}{\sigma_s^2} = \frac{R_s(T) - \bar{s}^2}{\sigma_s^2} = e^{-2\beta T} \quad (8B.4)$$

From (8B.4), the process s has the same form of exponential correlation function as do the components x and y. However, the correlation coefficient is doubled ($\beta_s = 2\beta$), or, equivalently, the time constant ($\tau_s = 1/\beta_s$) is halved.

Chapter 9

A Maximum Likelihood Expression for Data Association

9.1 INTRODUCTION

In this chapter, a general expression, based on a maximum likelihood approach, is derived for the optimal partitioning of observations into tracks. The derivation is based on Stein and Blackman [1], which in turn drew heavily from the pioneering work of Sittler [2]. Similar expressions are derived by Morefield [3] and Reid [4].

The main feature of the development is the computation of the probability associated with the partitioning of a group of observations (received over a number of scans) into tracks and false alarms (or returns from true targets that exist for a single scan). The logarithm of this probability is defined to be the score function. This result leads to a unified approach for the development of track initiation, confirmation, gating, and deletion logic. A mathematical foundation is thus developed for many of the expressions and techniques that were previously defined intuitively. Finally, a background is provided for subsequent chapters discussing advanced topics.

For notational convenience, expressions have been derived using a constant probability of detection (P_D). Because the expressions to be derived would be computed recursively, the extension to using time-variable P_D is direct.

The derived expression is directly applicable for an optimal batch processing algorithm. The derived optimal solution is generally not computationally feasible, however, for a real-time surveillance system. Thus, the application to the development of practical algorithms is discussed. A suboptimal, but computationally convenient, sequential correlation technique is developed. This derivation leads to a consistent relationship between the gates and the elements of the observation-to-track assignment matrix. Also, the expressions required for the implementation of the Bayesian techniques discussed in the next chapter are presented.

9.2 GENERALIZED TECHNIQUE DEVELOPMENT

Following Sittler [2], we will derive an expression giving the maximum likelihood solution to the problem of forming observations into tracks. First, the necessary elements are introduced. These include a model for track life that is used in determining track deletion criteria. Finally, the elements are defined in terms of simple models, combined and necessary manipulations are performed to give an algebraically convenient expression.

9.2.1 Technique Outline

Assume that we have a total of r observations which have been received during K scans of a search volume V. The problem is to partition these observations into sets of tracks and sets of single point observations. Single point observations include false alarms and observations from targets that produce a single detection. A number of hypotheses relating to this partitioning can be formed. The goal is to define an expression for computing the relative likelihood that each of these data association hypotheses is correct. This expression is defined to be the likelihood function. The relative likelihood of all possible ways to partition the data can be computed by substitution of the observed data into this expression.

No more than one observation per scan will be assigned to any given track. Also, it will be assumed that each observation was produced by a single source. Trunk and Wilson [5] develop a similar, but more complex, expression that is applicable to the condition where unresolved detections produced by more than one target are present.

Figure 9-1 illustrates the data association problem by giving four alternative ways in which observations received on three consecutive scans can be combined. Cases a and b represent the extremes where all observations are uncorrelated and where all observations are used to form tracks, respectively. Case c represents the condition where there are two tracks formed and two observations are uncorrelated. Finally, case d represents a disallowed (for our derivation) track formation because the two tracks have a common observation. This condition may appear in practice for crossing targets where an unresolved detection occurs, and a more general derivation that allows this situation is given in [5].

A given data partitioning hypothesis must first state how many independent sources (tracks and single point observations) were present during the data collection period (K scans). For notational convenience, we will refer to all single point sources as false targets. Also, define n_{FK} and n_K to be the numbers of false targets and true targets, respectively, that arose during the K scans. Then, $P_0 (n_{FK}, n_K)$ will give the probability associated with a

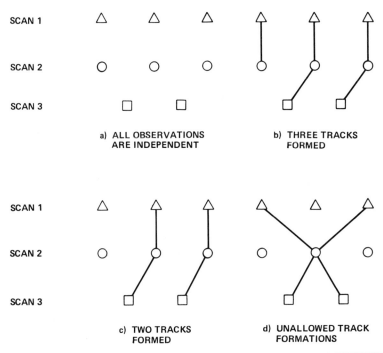

SCAN 1

SCAN 2

SCAN 3

a) ALL OBSERVATIONS
ARE INDEPENDENT

b) THREE TRACKS
FORMED

SCAN 1

SCAN 2

SCAN 3

c) TWO TRACKS
FORMED

d) UNALLOWED TRACK
FORMATIONS

FIGURE 9-1. EXAMPLES OF POSSIBLE DATA ASSOCIATION HYPOTHESES

particular choice of n_{FK} and n_K. Under the assumption that true and false targets arise independently, we have

$$P_0 (n_{FK}, n_K) = P_{0F} (n_{FK})\, P_{0T} (n_K)$$

An expression will be derived later for $P_{0T} (n_K)$ under the assumption that the targets arise at random in space and time. If, however, the number of targets were known (perhaps from previous surveillance information) to be N, the simpler expression would be

$$P_{0T} (n_K) = \delta(N) = \begin{cases} 1, & n_K = N \\ 0, & \text{otherwise} \end{cases}$$

Refer again to Fig. 9-1, which illustrates potential choices (taking $K=3$) for n_3 and n_{F3}. For this example, the cases illustrating allowable track formations give

Case a : $n_3 = 0$, $n_{F3} = 8$
Case b : $n_3 = 3$, $n_{F3} = 0$
Case c : $n_3 = 2$, $n_{F3} = 2$

Note that the extremes shown by cases a and b represent likely hypotheses only under the conditions of a high false target density and a high true target density (or for a known value of $n_3 = 3$), respectively.

Given that a particular hypothesis contains n_K true target tracks, the next step is to determine how long the tracks lasted. For this development a track will be assumed to last as long as the target exists within the scan volume. A target could cease to exist when it left the scan volume, or, as in the case of a ground target that is obscured, when it becomes undetectable. Thus, the term $P_{TL}(D|n_K)$ is defined to represent the probabilities associated with the track lengths (D) given that n_K target tracks are formed by a given hypothesis. Again considering the example where it is known that there are exactly N targets present during the entire data collection period, $P_{TL}(D|N)$ will be unity for track lengths equal to or greater than the surveillance time period (K scans), and zero otherwise.

For a given track length hypothesis (with probability defined by P_{TL}) the term $P_{DT}(NU|D)$ gives the probability of the particular detection sequences as defined by the number of track updates (NU). For example, if a given data association hypothesis states that a particular track has a length of D_i scans after initial detection, there can be up to D_i observations (beyond the initial observation) included in that track. Then, P_{DT} gives the probability associated with a particular choice for the number of observations included in that track.

Refer to cases b and c of Fig. 9-1, which illustrates the manner in which track length and update history enter the hypothesis formation. The two-point track given in case b can either result from the condition where the track length did not extend into the third scan or from a missed update (nondetection) on the third scan. These hypotheses can be compared with the hypothesis shown for case c where the two observations are uncorrelated. Then if, for example, the probability of detection is high ($P_D \cong 1.0$) and the expected track length is long the hypothesis shown in case c would be preferable; if the first two points did form a track there should have been a third point.

A final term, $P_{ER}(\tilde{y}|NU)$, relates to the set of residual errors (the differences between predicted and measured track positions). This term gives the probability that the given detection sequences defined by NU will produce observations with the particular residual values.

Referring again to Fig. 9-1, the inclusion of the third scan observations in the tracks shown for cases b and c represent significant deviations from a straight line path. Thus, the likelihood of these hypotheses would depend upon the assumed target dynamics model and the measurement model. If, for example, targets are modeled as having essentially straight-line trajectories and if the measurement error is assumed small, these hypotheses will be found to be unlikely.

Combining the terms discussed above, the desired likelihood expression, defined to be Q_K, can be written to include the conditional dependencies

$$Q_K = P_{ER}(\tilde{y}|NU) \, P_{DT}(NU|D) \, P_{TL}(D|n_K) \, P_0(n_K, n_{FK}) \qquad (9.1)$$

The expression given in (9.1) is to be evaluated for a given hypothesized set of n_K tracks. Thus, a more explicit form can be defined expressing Q_K as a product of terms for each track and each observation associated with each track:

$$Q_K = P_0(n_K, n_{FK}) \prod_{i=1}^{n_K} P_{TL}(D_i) \, P_{DT}(NU_i|D_i) \prod_{l=1}^{NU_i} P_{ER}(\tilde{y}_{il}) \qquad (9.2)$$

where, in summary,

$P_0(n_K, n_{FK})$ = probability that n_K true targets and n_{FK} false targets arise in the scan volume during the K scans

D_i = track length for track i

$P_{TL}(D_i)$ = probability of track length D_i

$P_{DT}(NU_i|D_i)$ = probability that track i produces NU_i detections (used for track update) given that the track length is D_i

$P_{ER}(\tilde{y}_{il})$ = probability of residual error $\tilde{y}_{il}$ for the lth observation included in the ith track

Equation (9.2) defines a partitioning of the r observations received on K scan into n_K true target tracks and n_{FK} false targets. Each of the n_K tracks is defined by its track length D_i and the NU_i observations included in the track with associated residual errors $\tilde{y}_{il}$.

Next, we will derive expressions for the terms given in (9.2). The expressions will be based on standard models. Similar developments could be performed starting with (9.2), but using other models.

Using expressions for the terms in (9.2), the maximum likelihood approach can be used to compute the relative likelihood of various data partitioning hypotheses. Using this approach, a likelihood function is formed by using the data (in this case, the time of arrival and the measured positions, velocities, *et cetera* of the observations) in the *a posteriori* probability expression given by (9.2). The relative likelihoods of various data association hypotheses are found by evaluating the expression using the measured data.

9.2.2 New Source Model

Assume that new sources arise at random within the scan volume V at a rate of β objects per scan per unit volume. The new source density is defined to include the density of false targets (clutter, false alarms, *et cetera*) β_{FT} and the density of true targets β_{NT}:

$$\beta = \beta_{FT} + \beta_{NT}$$

Separate expressions will be derived for true and for false targets. Comparable expressions can be derived [1] by considering the two types of new sources together. The approach chosen here, however, leads more conveniently to the expressions formulated in [4]. These expressions are later used in the development of techniques for multiple hypothesis tracking.

The derivation for false targets is presented, but an identical expression will be valid for true targets as long as the same arrival statistics are assumed for both. Assume that for each scan (we consider scan k) false targets arise at random in space. Consider small cells of volume Δ. The probability that a false target appears within a given cell is $\beta_{FT}\Delta$. Because Δ is assumed very small, the probability of more than one false target arising within a single cell is negligible. Thus, the probability that n_{Fk} false targets arise within a set of n_{Fk} cells (and that the other cells are empty) is

$$P_{0F}(n_{Fk}) = (\beta_{FT}\Delta)^{n_{Fk}} (1 - \beta_{FT}\Delta)^{N_C - n_{Fk}}$$

where

N_C = total number of cells within scan volume = V/Δ.

Since, by assumption, $N_C \gg n_{Fk}$, then

$$(1 - \beta_{FT}\Delta)^{N_C - n_{Fk}} \cong (1 - \beta_{FT}\Delta)^{N_C} = (1 - \beta_{FT}\Delta)^{V/\Delta}$$

Hence, letting the cell size Δ approach zero, we write

$$\lim_{\Delta \to 0} (1 - \beta_{FT}\Delta)^{V/\Delta} = \lim_{\Delta \to 0} \exp\left[\frac{V}{\Delta} \ln(1 - \beta_{FT}\Delta) \right]$$

$$= \exp\left[\frac{V}{\Delta} (-\beta_{FT}\Delta) \right] = \exp(-\beta_{FT}V)$$

Thus, as in [1, 2],

$$P_{0F}(n_{Fk}) = (\beta_{FT}\Delta)^{n_{Fk}} e^{-\beta_{FT}V}$$

The probability that n_k true target tracks are started on scan k and within a specified set of n_k cells is derived in a completely analogous manner to be

$$P_{0T}(n_k) = (\beta_{NT}\Delta)^{n_k} e^{-\beta_{NT}V}$$

Finally, combining the above expressions gives the probability (P_0) that there are exactly n_{FK} false targets and n_K true targets that arise on scans 1 to K and that these sources arise within a specific set of cells:

$$P_0(n_{FK}, n_K) = \prod_{k=1}^{K} P_{0F}(n_{Fk}) \, P_{0T}(n_k) = (\beta_{FT}\Delta)^{n_{FK}} (\beta_{NT}\Delta)^{n_K} e^{-\beta KV}$$

(9.3)

9.2.3 Track Length Model

Next, given that a true target was detected, we compute the conditional track length probability (P_{TL}). First, assume that the true target track length (τ) density function can be approximated by the exponential distribution:

$$f(\tau) = \frac{e^{-\tau/\tau_o}}{\tau_o}$$

where τ_o is the expected track length. The exponential track length assumption was introduced by Sittler [2] and has been found to match experimental data closely for a ship tracking problem in which targets crossed through a fixed surveillance area. However, for a particular implementation, τ_o may be chosen as a function of position because targets may be more likely to disappear from some parts of the scan volume than from others.

Define the expected track length in terms of the expected track length in scans (D_E) and the sampling interval T so that $\tau_o = D_E T$. Then, given data received through scan K, there are two possibilities for the track length (D_i) of true target track i. First, the track may have terminated before scan K with final length D_i. The probability that the track terminated during the time interval $D_i T$ to $(D_i + 1) T$, and thus had track length D_i, is

$$P_{TL1}(D_i) = \frac{1}{\tau_o} \int_{D_i T}^{(D_i + 1) T} e^{-\tau/\tau_o} \, d\tau = P_{TT} e^{-D_i / D_E}$$

(9.4a)

where

$$P_{TT} = 1 - e^{-1//D_E}$$

(9.4b)

Note that $\exp(-1/D_E)$ is the probability that the track continues for an additional scan so that P_{TT} is the probability that the track terminates.

The second alternative is that the track may still be present (at scan K) and thus will not terminate until some time in the future. The probability of this alternative is the probability that a track will have length greater than D_i. This probability is given by

$$P_{TL2}(D_i) = \frac{1}{\tau_o} \int_{D_iT}^{\infty} e^{-\tau/\tau_o} \, d\tau = e^{-D_i/D_E} \tag{9.4c}$$

Thus, the probabilities for the two track length alternatives differ only by the track termination factor P_{TT}. To summarize:

$$P_{TL}(D_i) = \begin{cases} P_{TL1}(D_i), & \text{source not present at scan } K \\ P_{TL2}(D_i), & \text{source still present at scan } K \end{cases} \tag{9.5}$$

Another useful expression is the conditional probability that the track length will be at least D scans given that it is at least D_o scans where $D = D_o + \delta$. The conditional probability that a track assumed now valid will last at least δ more scans is given by

$$P(D_i \geqq D \mid D_i \geqq D_o) = \frac{P_{TL2(D)}}{P_{TL2(D_o)}} = e^{-\delta/D_E}$$

Target tracks that exist only for the initial detection scan, and thus have zero track length, are essentially indistinguishable from false targets. The density of these one-point sources is $\beta_{NT} P_{TT}$, and this density can effectively be added to β_{FT}. Because this contribution is typically small and the combining of false targets and one-point true targets leads to some additional complexities in the notation, this point will not be considered in the subsequent derivations.

9.2.4 Detection and Track Update Model

Define:

$NU_i \triangleq$ number of detections (or updates), beyond the initial observation, for target track i;

P_D = probability of detection.

Then, the probability of a particular detection history (after initial detection) for the ith target track, which was available for D_i scans, is

$$P_{DT_i} = P_D^{NU_i} (1 - P_D)^{(D_i - NU_i)} \tag{9.6}$$

9.2.5 Tracking Error

Track initiation, duration, and updating models have been derived in the previous sections. The next step is to describe the subsequent (after initiation) prediction error statistics. As discussed in Chapter 2, assume a Kalman filter with residual covariance matrix of the form

$$S = HPH^T + R_c$$

where P and R_c are the Kalman prediction and measurement noise covariance matrices, respectively, and H is the measurement matrix. Also, the difference between the true and the expected measurement value, defined to be the residual (or innovation), is given by

$$\tilde{y}(k) = y(k) - H\hat{x}(k|k - 1)$$

Assume that for each of the NU_i points (beyond the initial one) associated with track i, the probability density of the residual error vector is Gaussian, given by

$$f(\tilde{y}) = \frac{e^{-d^2/2}}{(2\pi)^{M/2} \sqrt{|S|}}$$

where M is the measurement dimension, $|S|$ is the determinant of S and

$$d^2 = \tilde{y}^T S^{-1} \tilde{y}$$

We will again convert probability densities to finite probabilities within space cells of volume Δ. As before, we let subscript i denote track number and we introduce subscript l to denote the lth observation associated with that track. Thus, $\tilde{y}_{il}$ is defined to be the residual for the lth observation of the ith track. Probability densities are converted to probabilities by multiplying the probability density for a given residual error, $f(\tilde{y}_{il})$, by the small cell volume Δ. Then, the probability of the ith track having NU_i residual errors within NU_i cells of volume Δ (since Δ is assumed very small) is

$$P_{ER_i} = \Delta^{NU_i} \prod_{l=1}^{NU_i} f(\tilde{y}_{il}) \tag{9.7}$$

Note that the product on l is taken only over those scans for which an update on track i is available. Finally, the total error probability associated with all residual errors as taken over all tracks becomes

$$P_{ER} = \Delta^{n_{uK}} \prod_{i=1}^{n_K} \prod_{l=1}^{NU_i} f(\tilde{y}_{il})$$

where n_{uK} is the total number of updates for all tracks,

$$n_{uK} = \sum_{i=1}^{n_K} NU_i = r - n_K - n_{FK}$$

This completes specification of the models and the resulting distributions for the elements of the MTT data association expression given in (9.2). Next, these individual elements will be combined into an overall expression giving the *a posteriori* probability for any given combination of observations into tracks.

9.2.6   Composite Probability Expressions

Equation (9.2) gives a general expression for the probability (Q_K) associated with any particular data association hypothesis given K scans of data that produced r observations. Equations (9.3) through (9.7) give expressions for the general terms included in (9.2). Combining gives

$$Q_K = C \beta_{FT}^{n_{FK}} \beta_{NT}^{n_K} \prod_{i=1}^{n_K} \left[P_{TL}(D_i) P_D^{NU_i} (1 - P_D)^{(D_i - NU_i)} \prod_{l=1}^{NU_i} f(\tilde{y}_{il}) \right]$$

$$(9.8)$$

where $C = \Delta^r e^{-K\beta V}$. Thus, the arbitrarily chosen cell volume Δ and scan volume V are contained entirely in the constant C and will not affect the comparisons of probabilities derived from different data associations.

It is also of interest to present the likelihood function for the case where it is known that there are exactly N targets in the surveillance volume during the entire K scans. For this case, it can be assumed that initial estimates of the target positions are available. If the positions are essentially unknown (except to be within the surveillance volume) the uncertainty can be modeled by large initial position estimation standard deviations. Also, for this case, since the tracks are assumed to last for at least the K surveillance scans, note that,

$$P_{TL}(D_i) = \begin{cases} 1.0, & D_i \geq K \\ 0, & \text{otherwise} \end{cases}$$

Thus, for this case,

$$Q_K = C\beta_{FT}^{n_{FK}} \prod_{i=1}^{N} P_D^{NU_i} (1 - P_D)^{(K - NU_i)} \prod_{l=1}^{NU_i} f(\tilde{y}_{il})$$

Finally, the total number of false targets (n_{FK}) associated with the given data association hypothesis is

$$n_{FK} = r - \sum_{i=1}^{N} NU_i$$

The goal is to find the data association that maximizes Q_K. Equivalently, this goal is achieved through maximization of $\ln Q_K$. Thus, noting the exponential form of several of the expressions, it is convenient to consider the quantity

$$L_K' = \ln Q_K - \ln C \tag{9.9}$$

Finally, from (9.8) and (9.9) and upon expanding all terms, including $f(\tilde{y}_{il})$, L_K' becomes

$$L_K' = n_{FK} \ln \beta_{FT} + n_K \ln \beta_{NT} + \prod_{i=1}^{n_K} \left\{ \ln [P_{TL}(D_i)] + (D_i - NU_i) \ln (1 - P_D) \right.$$

$$\left. + \sum_{l=1}^{NU_i} \left(\ln \left[\frac{P_D}{(2\pi)^{M/2} \sqrt{|S_{il}|}} \right] - \frac{d_{il}^2}{2} \right) \right\} \tag{9.10}$$

Equation (9.10) gives a general expression to be maximized for a given data set, and L_K' may be considered to be a score associated with a particular way of combining the data (observations) into tracks. The combination giving the maximum score is the most likely. It would give the maximum *a posteriori* probability. For the purpose of having an appropriate reference, however, it is convenient to define a slightly modified expression that has zero score associated with choosing all observations to be from false targets. Thus, the reference is defined to be that case in which all observations are declared to be false targets so that no tracks are formed. Then, any valid tracks that are formed for other data association options must contribute a positive score.

With reference to (9.10), the score associated with forming no tracks is found by putting $n_{FK} = r$ so that L_K'(no tracks) $= r \ln \beta_{FT}$. Thus, the modified score function becomes

$$L_K = L'_K - r \ln \beta_{FT} = n_K \ln \frac{\beta_{NT}}{\beta_{FT}} + \sum_{i=1}^{n_K} \left\{ \ln \left[P_{TL} (D_i) \right] + (D_i - NU_i) \ln (1 - P_D) \right.$$

$$\left. + \sum_{l=1}^{NU_i} \left(\ln \left[\frac{P_D}{\beta_{FT} (2\pi)^{M/2} \sqrt{|S_{il}|}} \right] - \frac{d_{il}^2}{2} \right) \right\} \tag{9.11}$$

Equation (9.11) gives the final expression for the score associated with the formation of tracks from observations. The goal will be to maximize score. Choosing all observations to be uncorrelated leads to a score of zero. Thus, any track that is formed must lead to a score greater than zero.

To prepare for future developments, a convenient alternative representation of (9.8), (9.10), and (9.11) can be defined for data association hypotheses containing observations received on the most recent scan, K, and not assigned to previously established tracks. For these observations an alternative representation of (9.8) combines the new true target and new false target hypotheses (with probabilities β_{NT} and β_{FT}, respectively) into a single new source hypothesis with probability β. The result is that a term $\ln \beta$ in (9.10) and a term $\ln [\beta/\beta_{FT}]$ in (9.11) are used to represent the combined (true and false target) new source hypothesis. After receipt of the next scan of data the combined hypothesis must be split into true and false target hypotheses because additional terms become required to represent the true target hypothesis.

Equations (9.8) and (9.11) give expressions which could be used at scan K for the processing of all data received through that scan. This method, commonly referred to as batch processing, is generally not computationally feasible for a practical problem. Morefield [3], however, has developed a method for the solution of a similar expression (but upon assuming unity P_D) using integer programming.

In this chapter, we will outline the application of the expressions given in (9.8) and (9.11) to develop a suboptimal, but easily implemented, sequential method. Chapter 10 will discuss two other important applications that are more computationally involved. First, it is of interest to discuss the physical significance of the terms that have been developed.

9.3 APPLICATIONS

9.3.1 Interpretation of Terms

With reference to (9.11), four basic terms quantify the score associated with various aspects (initiation, length, missed observations, and received observations) of track formation. The first term, $\ln \beta_{NT}/\beta_{FT}$, is the score resulting from track initiation. This term increases as the density of true targets increases and as the density of false targets decreases. The second term, $\ln[P_{TL}(D_i)]$, represents the score associated with assigning track length D_i, and this term includes the penalty, discussed below, for track deletion. The third term, $(D_i - NU_i)\ln(1 - P_D)$, is a penalty term arising when detections are not received. This term approaches negative infinity for missed detections as P_D approaches unity. The final term is a sum over track updates of the incremental scores associated with those updates.

Next, we examine in more detail the terms related to track length. First, given that the track is currently valid, the probability associated with extending it another scan is e^{-1/D_E}. The probability associated with track length D_i is e^{-D_i/D_E}. If the track is deleted after D_i scans, however, there is the additional factor of $P_{TT} = 1 - e^{-1/D_E}$. For most cases, $D_E \gg 1$ so that

$$P_{TT} = 1 - e^{-1/D_E} \sim 1 - \left(1 - \frac{1}{D_E}\right) \sim \frac{1}{D_E}$$

Thus, the increment to the score function associated with the track length is

$$\ln[P_{TL}(D_i)] = \begin{cases} -\dfrac{D_i}{D_E}, \text{ track continuing} \\[2ex] -\dfrac{D_i}{D_E} + \ln P_{TT}, \text{ track deleted} \end{cases}$$

The term $\ln P_{TT} \cong -\ln D_E$ is effectively a penalty associated with track deletion; its relationship to track confirmation is discussed next.

9.3.2 Track Confirmation

To facilitate future developments, Table 9-1 defines a convenient set of track life stages. First, consider the transition from nonconfirmed (potential or tentative) to confirmed track status. The criterion that we will use is that a track becomes confirmed when it is assured of a positive score. This occurs when the score function becomes greater than the penalty term $(\ln P_{TT} \cong -\ln D_E)$ that must be added when deletion occurs. Then, given score $L_{i,k}$ for track i at scan k, a positive track score is assured if

$$L_{i,k} + \ln P_{TT} > 0 \tag{9.12}$$

Thus, when the inequality of (9.12) is satisfied, a grouping of observations into a track is assured of being statistically superior to the alternative that the observations are uncorrelated single points.

TABLE 9-1
TRACK LIFE STAGE DEFINITION

Track Type	Definition
Potential	A single point track, with initial score $\ln \beta_{NT}/\beta_{FT}$, that is still being considered as a possible first point for a grouping of two or more points.
Tentative	A grouping of two or more points for which the score, upon considering future deletion cost, is not assured of being positive.
Confirmed	A grouping of two or more points for which a positive score is assured.
Deleted	A grouping of two or more points leading to a positive score that is maximized by assuming that the track is terminated prior to scan K.

9.3.3   Hypothesis Tree Representation

Returning to (9.8), consider the formulation of alternative hypotheses for the combination of measurement data into tracks. We will use the notation $y_j(k)$ to refer to the jth observation received on scan k. Begin with an observation $(y_1(1))$ that is not used for update of an existing track. The two alternative hypotheses for this observation are false target and new target with probabilities proportional to β_{FT} and β_{NT}, respectively. When we consider an observation $(y_1(2))$ received on the next scan, five hypotheses now represent the various combinations of alternatives for the two observations. These alternative hypotheses and the corresponding probability densities are

H_1:   Both observations are false targets,

$$p(H_1) = \beta_{FT}\,\beta_{FT}$$

H_2:   First observation is a false target; second is a true target denoted new target two ($T2$),

$$p(H_2) = \beta_{FT}\,\beta_{NT}$$

H_3: First observation is a true target ($T1$); second is a false target and the first target ($T1$) is not detected,

$$p(H_3) = \beta_{NT}(1 - P_D) e^{-1/D_E} \beta_{FT}$$

H_4: First observation is a true target ($T1$) and the observation on the second scan is associated with the first target track ($T1$),

$$p(H_4) = \beta_{NT}(P_D) e^{-1/D_E} g_{11}$$

H_5: First observation is a true target ($T1$); second is another new target ($T2$) and the first target is not detected on the second scan,

$$p(H_5) = \beta_{NT} e^{-1/D_E}(1 - P_D) \beta_{NT}$$

The quantity g_{11} included in $p(H_4)$ is the Gaussian likelihood function associated with assigning the first (and only) observation received on the second scan to track $T1$. This is defined as

$$g_{11} = \frac{e^{-d_{11}^2/2}}{(2\pi)^{M/2} \sqrt{|S_1|}} \tag{9.13}$$

where d_{11}^2 is the normalized distance associated with the observation-to-track assignment and $|S_1|$ is the determinant of the residual covariance matrix for track $T1$.

The factors P_D and $(1 - P_D)$ are included in the expressions for the hypothesis probabilities to represent the probabilities of the target being detected and not detected, respectively, on the second scan. Finally, the factor e^{-1/D_E} in the last three probabilities represents the probability associated with extending the track for an additional scan.

Figure 9-2 shows the hypothesis tree representation of the hypothesis formation technique outlined above. Each node of the tree represents an alternative hypothesis; further branches are added to each node as a new data point is considered. Clearly, even in this most simple example, the number of hypotheses (branches) can grow very rapidly unless limiting techniques are applied.

Chapter 10 will discuss the multiple hypothesis tracking (MHT) method in detail. This technique involves maintaining multiple hypotheses while "pruning" those unlikely branches of the hypothesis tree. The simplest and most extreme form of pruning is formulation of alternative hypotheses as data are received and propagation of only a single hypothesis. This is the sequential correlation approach which will be developed further in this chapter.

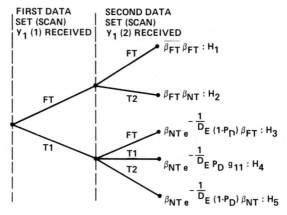

FIGURE 9-2. EXAMPLE OF HYPOTHESIS TREE

9.4   DEVELOPMENT OF A SEQUENTIAL CORRELATION TECHNIQUE

Next, we use (9.8) and (9.11) to develop a purely sequential method in which only the new data received on each scan are used for track initiation and track updating. The nearest-neighbor (NN) technique is assumed to be used for correlation. This purely sequential method is basically the technique that has been discussed previously in this book, but the expressions derived above now provide a mathematical guideline for the logic development.

The first requirement for a sequential correlation method is the track confirmation criterion defined in (9.12). Next, we continue with a simplified hypothesis tree representation to define gating and deletion criteria. Finally, the techniques will be extended to the resolution of multiple target/multiple observation conflict situations through use of the correlation (or assignment) matrix.

9.4.1   Gating and Deletion

Continuing with the example discussed in the previous section and shown in Figure 9-2, consider the decision regarding the possible assignment of the second scan's observation to the tentative new track formed on the first scan. This assignment is represented by H_4. Assume that it will be made if H_4 has at least 0.5 *a posteriori* probability of being correct. (It is more likely than all other hypotheses combined.) This condition is met if

$$p(H_4) > p(H_1) + p(H_2) + p(H_3) + p(H_5) \tag{9.14}$$

A sequential decision rule based on (9.14) seems "reasonable" because only H_4 eliminates the option of later declaring that the initial observation was from a single point source. If the second scan's observation $(y_1(2))$ is not assigned to the tentative track, the options to declare later $y_1(1)$ to be a single point observation and to declare $y_1(2)$ as either a new true or a false target remain available. Equation (9.14) is satisfied if

$$\beta_{NT} \, e^{-1/D_E} \, P_D \, g_{11} > \beta_{FT} \, (\beta_{FT} + \beta_{NT}) + \beta_{NT} \, e^{-1/D_E} \, (1 - P_D) \, (\beta_{FT} + \beta_{NT})$$

$$= \beta_{FT} \, \beta + \beta_{NT} \, \beta \, e^{-1/D_E} \, (1 - P_D)$$

or, dividing both sides by $\beta_{NT} \beta \, e^{-1/D_E} \, (1 - P_D)$,

$$\frac{P_D \, g_{11}}{\beta (1 - P_D)} > \frac{\beta_{FT} + \beta_{NT} \, e^{-1/D_E} \, (1 - P_D)}{\beta_{NT} \, e^{-1/D_E} \, (1 - P_D)}$$

Finally, taking logarithms and noting the form of g_{11}, from (9.13), gives a gating condition for the possible assignment of $y_1(2)$ to $T1$, which is written thusly,

$$d_{11}^2 < 2 \ln \left[\frac{P_D}{(1 - P_D) \, \beta \, (2\pi)^{M/2} \, \sqrt{|S_1|}} \right]$$

$$-2 \ln \left[\frac{\beta_{FT} + \beta_{NT} \, e^{-1/D_E} \, (1 - P_D)}{\beta_{NT} \, e^{-1/D_E} \, (1 - P_D)} \right] \tag{9.15}$$

The first term on the right of (9.15) represents the standard gate derived in [1, 6] and previously presented in this book. The non-zero value of the second term is derived from the β_{FT} term contributed by hypotheses H_1 and H_2. It represents a decrease in the gate that results, in effect, from the option to delete the track and declare the single point to be a false alarm. As the false target density (β_{FT}) decreases with respect to β_{NT}, this term becomes negligible.

The next extension is to a potential (single-point) track for which N_m consecutive scans have elapsed without a second point being added to the track and for which update with a new observation is now being considered. Basically, the same hypothesis tree as shown in Fig. 9-2 can be drawn for this case. However, the probabilities associated with the hypotheses that include $T1$ as a valid track now have the factor $(1 - P_D)^{N_m} e^{-N_m/D_E}$ to account for the N_m consecutive missed detections and the extension of the track for N_m scans. Thus, basically the same hypotheses are associated with the potential inclusion of a new observation, and the probabilities are

$$p(H_1) = \beta_{FT}\,\beta_{FT}$$

$$p(H_2) = \beta_{FT}\,\beta_{NT}$$

$$p(H_3) = \beta_{NT}\,e^{-(N_m + 1)/D_E}\,(1 - P_D)^{N_m + 1}\,\beta_{FT}$$

$$p(H_4) = \beta_{NT}\,e^{-(N_m + 1)/D_E}\,(1 - P_D)^{N_m}\,P_D\,g_{11}$$

$$p(H_5) = \beta_{NT}\,e^{-(N_m + 1)/D_E}\,(1 - P_D)^{N_m + 1}\,\beta_{NT}$$

As before, satisfaction of (9.14) will be the criterion required for the observation to be assigned to the track. Then, the requirement for track update becomes

$$\beta_{NT}\,e^{-(N_m + 1)/D_E}\,(1 - P_D)^{N_m}\,P_D\,g_{11} > \beta_{FT}\,\beta + \beta_{NT}\,e^{-(N_m + 1)/D_E}\,(1 - P_D)^{N_m + 1}\,\beta$$

or

$$\frac{P_D\,g_{11}}{\beta\,(1 - P_D)} > \frac{\beta_{FT} + \beta_{NT}\,[(1 - P_D)\,e^{-1/D_E}]^{N_m + 1}}{\beta_{NT}\,[(1 - P_D)\,e^{-1/D_E}]^{N_m + 1}}$$

Finally, again taking logarithms, the gating condition becomes

$$d_{11}^2 < 2\ln\left[\frac{P_D}{(1 - P_D)\,\beta\,(2\pi)^{M/2}\,\sqrt{|S_1|}}\right]$$

$$-2\ln\left\{\frac{\beta_{FT} + \beta_{NT}\,[(1 - P_D)\,e^{-1/D_E}]^{N_m + 1}}{\beta_{NT}\,[(1 - P_D)\,e^{-1/D_E}]^{N_m + 1}}\right\} \tag{9.16}$$

Thus, (9.16) represents the generalization of (9.15) for $N_m \geqq 1$.

Referring to (9.16), note that the gate decreases as the number of misses increases. First, the elements of the covariance matrix S_1 increase with extrapolation time so that the first term on the right-hand side of (9.16) decreases. Also, the magnitude of the second, negative factor increases as N_m increases.

The next extension is to the general case for tentative tracks. Assume that the track history after reception of the original point led to the probability p_{ci} associated with extending the track (track number i). For example, for the case above of N_m scans without update, p_{ci} is

$$p_{ci} = [e^{-1/D_E}\,(1 - P_D)]^{N_m} \tag{9.17}$$

In general, there may also be factors of $P_D g$, such as those that arise in hypothesis H_4 defined above, for the cases of track update which do not satisfy the confirmation criterion. For this general case, the gating relationship (for assigning observation j to track i) becomes

$$d^2_{ij} < 2 \ln \left[\frac{P_D}{(1 - P_D)\, \beta\, (2\pi)^{M/2} \sqrt{|S_i|}} \right]$$

$$-2 \ln \left[\frac{\beta_{FT} + \beta_{NT}\, p_{ci}\, e^{-1/D_E}\, (1 - P_D)}{\beta_{NT}\, p_{ci}\, e^{-1/D_E}\, (1 - P_D)} \right] \tag{9.18}$$

Next, consider a confirmed track that achieved maximum score at scan k_m. Assume that the probability density associated with extending the track beyond k_m is p_c. The usual condition will be that N_m consecutive misses occurred so that p_c will again be given by (9.17). However, p_c may also contain factors of P_{Dg} to account for observations that were included in the track but that did not raise the score beyond its previously achieved maximum value.

There are now three hypotheses associated with the potential inclusion of another observation into the track and the probabilities given are those associated with the events occurring after the maximum score was achieved. Note that all hypotheses would include a term representing the track probability at the time of maximum score. However, this term is not included since it will be contained in all hypotheses and thus will cancel in the comparison. Thus, the three hypotheses and their probabilties are

H_1:   Track ended at scan k_m and should be deleted retroactively to that scan. The potential updating observation is from a new source,

$$p(H_1) = P_{TT}\, \beta$$

H_2:   The track is continued but the observation is from a new source,

$$p(H_2) = p_c\, e^{-1/D_E} (1 - P_D)\, \beta$$

H_3:   The track is continued and the observation is assigned to the track,

$$p(H_3) = p_c\, e^{-1/D_E}\, P_D\, g$$

where g is the Gaussian likelihood function associated with the assignment of the observation to the track. For simplicity of representation the hypotheses that consider the potential updating observation to be from a false target and from a new true target have been combined because the result, in terms of the defined gate, will be the same.

The condition for assigning the observation to the track is

$$p(H_3) > p(H_1) + p(H_2) \tag{9.19}$$

Equation (9.19) gives

$$p_c\, e^{-1/D_E}\, P_D\, g > P_{TT}\, \beta + p_c\, e^{-1/D_E} (1 - P_D)\, \beta$$

or

$$\frac{P_D \, g}{\beta \, (1 - P_D)} > \frac{P_{TT} + p_c \, e^{-1/D_E} (1 - P_D)}{p_c \, e^{-1/D_E} (1 - P_D)}$$

Finally, the gating condition (for assigning observation j to track i) becomes

$$d^2_{ij} < 2 \ln \left[\frac{P_D}{(1 - P_D) \, \beta \, (2\pi)^{M/2} \, \sqrt{|S_i|}} \right]$$

$$-2 \ln \left[\frac{P_{TT} + p_{ci} \, e^{-1/D_E} (1 - P_D)}{p_{ci} \, e^{-1/D_E} (1 - P_D)} \right] \tag{9.20}$$

To summarize, the gating relationships derived in (9.16), (9.18), and (9.20) all have the same form. Consider the possible assignment of observation j to track i and define the standard gate

$$G_i(1) = 2 \ln \left[\frac{P_D}{(1 - P_D) \, \beta \, (2\pi)^{M/2} \, \sqrt{|S_i|}} \right] \tag{9.21}$$

In all cases, the gating requirement on the normalized distance function is

$$d^2_{ij} < G_i(1) - \Delta G_i \overset{\Delta}{=} G_i \tag{9.22}$$

Define p_{ci} to be the probability associated with continuing track i beyond the initial point for a nonconfirmed track and beyond the scan where the maximum score was achieved for a confirmed track. Then,

$$\Delta G_i = \begin{cases} 2 \ln \left[\dfrac{r_{FN} + p_{ci} \, e^{-1/D_E} (1 - P_D)}{p_{ci} \, e^{-1/D_E}(1 - P_D)} \right], \text{ nonconfirmed track} \\[3mm] 2 \ln \left[\dfrac{P_{TT} + p_{ci} \, e^{-1/D_E} (1 - P_D)}{p_{ci} \, e^{-1/D_E}(1 - P_D)} \right], \text{ confirmed track} \end{cases} \tag{9.23}$$

where

$$r_{FN} = \beta_{FT} / \beta_{NT} = \text{ratio of false to true new targets}$$

$$P_{TT} = 1 - e^{-1/D_E} \cong \frac{1}{D_E} = \text{probability associated with track termination}$$

The usual condition for airborne radar MTT systems is that confirmation occurs after a second observation is assigned to the track. Also, for confirmed tracks the maximum (or close to the maximum) score is reached each time an observation is assigned to the track. Thus, for both tentative and confirmed tracks the usual case is that p_{ci} is given by (9.17).

Equations (9.17), (9.21), (9.22), and (9.23) define a gating relationship that includes all aspects of track quality. As track updates are missed the gate decreases through the factor $-\triangle G_i$. Also, as extrapolation time increases, the term $|S_i|$ increases so that $G_i(1)$ decreases. Thus, the final result is that the gate G_i can become small and, as discussed below, a convenient deletion criterion can be derived based upon G_i.

The normalized distance d_{ij}^2 has the chi-square distribution with M degrees of freedom (χ_M^2) where M is the measurement dimension. Thus, using standard statistical tables we can readily obtain the theoretical probability of a valid observation not satisfying the gating relationship $d_{ij}^2 < G_i$. Alternatively, the expressions given in Table 4-1 can be evaluated. Then, a convenient deletion rule is to delete a track when this probability of satisfying the gate falls below some acceptable level. Usually this can be approximated by a rule that leads to deletion upon N_D consecutive missed deletions.

While the gate decreases primarily due to missed updates and the resultant required track extrapolation, the rate at which G_i decreases is also a function of the geometry. Thus, although it is convenient and usually accurate to define the deletion criterion to be N_D consecutive missed update attempts, the value of N_D should be chosen as a function of the sampling interval and the geometry. This approach is illustrated below with an example from a typical airborne radar TWS system.

9.4.2 TWS System Gating and Deletion Example

We wish to define a simple track deletion criterion for confirmed tracks based upon N_D consecutive missed detections. A TWS system with fixed sampling interval T sec is considered. However, there are two search modes in which the system can operate so that values for T of 3.0 and 1.0 s are considered. The probability of detection (P_D) is a function of range (R). Thus, the quantity N_D should be a function of both T and R.

The approach will be to examine the behavior of the score function and the gate as computed by the adaptive system defined above. This will be used to determine the best choice of N_D for the fixed deletion criterion method.

Figure 9-3 gives a typical example of the computed gates as a function of range for the two values (1.0 and 3.0 s) of sampling interval. In order to test the deletion logic for the adaptive system and to determine the

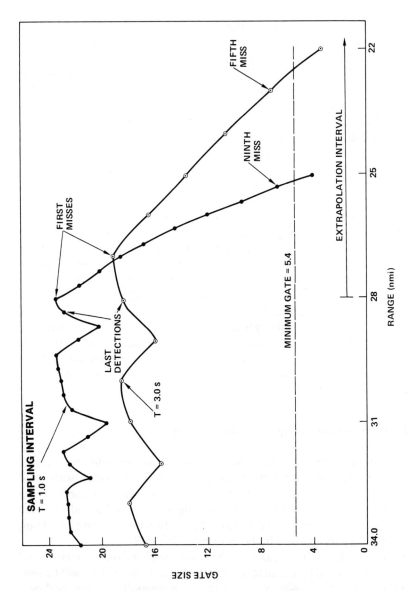

FIGURE 9-3. EXAMPLE OF GATE BEHAVIOR AND RESULTANT DELETION

corresponding number of consecutive misses for a fixed deletion criterion, the case where no detections were received after the target reached 28 nmi was simulated. A four-dimensional measurement (range, range rate, azimuth and elevation angles) was assumed and the minimum allowable gate was chosen to be 5.4.

Referring to Figure 9-3, the track deletion criterion ($G < G_{MIN} = 5.4$) occurs after five consecutive misses for the $T = 3.0$ s case and after nine consecutive misses for the $T = 1.0$ s case. Given these numbers of consecutive misses, Fig. 9-3 shows that the gate size for the next scan falls below the required minimum value of 5.4. Due to the random number sequences a missed detection occured for the $T = 1.0$ s case just before the forced extrapolation began while a detection was received for the second ($T = 3.0$ s) case just before the forced extrapolation.

Deletion occurred sooner (9.0 s after the last detection) for the shorter sampling interval but required more misses. Thus, a deletion criterion based upon either total elapsed time or number of misses alone is insufficient if consideration of the sampling interval is not included. Also, the deletion criterion was found to be a function of range, with more consecutive misses allowed at longer ranges before deletion occurred. This is due to the lower P_D (less penalty for a miss) and the smaller rate of growth of the residual covariance matrix (less target angular dynamics) at longer range.

Finally, considering typical new target and false alarm densities, the probabilitiy of false correlation, P_{FC}, as computed using (7.14), was very small ($P_{FC} \gtrsim 0.001$) for both cases until after extrapolation. Upon extrapolation, P_{FC} reached the maximum values of 0.005 for the shorter sampling interval ($T = 1.0$ s) case and 0.014 for the $T = 3.0$ s case. The rapid decrease in the gate size effectively limited P_{FC} for the assumed conditions of corruption only through false alarms and new sources. However, for closely spaced interacting target tracks the miscorrelation problem, with the assumed nearest-neighbor correlation method, would be much more severe.

9.4.3 Deletion Based on Score Function

As discussed in [1, 2], track deletion can also be defined using the score function. For a confirmed track with maximum score occuring at scan k_m the positive score $L_{i,k_m} + \ln P_{TT}$ is assured. This represents the maximum score achieved at scan k_m plus the track termination term. This score can always be achieved by terminating the track after scan k_m. Similarly, for a nonconfirmed track, the zero score associated with dissolving the track is assured. Thus, as a track degrades, with the resultant decrease in score, it is convenient to compare the present score with the maximum assured score that could be obtained by track deletion. For a confirmed track, the decision would be to terminate the track retroactive to scan k_m. A nonconfirmed track would be dissolved with all observations taken to be derived from independent one-point sources.

Figure 9-4 shows the behavior of the score function for the $T = 1.0$ s case of the example given in the previous section. The score function is shown to increase, after an update occurs, on the last scan before the extrapolation occurs. Then, as misses occur the score function drops rapidly and after five consecutive misses the score falls below the maximum assured value, which for this case (using $D_E = 60$ scans) is

$$L_{i,k_m} + \ln P_{TT} = 200.5 - 4.1 = 196.4$$

However, results have shown that, for the purposes of track deletion, an increment ΔL_L should be added to the score function to account for a potential loss due to premature track deletion. As shown in Fig. 9-4, adding ΔL_L to the present score gives the anticipated score that might occur in the next scan if the track is not deleted and a correlating observation is received.

The recommended value for ΔL_L is given by

$$\Delta L_L = -\frac{.1}{D_E} + \ln \left[\frac{P_D}{\beta_{FT} (2\pi)^{M/2} \sqrt{|S|}} \right] - \frac{\bar{d}^2}{2} - \ln \left[\frac{\beta}{\beta_{FT}} \right]$$

$$= -\frac{1}{D_E} + \ln \left[\frac{P_D}{\beta (2\pi)^{M/2} \sqrt{|S|}} \right] - \frac{\bar{d}^2}{2} \tag{9.24}$$

Referring to (9.24), the term $\bar{d}^2/2$ represents the expected normalized distance associated with a potential update. For the case of a four-dimensional measurement, $\bar{d}^2/2$ is 2 (since d^2 has the χ_4^2 distribution). Also, the term $\ln [\beta/\beta_{FT}]$ represents the score that would have been derived if the potential track update were designated to be a new source.

Referring again to Fig. 9-4, after nine consecutive misses the value of the score function plus the premature deletion loss term ΔL_L finally falls below the deletion threshold. Thus, referring also to Fig. 9-3, the same deletion criterion (nine consecutive misses) results for the criteria based on the gate size and the score function. The criteria were also found to agree for the case with the $T = 3.0$ s sampling interval.

9.4.4 Comparison with a Standard Approach

Reference [1] compared performance which was derived using a sequential score function approach, similar to that derived above, with performance

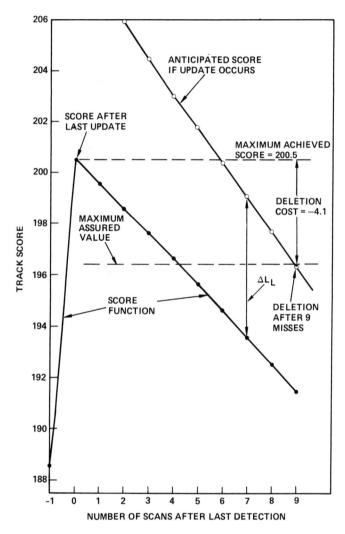

FIGURE 9-4. DELETION BASED UPON SCORE FUNCTION

derived using a more standard technique. The standard technique used fixed parameters, such as rectangular gates set at the three-standard-deviation level, and fixed confirmation and deletion criteria. The sampling interval was taken to be 1.0 s. Table 9-2 summarizes typical comparative results taken from [1].

Table 9-2 shows the probability of false decision ($P_{FD} = 1 - P_{CD}$) and the expected deletion time. Results are shown for tracks formed on a single true target and on false alarms (false tracks). Results were based upon 1000 Monte Carlo runs that provided over 10,000 decision opportunities. Thus, the three-standard-deviation confidence limits on the computed P_{FD} are about ± 0.0025 for the case of a true target track. The expected deletion time refers to the time required to delete a true target track after the target was taken to be no longer producing detections and the time required to delete a track initiated on a false alarm. Finally, the probability of premature track deletion was found to be about the same for both methods.

Referring to Table 9-2, the score function method led to distinct decreases in the probabilities of false decision and the time required to delete false target tracks and true target tracks which are no longer active. The results were somewhat less significant for a less difficult case that was also examined in [1].

TABLE 9-2
COMPARATIVE FALSE DECISION PROBABILITIES (P_{FD})
AND TRACK DELETION TIMES

	True Target Track		*False Alarm Track*	
	P_{FD}	Average Deletion Time(s)*	P_{FD}	Average Deletion Time(s)
Method Using Score Function	0.061	4.32	0.122	3.13
Standard Method	0.091	5.70	0.167	4.60

*Time after true target track terminates.

9.5 EXTENSION TO MULTIPLE OBSERVATION-TO-TRACK CORRELATIONS

Logic has been developed to define necessary conditions (gates) for observation-to-track pairing in a sequential system. However, in a multiple-target environment, there may be many conflicting pairings that satisfy these necessary conditions. Ideally, these conflict situations should be handled by deferring decision until more data are received. This ideal approach requires the use of branching or multiple hypothesis tracking methods as discussed in the next chapter. Here, we complete discussion of the suboptimal nearest-neighbor sequential approach.

Assuming that computational requirements dictate that a purely sequential nearest-neighbor correlation approach be taken, the multiple observation/multiple track conflict situation is typically handled by use of a correlation (or assignment) matrix. We will define an assignment matrix for use in resolving conflicts that is consistent with the relationships developed above. Once the elements are defined, the solution is reduced to that of the classical assignment problem (discussed in Chapters 4 and 14) with the goal of assigning observations to tracks in such a way as to maximize the total score.

The form of the assignment matrix is general for any number of observations and any number of existing tracks. Assume there are n tracks (some may be potential or tentative) and that s observations are received. Only those observation-to-track correlations which satisfy the gating criterion of (9.22) are allowable. Then, a two-dimensional matrix is formed with track number ($i = 1, 2, \ldots, I$) along the vertical axis and observation number ($j = 1, 2, \ldots, J$) along the horizontal axis. The elements of the matrix (p_{ij}) represent the probabilities associated with assigning observation j to track i.

Some of the possible assignments are not allowed because of the gating considerations discussed above. For these pairings some arbitrarily small probability may be used for the appropriate matrix elements so that a nonallowable correlation is denoted by X. Also, a no-track row and a no-observation column are included in the matrix. Thus,

I = total number of rows = $n + 1$
J = total number of columns = $s + 1$

Figure 9-5 shows a typical assignment matrix for n and s where both are 3. The values for n and s, however, might be anything, including 1. Referring to Fig. 9-5, we now define the elements. First, using a development similar to that leading to the gating relationships of (9.16) through (9.20), the elements p_{ij}, associated with assigning observation j to track i, are

$$p_{ij} = p_{ci}\, P_D\, g_{ij}\, e^{-\frac{1}{D_E}} \qquad (9.25)$$

Similarly, the probability associated with choosing no observation for assignment to track i is

$$p_{iJ} = \begin{cases} r_{FN} + p_{ci}\, e^{-1/D_E}\, (1 - P_D) \text{ , nonconfirmed tracks} \\ P_{TT} + p_{ci}\, e^{-1/D_E}\, (1 - P_D) \text{ , confirmed tracks} \end{cases} \qquad (9.26)$$

Finally, the probability associated with assigning an observation to no track

OBSERVATIONS (j)			
TRACKS (i)	y_1	y_2	y_3	NO OBSERVATION
T1	P_{11}	X	P_{13}	P_{14}
T2	X	P_{22}	X	P_{24}
T3	P_{31}	P_{32}	X	P_{34}
NEW SOURCE	β	β	β	X

FIGURE 9-5. EXAMPLE OF CORRELATION MATRIX
BEFORE MODIFICATION

is the probability that the observation is from a new source:

$$p_{Ij} = \beta_{FT} + \beta_{NT} = \beta$$

The probabilities given in (9.25) and (9.26) can be derived by first noting that p_{ci} is defined to be the probability associated with continuing track i beyond the initial point for a nonconfirmed track and beyond the scan where the maximum score was achieved for a confirmed track. Then, the additional term $(P_D g_{ij} e^{-1/D_E})$ in (9.25) represents the probability associated with update of track i with observation j.

Given that track update does not occur, the probability term p_{iJ} of (9.26) is the sum of probabilities representing two possible events. First, the term $p_{ci} e^{-1/D_E}(1 - P_D)$ represents the probability associated with track continuation given that no observation is assigned. The term P_{TT} represents the probabilitiy associated with the second alternative, track deletion, for a confirmed track. The term $r_{FN} = \beta_{FT}/\beta_{NT}$ represents the likelihood that the initial point was a false target and is associated with the option to dissolve a nonconfirmed track. Finally, note that all probability expressions have been divided by the probability β_{NT} that the initial point of the track was from a true target.

The problem is to assign the observations (y_j) to tracks (or to the no-track option) so that the product of the probabilities associated with the assignments is maximized. For example, from Fig. 9-5, one possible combination of assignments gives y_1 to $T1$ and y_2 to $T3$. This leaves y_3 declared to be a new source and $T2$ with no observation. The associated probability is the product $p_{11} p_{32} \beta p_{24}$.

As illustrated above, the probabilities associated with the various assignment options consist of products of the individual assignment probabilities.

The optimal solution is to examine all possible combinations which satisfy the gating conditions and to choose that combination with the highest probability. An equivalent solution is to take logarithms of all the individual probabilities and to choose that solution which maximizes the sum of the logarithms of the individual probabilities. Note that by taking logarithms we have returned to the score function formulation.

As a first step in simplifying the correlation matrix, we take the logarithm of all the elements and define:

$$c'_{ij} = \ln p_{ij}, \quad c'_{iJ} = \ln p_{iJ}$$
$$c'_{Ij} = \ln p_{Ij} = \ln \beta$$

Continuing simplification of the assignment matrix, we note that any value can be subtracted from all elements in a given column of all elements in a given row without changing the solution. This is because there must be an assignment made for each observation and each track. Therefore, adding a constant value to each element in a given row (or in a given column) will not change the relative rating of the various options which will all include this increment. Thus, first we subtract $c'_{Ij} = \ln \beta$ from all elements in the matrix for $j < J$. Then, we subtract c'_{iJ} from each element in all rows $i = 1, \ldots, n$. Finally, we multiply all elements by the factor 2. The remaining non-zero elements are found, after some manipulations using (9.25) and (9.26), to be

$$c_{ij} = 2 [\ln p_{ij} - \ln \beta - \ln p_{iJ}]$$

$$= 2 \ln \left[\frac{P_D}{(1 - P_D) \beta (2\pi)^{M/2} \sqrt{|S_i|}} \right] - d^2_{ij} - \Delta G_i \tag{9.27}$$

where ΔG_i is defined by (9.23).

Using Equations (9.21), (9.22), and (9.27), the non-zero matrix elements are

$$c_{ij} = G_i - d^2_{ij}$$

The elements in the last row (c_{Ij}) and the last column (c_{iJ}) are zero. Figure 9-6 shows the modified matrix.

Figure 9-7 gives an example for the solution of the modified correlation matrix with hypothetical numerical values based on the example given in Table 7-2. We assume three observations and three tracks. Also, for simplicity, assume that all three tracks are confirmed and that $P_{TT} \ll P_{ci}$ so that $\Delta G_i \sim 0$. Then, for this two-dimensional measurement ($M = 2$) example, the parameter values (assuming $\beta_{NT} \cong 0$) are taken to be

$$\beta = P_{FA} = 10^{-4}, \quad P_D = 0.69, \quad \sigma_{\tilde{x}} = \sigma_{\tilde{y}} = 10$$

OBSERVATIONS			
TRACKS	y_1	y_2	y_3	NO OBSERVATION
T1	c_{11}	X	c_{13}	0
T2	X	c_{22}	X	0
T3	c_{31}	c_{32}	X	0
NEW SOURCE	0	0	0	X

$$c_{ij} = G_i - d^2_{ij}$$

FIGURE 9-6. EXAMPLE OF CORRELATION MATRIX AFTER FIRST MODIFICATION

OBSERVATIONS			
TRACKS	y_1	y_2	y_3	NO OBSERVATION
T1	6	X	2	0
T2	X	4	X	0
T3	3	5	X	0
NEW SOURCE	0	0	0	X

FIGURE 9-7. NUMERICAL EXAMPLE OF ASSIGNMENT MATRIX

Thus, as computed in Table 7-2, G is approximately 7.

Hypothetical values for the d^2_{ij} for which the gating relationship is satisfied are

$$d^2_{11} = 1, \quad d^2_{13} = 5, \quad d^2_{22} = 3, \quad d^2_{31} = 4, \quad d^2_{32} = 2$$

Using $G = 7$ and the values for d^2_{ij} given above leads to the assignment matrix given in Fig. 9-7. Note that the assignments are now made in such a way as to maximize the associated score. The solution that achieves this is y_1 to $T1$, y_2 to $T3$ and y_3 to a new source. The summed score for this solution is 11, while the score for the solution (y_1 to $T3$, y_2 to $T2$ and y_3 to $T1$) assigning all observations to existing tracks is 9.

For the purpose of solution by the optimal assignment algorithm, the assignment matrix is modified by one more step. First, the last (no observation) column is eliminated. Then, a row is added for each observation to represent the assignment of that observation to a new track. Figure 9-8 shows the final assignment matrix form. Unfortunately, the addition of the extra rows makes the solution of the assignment matrix more complex.

OBSERVATIONS			
TRACKS	y_1	y_2	y_3
T1	c_{11}	c_{12}	c_{13}
T2	c_{21}	c_{22}	c_{23}
T3	c_{31}	c_{32}	c_{33}
NEW TRACK 1	0	X	X
NEW TRACK 2	X	0	X
NEW TRACK 3	X	X	0

FIGURE 9-8. FINAL FORM OF ASSIGNMENT MATRIX FOR SOLUTION USING OPTIMAL ASSIGNMENT ALGORITHM

9.6 SUMMARY

An expression has been derived for the optimal (most likely) partitioning of observations into tracks. This expression leads to considerable insight into the data association problem. First, this expression consists of terms whereby each has physical significance relative to the elements (initiation, length, missed observations, and received observations) of track formation. Also, this expression leads directly to a sequential processing algorithm in which track initiation and deletion, gating, and an assignment matrix are defined in a mathematical manner. This contrasts with the *ad hoc* definition of these functions which frequently occurs.

The derived gating expressions show how the gate should adapt to track quality. As track quality degrades the gate should decrease so that a minimum gate size criterion is convenient for determining when to delete a track. The elements of the assignment matrix (for use in resolving multiple observation/ multiple track conflict situations) now become the difference between the gate and the normalized distance. Finally, results derived in order to compare the score function-based sequential approach described above and a more standard method were favorable to the score function approach.

Inherent limitations exist for the sequential nearest-neighbor approach, regardless of the implementation. Thus, as computational capabilities increase, the emphasis will shift towards more accurate methods. The next chapter discusses two of these methods.

REFERENCES

1. Stein, J.J., and S.S. Blackman, "Generalized Correlation of Multi-Target Track Data," *IEEE Transactions on Aerospace and Electronic Systems*, AES-11, Nov. 1975, pp. 1207–1217.
2. Sittler, R.W., "An Optimal Data Association Problem in Surveillance Theory," *IEEE Transactions on Military Electronics*, MIL-8, April 1964, pp. 125–139.
3. Morefield, C.L., "Application of 0-1 Integer Programming to Multitarget Tracking Problems," *IEEE Transactions on Automatic Control*, AC-22, June 1977, pp. 302–312.
4. Reid, D.B., "An Algorithm for Tracking Multiple Targets," *IEEE Transactions on Automatic Control*, AC-24, Dec. 1979, pp. 843–854.
5. Trunk, G.V., and J.D. Wilson, "Track Initiation of Occasionally Unresolved Radar Targets," *IEEE Transactions on Aerospace and Electronic Systems*, AES-17, Jan. 1981, pp. 122–130.
6. Sea, R.G., "Optimal Correlation of Sensor Data with Tracks in Surveillance Systems," *Proceedings of the Sixth Conference on System Sciences*, Honolulu, HI, Jan. 1973, pp. 424–426.

Chapter 10

The Bayesian Probabilistic Approach

10.1 INTRODUCTION

This chapter summarizes two important methods for data association that have been developed based upon use of the *a posteriori* probability as calculated using Bayes' rule. These techniques are computationally involved and go beyond the simpler approaches discussed in previous chapters. However, they represent the direction in which future MTT system design will proceed as improved computational capabilities are utilized.

Bayes' rule may be written, for our application, as

$$P(H_i|D) = \frac{P(D|H_i)\,P(H_i)}{P(D)} \tag{10.1}$$

where H_i is identified as a hypothesis concerning the origin of received measurement data. This hypothesis will, in general, contain some groupings of observations into tracks and the identification of other observations to be false alarms. Also, D is defined to be the most recently received data set. Then,

$P(H_i)$ = *a priori* (before the reception of data set D) probability that hypothesis H_i is correct

$P(D|H_i)$ = probability of receiving D given H_i

$P(H_i|D)$ = *a posteriori* (after the reception of data set D) probability of H_i

$P(D)$ = $\sum_i P(D|H_i)P(H_i)$ = probability of receiving data set D

Also, note that $P(D)$ is effectively just a normalizing constant so that the computation of $P(H_i|D)$ is given by

$$P'(H_i|\mathrm{D}) = P(D|H_i)\,P(H_i)$$

and $\tag{10.2}$

$$P(H_i|\mathrm{D}) = \frac{P'(H_i|\mathrm{D})}{\sum_i P'(H_i|D)}$$

Finally, the *a posteriori* probability, $P(H_l|D)$, becomes the *a priori* probability for use upon receipt of the next data set.

Equation (10.1), or equivalently (10.2), provides a convenient recursive means for computing the probabilities that the various hypotheses concerning the origin of the received data are correct. Using the recursive nature of the solution, the probability of a given data-association hypothesis is obtained from $P(H_l)$. Then, after each data set is received, the *a posteriori* probabilities, $P(H_l|D)$, are computed from $P(H_l)$ and the probability, $P(D|H_l)$, of receiving the data D given H_l. Finally the *a posteriori* probabilities, $P(H_l|D)$, become the *a priori* probabilities, $P(H_l)$, when the next data set is received. This is a more formalized representation of the branching process discussed in Chapter 4, and it assures the consistency of the data-association hypotheses.

In effect, this approach allows a modified version of batch processing to be performed. Whenever difficult correlation decisions arise, a final decision is postponed and alternative hypotheses, H_l, are formed and re-evaluated when later data are received. Thus, use of later measurements is allowed to aid in evaluating difficult prior correlation decisions.

The approach outlined above is referred to as multiple hypothesis tracking (MHT) and an early formulation was given by Singer, Sea, and Housewright [1]. However, the authors only considered a single target in clutter and did not address the problem of track initiation. Allowing for multiple targets and for new track initiation can lead to complex bookkeeping and to a rapid growth in the number of hypotheses formed.

Fortunately, Reid has presented [2,3] a structure (denoted Reid's algorithm) which makes MHT appear feasible in the light of expected increases in computational capabilities. The next section outlines a MHT tracking technique based on Reid's algorithm and an approach developed by Chong [4]. Chapter 14 will discuss a particular implementation in more detail.

Most of the correlation techniques previously discussed in this book have been based on the nearest-neighbor approach where, at most, a single observation is assigned to a given track and observations are assigned, at most, to one track. The MHT method basically pursues this approach, but may hold in abeyance the final decision as to which single observations are to be assigned to which single tracks. An alternative approach, the joint probabilistic data association (JPDA) method [5,6,7] incorporates all observations within the neighborhood of the predicted target position to update the position estimate using an *a posteriori* probability weighted sum of residuals.

The JPDA method, which is summarized in Section 10.3, is an alternative method also based on Bayes' rule. Again, various hypotheses regarding the origin of received data are formed, but the final decisions as to the track parameters are made sequentially. Hypotheses are immediately combined so that no decisions are held in abeyance. All track uncertainty is modeled in the track covariance matrices for this method.

10.2 MULTIPLE HYPOTHESIS TRACKING

For most MTT applications there will at any given time be a number of plausible ways to partition observation data into tracks and false targets (false alarms). If the standard sequential processing approach is taken, the most likely combination will be chosen after each data set is received. However, using the multiple hypothesis tracking (MHT) approach, a number of candidate hypotheses will be generated and evaluated later as more data are received. Thus, the capability of using later measurements to aid prior correlation decisions is allowed. However, the method is recursive so that data sets only need be processed as they are received.

As an example of MHT implementation, consider the hypothesis $(H_{l'})$ concerning the origin of previous data. Also, define $P(H_{l'})$ to be the probability that $H_{l'}$ is correct. Now, consider what happens when a new data set is received. For simplicity, consider the receipt of a single observation and, in addition, assume there are $N_{l'}$ tracks presently included in $H_{l'}$. For this case, the single hypothesis $H_{l'}$ can generate up to $N_{l'} + 2$ hypotheses (denoted H_l), representing the possible assignment of the observation to each of the prior $N_{l'}$ tracks plus the identification of the observation to be a new target or a false alarm. This number, however, may be decreased through the use of gating.

Next, the associated probabilities, $P(H_l)$, are calculated using the expressions derived in Chapter 9. There are three alternative types of new hypotheses whose probabilities are computed using Bayes' rule:

(1) The observation is a false target and no reports were generated by the N_l' tracks

$$P(H_l) = \frac{\beta_{FT}(1-P_D)^{N_l'}}{C} P(H_{l'}) \tag{10.3a}$$

(2) The observation (denoted observation j) comes for the ith track included in the prior hypothesis

$$P(H_l) = \frac{(1-P_D)^{N_l'-1} P_D g_{ij}}{C} P(H_{l'}) \tag{10.3b}$$

(3) The observation is from a new target

$$P(H_l) = \frac{\beta_{NT}(1-P_D)^{N_l'}}{C} P(H_{l'}) \tag{10.3c}$$

Here, g_{ij} is the Gaussian density (likelihood) function associated with the assignment of the jth observation to the ith track of H_l',

$$g_{ij} = \frac{e^{-\frac{d_{ij}^2}{2}}}{(2\pi)^{M/2} \sqrt{|S_i|}}$$

The terms d_{ij}^2 and $|S_i|$ are the normalized distance function and the determinant of the residual matrix (Chapter 4), respectively and C is the normalizing constant.

The expressions given in (10.3) do not include the track deletion option. The manner in which track deletion can be included in the MHT formulation will be discussed later. Also, the factor, e^{-1/D_ε}, associated with extending the track life will be omitted. This factor typically can be approximated by unity.

The growth of hypotheses must be limited if the implementation is to be feasible. The first opportunity for limiting hypotheses is to require an observation to satisfy a gating relationship, such as discussed in Chapters 4 and 9, before any of the N_l' track associations are considered to be potentially valid. This, in general, will lead to an introduction, in (10.3b), of the factor P_{Gi} giving the probability that a valid observation will fall within the gate of the ith track. However, since P_G is usually large ($P_G \cong 1$), it will be approximated by unity.

Second, there must be a "pruning" method to eliminate low probability hypotheses. A third simplifying approach is to combine hypotheses whose effects are similar. For example, when considering the hypotheses associated with a single track, Reference [1] defined the N-scan memory filter whereby those track hypotheses that contain the same observation from the present scan, and for which the N previous (not including the present) observation-to-track associations are the same, are combined. For our purposes, it is more convenient to define N-scan algorithms as those that combine hypotheses (or the associated tracks) in which the last N (including the present) observation-to-track associations are the same. Another technique is to combine hypotheses with the same number of tracks if the tracks pass some measure of similarity based upon the state estimates and covariances.

Reid [2] introduced the concept of clustering of hypotheses. Using this method of simplification, hypotheses that do not interact are considered separately. This method reduces the number of probability calculations that must be performed by effectively breaking a large problem into a set of smaller ones which are solved in parallel. The concepts of pruning, combining, and clustering hypotheses will be discussed in more detail below.

Figure 10-1 gives an overview of MHT logic implementation. Hypotheses are formed as data are received. Hypotheses consist of tracks whose state estimates are updated, usually with standard Kalman filtering techniques,

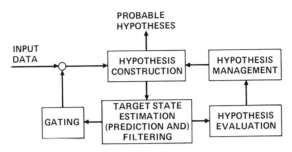

FIGURE 10-1. OVERVIEW OF MULTIPLE HYPOTHESIS
TRACKING LOGIC

as new data are received. The state estimates and covariances are used to form gates so that when the next data set is received the generation of very unlikely hypotheses can be avoided. Additional hypothesis evaluation and management techniques (such as pruning, combining, and clustering) are also required to limit the number of hypotheses.

As in previous developments, assume that a single true target generates no more than one report. Further, assume that the report data sets are ordered correctly in time. We initially consider only the most common type of sensor, the type 1 sensor, such as a radar, for which the lack of a detection in a given region can be used to infer, through the term $(1 - P_D)$, that there is no target within that region. However, the modification for a type 2 sensor, where the lack of a detection may not imply the absence of a target, is straightforward.

An example of a type 2 sensor is the radar warning receiver that can only detect target presence when the target is transmitting. For this type of sensor the lack of a target detection does not necessarily imply that a target is not present. (It may just not be using its transmitting radar.) Thus, as discussed below, the factor $1 - P_D$ does not enter the probability calculations when no target detection occurs with the type 2 sensor.

10.2.1   The Hypothesis Tree

Central to the MHT approach is the formation of a hypothesis tree. This concept is illustrated with a standard example in which two sets of data each containing two observations are received. Figure 10-2 illustrates the formation of a hypothesis tree. The notation is

FA: observation taken to be a false alarm;
$NT1$: observation initiates the new track number 1. Thereafter, the track is referred to as $T1$;
$T1$:   observation associated with existing track 1.

Using standard MHT implementation techniques, the numbering system will be a measurement-oriented scheme in the sense that hypotheses are formulated based on possible alternatives for the measurements. This is in contrast to other approaches, such as the branching scheme discussed in Chapter 4, in which the numbering is track-oriented.

To illustrate the technique for hypothesis tree formation, we will go through each step of the example shown in Fig. 10-2. First, denoting $y_j(k)$ to be the $j$ith observation received on scan k, observations $y_1(1)$ and $y_2(1)$ can either be labeled as false alarms (FA) or new tracks ($NT1, NT2$). Thus, after the first observation is received there are just two branches with hypotheses as defined

$$H_1 : y_1(1) = FA, H_2 : y_1(1) \text{ becomes } NT1$$

It is very important to define an efficient scheme for numbering and recording hypotheses and tracks as they are formed. Following [2,3], such an approach is developed below. First, it is always possible that the observation may be declared a false alarm. Only for this option will each hypothesis and each track retain their previous number. Thus, for the example above, upon receipt of observation $y_2(1)$ we first have that H_1 and H_2 become

$$H_1: y_1(1) = FA, \; y_2(1) = FA$$
$$H_2: y_1(1) = NT1, \; y_2(1) = FA$$

Next, the observation is considered for correlation with existing tracks. However, since no tracks existed prior to the receipt of the initial observations, $y_j(1)$, and since the observation cannot correlate with $NT1$ (because we assumed that a single target produces no more than one observation per scan), no associations with existing tracks are allowed at this time. Finally, the option to allow the observation to start a new track must be considered so that two more hypotheses are created:

$$H_3: y_1(1) = FA, \; y_2(1) = NT2$$
$$H_4: y_1(1) = NT1, \; y_2(1) = NT2$$

Even for the simple example considered so far, it can be seen that an identical track will often appear in more than one hypothesis. Thus, for example, $NT1$ appears in both H_2 and H_4. It would be computationally inefficient to process the same track over again for each hypothesis as observations are considered for association with the various hypotheses. Thus, another indexing scheme must be developed in order to cross reference which hypotheses contain what tracks and which tracks are contained within what hypotheses. To implement the required cross referencing and other data manipulations associated with MHT, it may be best to use a computer

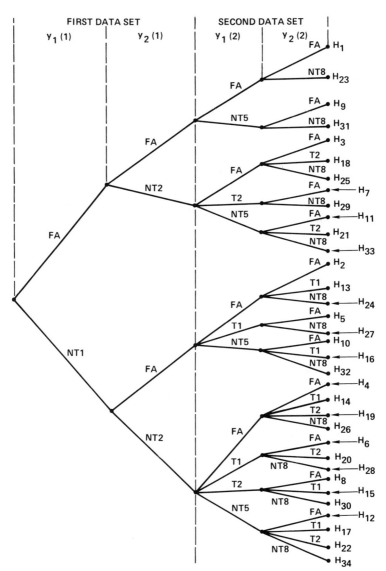

FIGURE 10-2. HYPOTHESIS TREE REPRESENTATION

language, such as PASCAL, that provides more general data types and more extensive data structures ([8]; *see* also Chapter 14). Also, it may be noted that the language, Ada, designed to be used for development of future military systems, has these appropriate data structures.

To continue, consider the first observation $y_1(2)$ from the second data set. Again, we first allow the option for $y_1(2)$ to be a false alarm. Thus, the continuation of the first four hypotheses becomes

H_1: $y_1(1) = FA$, $y_2(1) = FA$, $y_1(2) = FA$
H_2: $y_1(1) = NT1$, $y_2(1) = FA$, $y_1(2) = FA$
H_3: $y_1(1) = FA$, $y_2(1) = NT2$, $y_1(2) = FA$
H_4: $y_1(1) = NT1$, $y_2(1) = NT2$, $y_1(2) = FA$

Next, assuming that the gating relationships are satisfied, consider the potential association of $y_1(2)$ with tracks $T1$ and $T2$. Since $T1$ is contained in the previous hypotheses H_2' and H_4' (note that primes (') refer to the previous ordering), we have two more current hypotheses linking $y_1(2)$ with $T1$. Also, with the inclusion of $y_1(2)$, track $T1$ must be redefined to be $T3$ (since $T1$ may also be used to link with $y_2(2)$). Thus, the next two current hypotheses are

H_5: $y_1(1) = NT1$, $y_2(1) = FA$, $y_1(2) \rightarrow T1 = T3$
H_6: $y_1(1) = NT1$, $y_2(1) = NT2$, $y_1(2) \rightarrow T1 = T3$

Similarly, for the two options to assign $y_1(2)$ to $T2$,

H_7: $y_1(1) = FA$, $y_2(1) = NT2$, $y_1(2) \rightarrow T2 = T4$
H_8: $y_1(1) = NT1$, $y_2(1) = NT2$, $y_1(2) \rightarrow T2 = T4$

Finally, the hypotheses associated with the new track option are

H_9: $y_1(1) = FA$, $y_2(1) = FA$, $y_1(2) = NT5$
H_{10}: $y_1(1) = NT1$, $y_2(1) = FA$, $y_1(2) = NT5$
H_{11}: $y_1(1) = FA$, $y_2(1) = NT2$, $y_1(2) = NT5$
H_{12}: $y_1(1) = NT1$, $y_2(1) = NT2$, $y_1(2) = NT5$

As shown in Fig. 10-2, the process continues with observation $y_2(2)$.

Next, we introduce a compact representation to simplify recording the data permutations. Following the method of Reid [2], Table 10-1 gives this representation for our example. Each row represents a single hypothesis, which, in this notation, is a series of track numbers to which the observations are assigned. There is one column for each observation. The track numbers are the previous track numbers and the numbers in parentheses are the numbers that the tracks are given after the observations are assigned. The number 0 refers to the false target (or false alarm) assignment.

Table 10-1
Representation of Hypothesis Matrix

Hypothesis Number	First Data Set		Second Data Set		Track Numbers Contained in Hypothesis
	$y_1(1)$	$y_2(1)$	$y_1(2)$	$y_2(2)$	
1	0	0	0	0	0
2	1	0	0	0	1
3	0	2	0	0	2
4	1	2	0	0	1,2
5	1	0	1(3)	0	3
6	1	2	1(3)	0	2,3
7	0	2	2(4)	0	4
8	1	2	2(4)	0	1,4
9	0	0	5	0	5
10	1	0	5	0	1,5
11	0	2	5	0	2,5
12	1	2	5	0	1,2,5
13	1	0	0	1(6)	6
14	1	2	0	1(6)	2,6
15	1	2	2(4)	1(6)	4,6
16	1	0	5	1(6)	5,6
17	1	2	5	1(6)	2,5,6
18	0	2	0	2(7)	7
19	1	2	0	2(7)	1,7
20	1	2	1(3)	2(7)	3,7
21	0	2	5	2(7)	5,7
22	1	2	5	2(7)	1,5,7
23	0	0	0	8	8
24	1	0	0	8	1,8
25	0	2	0	8	2,8
26	1	2	0	8	1,2,8
27	1	0	1(3)	8	3,8
28	1	2	1(3)	8	2,3,8
29	0	2	2(4)	8	4,8
30	1	2	2(4)	8	1,4,8
31	0	0	5	8	5,8
32	1	0	5	8	1,5,8
33	0	2	5	8	2,5,8
34	1	2	5	8	1,2,5,8

To summarize, the eight tracks that were formed are defined below in terms of the component observations. Tracks can contain two observations at most. For those tracks that do contain two observations, the component observations are defined within the brackets.

(i) *One Point Tracks*

$$T1 = y_1(1), \quad T2 = y_2(1)$$
$$T5 = y_1(2), \quad T8 = y_2(2)$$

(ii) *Two Point Tracks*

$$T3 = [y_1(1), y_1(2)], \quad T4 = [y_2(1), y_1(2)]$$
$$T6 = [y_1(1), y_2(2)], \quad T7 = [y_2(1), y_2(2)]$$

As shown in Fig. 10-2 and Table 10-1, 34 hypotheses result from these two small data sets, but there are only eight tracks. To illustrate the potential rapid growth of the number of hypotheses, the addition of one more data set with two observations increases the potential number of hypotheses to over 500 [4]. Clearly the growth of the hypothesis tree must be limited. The probability calculations required for ranking and pruning hypotheses are discussed next.

10.2.2 Hypothesis Probability Calculations

By extending the relationships given by (10.3), a method is obtained for updating the probabilities associated with the hypotheses that include the new data set. First, assuming that all tracks have the same probability of detection, (P_D), the probabilities, $P(H_i')$, for all prior hypotheses are multiplied by the factor $(1-P_D)^{N_i}$. This represents the condition where none of the prior tracks is assigned an observation. This assumes that all tracks are illuminated and that a type 1 sensor is used. The factor $(1-P_D)$ would not be applied to tracks that are not within the scan volume, nor when using a type 2 sensor for which a nondetection does not imply the absence of a target.

Next, each branch that hypothesizes a new target is multiplied by the new target density β_{NT}. Similarly, a factor β_{FT} multiplies the prior probabilities for hypothesis branches that assume a false target. Also, for each branch that assigns the jth observation to the ith track of the prior hypotheses the factor

$$\frac{g_{ij}}{(1-P_D)}$$

multiplies the prior probabilities. Thus, a relatively simple probability update process occurs. The final step is to normalize the probabilities of each branch by dividing the previously computed probability by the sum of the probabilities from all branches. This calculation is performed in order to provide the probabilities typically required for the pruning and combining operations discussed next.

An alternative computational method is to use the logarithm of the above probability (or the related score function). Then, using the methods discussed in Chapter 9, the score associated with each track can be computed. Finally, the total score associated with a hypothesis is the sum of the scores from all the tracks contained within the hypothesis. Chapter 14 will discuss in more detail an implementation based on use of this score function.

Using the logarithm of the probability prevents the problem of computer underflows associated with potentially small probabilities. However, before the pruning hypothesis management technique (discussed next) is used, it may be convenient to convert from the logarithms (or score functions) back to probabilities.

10.2.3 Pruning Hypotheses

The manner in which branches are eliminated (or pruned) from the hypothesis tree is, like many issues in MTT, highly dependent upon the application. One technique is to remove hypotheses with probabilities that fall below some fixed predetermined threshold. A disadvantage of this type of pruning is that it does not take into consideration the computational resources. For example, branches may be pruned even if there are fewer hypotheses than the system can easily tolerate.

Another approach to pruning, called the breadth approach, is to allow only a predetermined fixed number (M) of hypotheses to be maintained. This technique involves ranking the hypotheses and choosing only the M most likely, as measured either by the probabilities or the score functions. A similar method is to rank and sum the probabilities of the more likely hypotheses. When this sum exceeds a threshold the remaining hypotheses are then deleted.

Pruning methods based upon ranking require a large amount of computation time to order the hypotheses at each frame. Thus, from a computational point of view, the threshold method may be preferable.

The extreme case of pruning is the standard sequential approach where only the most likely hypothesis is maintained. The type of pruning to be used is probably best chosen upon experimentation with the particular application. Further discussion of pruning is given in Chapter 14.

10.2.4   Combining Hypotheses

As data are accumulated certain hypotheses may tend to become similar. For example, two hypotheses might differ only with regard to correlation uncertainties that occurred several scans ago. Then, if the tracks involved in the previous correlation uncertainties have received the same recent updates, the past data associations (from several scans prior) may no longer be important and the hypotheses can be combined.

The technique recommended by Reid [2] is to combine hypotheses with similar effects. This is accomplished by first determining which hypotheses have the same number of tracks. Then, it must be determined if each track in one hypothesis has a corresponding track that is similar to it in the other hypothesis. There are basically two approaches for determining if track pairs are similar.

The first technique for determining track similarity is the N-scan approach in which (by the definition used in this book) tracks that have data points from the last N data scans in common are combined. For example, if N is chosen to be two, all tracks with the same observations from the last two scans would be considered similar.

Figure 10-3 illustrates a crossing target condition where the continuous lines represent tracks ($T1$, $T2$) from hypothesis one and the dashed lines represent tracks ($T3$, $T4$) from hypothesis two. The one-scan ($N=1$) approach would combine these hypotheses since the track pairs ($T1$, $T3$) and ($T2$, $T4$) both have common data points from the last scan. However, the velocity and acceleration estimates for the elements of these track pairs may be quite different even though the last data point is common. Thus, if the N-scan criterion is used to determine similarity it seems apparent that the

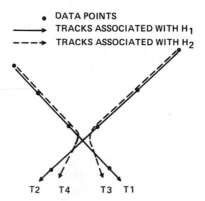

FIGURE 10-3. CROSSING TARGET DATA ASSOCIATION PROBLEM

choice must be $N \geqq 2$. Finally, it should be noted that only those tracks which received updating measurements on the last N scans can be directly determined to be similar. However, the logic is readily extended to include tracks that have the last N observations in common, even though these observations may not have been received consecutively on the last N scans.

The alternative track similarity criterion recommended by Reid [3] is to compare the track state distributions. The track distributions basically should contain all of the included measurement information. Reference [3] recommends the following tests, using both state estimates and covariance quantities, for comparing target track A of one hypothesis with target track B of another hypothesis. Similarity is declared if:

$$| x_{Ai} - x_{Bi} | \leqq \beta \sqrt{p_{Aii} + p_{Bii}} \tag{10.4}$$

and

$$p_{Aii} < \gamma p_{Bii} , \quad p_{Bii} < \gamma p_{Aii}$$

where i is indexed over all the estimation states. Reference [3] recommends typical values of $\beta = 0.1$ and $\gamma = 2.0$.

Once it has been determined that hypotheses can be combined, each track pair can be combined using the formulas [3]:

$$x = \frac{p_1 x_A + p_2 x_B}{p_1 + p_2} \tag{10.5}$$

with covariance matrix P written thusly,

$$P = \frac{p_1 P_A + p_2 P_B + \dfrac{p_1 p_2}{p_1 + p_2} (x_A - x_B)(x_A - x_B)^T}{p_1 + p_2}$$

where p_1 and p_2 refer to the probabilities associated with the two hypotheses being combined. A simpler alternative, which bypasses the operations of (10.5), is merely to drop the similar hypothesis with the lower probability. In either case, the probability (p_c) associated with the combined (or remaining) hypothesis becomes the sum of the probabilities of the similar hypotheses $(p_c = p_1 + p_2)$.

Another approach to combining hypotheses is to begin by combining tracks. Again, either the N-scan criterion or similarity tests, such as given by (10.4), would be used. Then, some criterion, such as smaller covariance matrix elements or the larger track score, would be used to determine which of the similar tracks is to be maintained. Finally, the track that remains will replace the other similar tracks in all hypotheses containing those tracks.

Once similar tracks are replaced it may be that two or more hypotheses will have identical track lists. If this occurs, only one of the hypotheses should be maintained. Again the probability of the one hypothesis that is retained should be augmented by the probabilities of the similar hypotheses that are deleted.

10.2.5   Operations with Hypothesis Matrix

Table 10-1 illustrates the hypothesis matrix in which there is a row for each hypothesis and a column for each measurement. For the example shown in Table 10-1, there were 34 hypotheses formed for only two scans of data with only two observations per scan. Clearly, the number of hypotheses must be reduced. Thus, simplifying operations designed to reduce the number of hypotheses are discussed next. The simplifying operations can be performed upon examination of the hypothesis matrix once the pruning and combining operations discussed above are performed. These operations will be illustrated through continuation of the hypothetical example discussed above.

Assume that the data points $y_1(2)$ and $y_2(2)$ both fall within the validation gates of both tentative tracks that were initiated on the previous scan. Figure 10-4 illustrates a possible situation with these conditions. Under these conditions and further assuming a low probability of false alarm, it could occur that only the hypotheses (H_{15} and H_{20}) which contain two, two-point

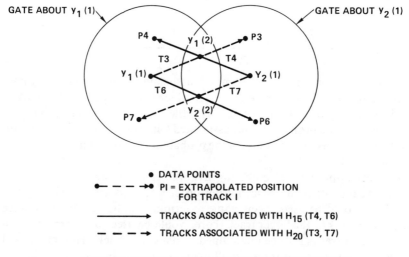

FIGURE 10-4. HYPOTHESIZED TRACK FORMATION FOR TWO
DATA SCANS

tracks would survive pruning. Under this condition (where all hypotheses except H_{15} and H_{20} are deleted), a situation has arisen where all the entries of a column, or in this case two columns, are the same. The only entries below $y_1(1)$ and $y_2(1)$ are $T1$ and $T2$, respectively. Thus, data points $y_1(1)$ and $y_2(1)$ can only be associated with tracks $T1$ and $T2$, respectively, so that tracks $T1$ and $T2$ are considered confirmed. The first two columns of the hypothesis matrix can be deleted and all rows except those corresponding to H_{15} and H_{20} are deleted. The question remains which of the tracks ($T3$, $T4$, $T6$, $T7$) that continued the original tracks ($T1$, $T2$) are valid.

Figure 10-4 shows the tracks ($T3$, $T4$, $T6$, $T7$) that remain and the predicted positions ($P3$, $P4$, $P6$, and $P7$). Figure 10-5 shows hypothetical validation regions around the predicted positions of these tracks for the time of the next scan's data. Assume that two observations ($y_1(3)$, $y_2(3)$) are received on the next scan, with their positions with respect to the gates as shown in Fig. 10-5. Table 10-2 shows the new hypothesis matrix with H_{15} and H_{20} being renumbered H_1 and H_2 and with hypotheses for the new data also shown. In general, computer storage considerations may also dictate a renumbering of tracks, but, for the purpose of presentation, we will continue the sequential numbering begun in Table 10-1. Thus, the option to update $T6$ with $y_1(3)$ leads to $T9$ with $T10$ and $T12$ representing new tracks started by $y_1(3)$ and $y_2(3)$, respectively, and so forth.

TABLE 10-2
FULL HYPOTHESIS MATRIX AFTER THIRD DATA SCAN

Hypothesis Number	Second Data Scan		Third Data Scan	
	$y_1(2)$	$y_2(2)$	$y_1(3)$	$y_2(3)$
1(15)	4	6	0	0
2(20)	3	7	0	0
3	4	6	6(9)	0
4	4	6	10	0
5	3	7	10	0
6	4	6	0	4(11)
7	4	6	6(9)	4(11)
8	4	6	10	4(11)
9	4	6	0	12
10	3	7	0	12
11	4	6	6(9)	12
12	4	6	10	12
13	3	7	10	12

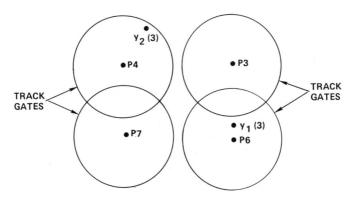

FIGURE 10-5. GATES AND OBSERVATIONS FOR THE THIRD DATA SCAN

Referring to Fig. 10-5 the data point $y_1(3)$ is very close to the predicted position ($P6$) of track 6. As a result, only those hypotheses that associate $y_1(3)$ with $T6$ (to form $T9$) are assumed to survive pruning. On the other hand, three options remain for $y_2(3)$ because it is not so close to $P4$. Thus, pruning leads to the reduced hypothesis matrix shown in Table 10-3. Note from this matrix that $T9$ is included in all three hypotheses. Thus, the existence of track $T9$ is assured and it is removed from these hypotheses to form a new cluster as discussed next.

10.2.6 Hypothesis Clustering

A cluster is a group of hypotheses, and associated tracks, that does not interact with any other group of hypotheses (contained within other clusters). The hypotheses within a cluster will not share observations with the hypotheses within any other cluster.

TABLE 10-3
REDUCED HYPOTHESIS MATRIX AFTER THIRD SCAN DATA

Hypothesis Number	Third Scan Data	
	$y_1(3)$	$y_2(3)$
1(3)	9	0
2(7)	9	11
3(11)	9	12

As an example of clustering, from above, the track

$$T9 = [y_1(1), y_2(2), y_1(3)]$$

is contained in all three hypotheses shown in Table 10-3. This track can be removed to start a new cluster with the single hypothesis containing the single track $T9$. This operation (splitting the cluster) is valid because none of the observations contained within $T9$ are contained within the tracks comprising the three hypotheses remaining in the previous cluster. To verify this, note that the composition of the three remaining hypotheses is

H_1: $T4 = [y_2(1), y_1(2)]$, $y_2(3) = FA$
H_2: $T11 = [y_2(1), y_1(2), y_2(3)]$
H_3: $T4 = [y_2(1), y_1(2)]$, $y_2(3) = NT12$

The above example, depicted in Fig. 10-4, represents a simple case of targets passing by each other while heading in different directions. This is a case where cluster splitting is most applicable.

The basic purpose of clustering is to divide the large tracking problem into a number of smaller ones that can be solved independently. This can greatly reduce the number of hypotheses that must be maintained. For example, if two clusters with ten hypotheses each remain combined into one cluster, there are 100 hypotheses required. Each cluster will have its own set of observations and tracks, a hypothesis matrix and a set of probabilities associated with the hypotheses. The steps involved in clustering are outlined next.

A new cluster is initiated any time an observation is received that does not fall within the gates of any track contained in an existing cluster. The cluster is initiated on the observation using the alternatives (true target or false alarm) associated with its source. Also, as in the above example, a new cluster is initiated on a track that is contained in all hypotheses of a previous cluster. The track is then removed from the old cluster.

In order that clusters remain distinct, the gates of the tracks within the clusters must not overlap. Thus, when an observation falls within the gates of two or more tracks from different clusters, the clusters are merged. The merging must be done before the observation is processed. New hypotheses are formed from all combinations of the hypotheses in the clusters being merged. The set of tracks and observations in the new "supercluster" is the sum of those in the prior clusters. The number of hypotheses in the new supercluster is the product of the number of hypotheses in the prior clusters and the associated probabilities are products of the prior probabilities. For example, consider the merging of a cluster with two hypotheses each with probability $1/2$ and a cluster having three hypotheses each with probability $1/3$. The result will be a supercluster with six hypotheses each with probability $1/6$.

10.2.7 Other Implementation Issues

As discussed in Chapter 9, any general development of expressions for evaluating data-association alternatives for the MTT problem should explicitly contain the track deletion option. Airborne targets indeed fly outside the radar scan volume and get shot down. Ground targets can effectively disappear by moving behind obstacles or just by stopping in regions of heavy background clutter. Thus, situations can occur where otherwise valid hypotheses become degraded because one of the associated target tracks is no longer present. To ensure that this situation does not occur, the track deletion option should be allowed and, upon deletion, the appropriate hypothesis probabilities can be modified.

Direct use of the deletion option for all tracks within a hypothesis would create unnecessary additional hypotheses. The preferred alternative is to examine individual tracks for deletion. Then, when the deletion alternative is preferable to maintaining a track, the track can be deleted in all those hypotheses containing it.

As discussed in previous chapters, the deletion criterion can be based on a simplified miss criterion (such as N_D consecutive misses), or on use of a mathematical criterion function (such as the score function). Then, once deletion occurs, the track will either be removed from all hypotheses that previously contained it, or at least identified as not being a candidate for future association. Also, the probabilities associated with these hypotheses should be multiplied by a factor, f_D, which accounts for the choice of the more likely option that the track has terminated. For example, if the N_D consecutive miss deletion criterion is used and upon assuming large D_E such that the deletion penalty term $(1 - e^{-1/D_E}) \cong 1/D_E$, f_D becomes

$$ f_D \cong \frac{1}{D_E(1-P_D)^{N_D}} $$

Another practical problem that arises is the presentation of target track information to the outside. For example, in an airborne radar application, the pilot will want to see estimated target positions displayed; he probably does not wish to be concerned with the details of the hypothesis tree. The problem is how to display, at any given time, some "best" representation of the number of targets present and the associated estimates of their kinematics (and, possibly, their attributes). Some of the issues involved in the presentation of this information are discussed next.

If the number of targets were known, estimates of target positions could be obtained by averaging over the position estimates from those hypotheses containing that number of targets. For example, in the simplest case where a single target is assumed present, Reference [1] shows that the minimum mean-squared error criteria is satisfied by forming the composite estimate from a weighted sum of the individual hypothesis estimates. The weighting is the associated hypothesis probabilities. However, this approach cannot generally be extended to the condition where an unknown number of targets exists.

The most direct approach is to present only the confirmed tracks within the hypothesis with the highest probability. Problems may arise with this approach, however, if there are several hypotheses that have similar probabilities but differ in track content. It may be confusing to the user if the hypotheses (and their associated tracks) presented change frequently. The best approach probably is to define some composite of the highest probability hypotheses so that this composite will not change erratically.

10.3 THE ALL-NEIGHBORS DATA ASSOCIATION APPROACH (PDA, JPDA)

We next consider an approach whereby multiple hypotheses are effectively formed after each scan of data, but where these hypotheses are combined before the next scan of data is processed. The result of this is that the updated estimate for a given track may contain contributions from more than one observation. Thus, the term "all-neighbors," referring to track update using all neighboring observations within some gated region, is applied.

An all-neighbors approach to correlation under the assumption of a single target in clutter was first presented by Bar-Shalom and Tse [5]. The method was denoted probabilistic data association (PDA), and it leads to an appropriately modified tracking filter called PDAF. Later results [6,7] showed that the PDA did not perform well in the presence of multiple targets, so a modified method (denoted JPDA) was derived to include the presence of multiple targets.

The JPDA is basically a special case of the MHT method discussed in the previous section. Because of the relative simplicity and practical importance of its application, however, the JPDA will be discussed separately and the details of its implementation will be outlined in this section. First, the basic principles will be given in a discussion of the PDA. Then, the extension to the JPDA will be outlined through the use of an example.

Several points should be noted about the JPDA (and PDA). First, this approach has no explicit provision for track initiation. Thus, a separate track initiation function, such as the operator-interactive process mentioned in [7], must be defined. Also, the method is target-track oriented so that probabilities are computed with reference to the assumed previously established tracks. This contrasts with the measurement orientation of the MHT method, in which options are computed for the measurements. As stated in [6], however, for most applications, the differences in these orientations are largely philosophical because essentially the same calculations are ultimately performed.

10.3.1 The PDA Method

Consider the case of a single established target track in the presence of extraneous returns, such as clutter. Define P_D to be the probability of detection and assume the gate is sufficiently large that the target return, when present, will fall within the track gate ($P_G \cong 1.0$). Further, assume the extraneous return density to be Poisson with density β (note that β now includes new targets and false returns, $\beta = \beta_{NT} + \beta_{FT}$).

Given N observations within the gate of track i, there are $N+1$ hypotheses that can be formed. The first (denoted H_0) is the case in which none of the observations is valid. Using the results of Chapter 9, the probability of H_0 is proportional to p'_{i0}, where

$$p'_{i0} = \beta^N (1 - P_D) \tag{10.6a}$$

Similarly, the probability of the hypothesis H_j ($j = 1, 2, \ldots, N$) that observation j is the valid return is proportional to

$$p'_{ij} = \frac{\beta^{N-1} P_D e^{-\frac{d_{ij}^2}{2}}}{(2\pi)^{M/2} \sqrt{|S_i|}}, \quad j = 1, 2, \ldots, N \tag{10.6b}$$

Finally, the probabilities (p_{ij}) associated with the $N+1$ hypotheses are computed through the normalization equation:

$$p_{ij} = \frac{p'_{ij}}{\sum\limits_{l=0}^{N} p'_{il}}$$

The factor β^{N-1} cancels during the normalization process, and thus is not required in the computation of p_{ij}. Therefore, a convenient simplified form becomes

$$p_{ij} = \begin{cases} \dfrac{b}{b + \sum\limits_{l=1}^{N} \alpha_{il}}, & j = 0 \text{ (no valid observation)} \\[4ex] \dfrac{\alpha_{ij}}{b + \sum\limits_{l=1}^{N} \alpha_{il}}, & 1 \leq j \leq N \end{cases} \tag{10.7}$$

where

$$b = (1 - P_D)\,\beta\,(2\pi)^{M/2}\,\sqrt{|S_i|}$$

$$\alpha_{ij} = P_D e^{-\frac{d_{ij}^2}{2}}$$

The next step, after computation of the probabilities using (10.6) and (10.7), is to merge hypotheses. The resulting method is summarized from Bar-Shalom and Tse [5]. First, the residual, for use in the Kalman filter update equation, is a weighted sum of the residuals associated with the N observations:

$$\tilde{y}_i(k) = \sum_{j=1}^{N} p_{ij}\,\tilde{y}_{ij}(k) \tag{10.8}$$

where

$$\tilde{y}_{ij}(k) = y_j(k) - H\hat{x}_i(k\,|\,k-1)$$
$$y_j(k) = \text{observation } j \text{ received at scan } k$$

For notational convenience, the subscript i, denoting track i, will be omitted whenever there ought to be no ambiguity in referring to the Kalman filter quantities. Then, the standard Kalman filter update equation is used:

$$\hat{x}(k\,|\,k) = \hat{x}(k\,|\,k-1) + K(k)\,\tilde{y}(k) \tag{10.9}$$

with the gain, $K(k)$, computed using (2.11). However, the covariance, at scan k, is modified according to the equation:

$$P(k\,|\,k) = P^\circ(k\,|\,k) + dP(k) \tag{10.10}$$

where $P^\circ(k\,|\,k)$ is the Kalman covariance that would be computed if a single return were present and $dP(k)$ is an increment added to reflect the effect of uncertain correlation. The equations defining $P^\circ(k\,|\,k)$ and $dP(k)$ are

$$P^\circ(k\,|\,k) = p_{i0}\,P(k\,|\,k-1) + (1 - p_{i0})\,P^*(k\,|\,k)$$

$$dP(k) = K(k)\left[\sum_{j=1}^{N} p_{ij}\tilde{y}_{ij}\tilde{y}_{ij}^T - \tilde{y}_i\tilde{y}_i^T\right]K^T(k) \tag{10.11}$$

and $P^*(k\,|\,k)$ is the standard Kalman covariance, as computed from (2.11),

$$P^*(k\,|\,k) = [I - K(k)H]\,P(k\,|\,k-1)$$

The term $dP(k)$ increases the covariance according to both the *a posteriori* probabilities (or uncertainties) and the spread of the observations found within the track gate. For example, for a single observation within the gate, using (10.8) and (10.11) and dropping subscript i, for track i, we have

$$\tilde{y} = p_1 \tilde{y}_1$$

$$dP(k) = K \left[p_1 \tilde{y}_1 \tilde{y}_1^T - \tilde{y}\tilde{y}^T \right] K^T = p_1(1-p_1) K \tilde{y}_1 \tilde{y}_1^T K^T$$

which gives a maximum correction for uncertainty when the probability that the observation is valid (p_1) is 0.5. Similarly, if there are two measurements in the gate and each has probability 0.5 of validity ($p_1 = p_2 = 0.5$, $p_0 = 0$), the covariance correction term becomes

$$dP = 0.25 \, K \, (\tilde{y}_1 - \tilde{y}_2)(\tilde{y}_1 - \tilde{y}_2)^T K^T$$

Equations (10.7) through (10.11) define the PDA. Results for a single target in clutter [5] have shown a significant decrease in the number of lost tracks when the PDA method is compared with a standard nearest-neighbor correlation method. However, an extension, discussed next, is required if multiple target tracks are considered.

10.3.2   Extension to JPDA

The JPDA method is identical to the PDA except that the association probabilities are now computed using all observations and all tracks. The state estimation gain and covariance are computed as before, using (10.8) through (10.11). The probability computation of (10.7) must be extended, however, to include multiple tracks.

Consider the typical type of conflict situation, such as shown in Fig. 10-6, in which multiple observations fall within the validation gates of multiple target tracks. In this example, there are three observations ($O1$, $O2$, $O3$) within the gate of the predicted position ($P1$) of the first track ($T1$),

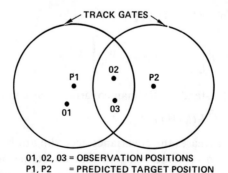

O1, O2, O3 = OBSERVATION POSITIONS
P1, P2   = PREDICTED TARGET POSITION

FIGURE 10-6. EXAMPLE OF CORRELATION CONFLICT CONDITION
SUITABLE FOR JPDA

while 'only $O2$ and $O3$ are within the gate of the second track $(T2)$. The JPDA will compute a weighted residual for $T1$ based upon the three observations, but the weights for $O2$ and $O3$ will be reduced to account for their presence within the gate of $T2$. The residual for $T2$ will be formed using $O2$ and $O3$.

Following the earlier approach of this chapter we will continue with the hypothesis matrix method and illustrate the required probability computations by example. References [6,7] present an alternative, more formalized approach. The difference between the hypothesis matrix method previously defined and this application is that because the JPDA is target-oriented, the hypothesis matrix will now show hypotheses for the alternatives with respect to the target tracks. Table 10-4 gives the hypothesis matrix and the associated hypothesis probabilities for this example. The numbers represent the observations assigned to the tracks, and 0 represents the assignment of no observation to a given track. Also, as previously defined, g_{ij} is the Gaussian likelihood function associated with the assignment of observation j to track i.

Table 10-4 shows the structure for computing the hypothesis probabilities $P'(H_l)$. Defining N_o and N_T to be the numbers of observations and tracks, respectively, note that certain common factors may appear in all $P'(H_l)$. If $N_o > N_T$, as in our example, the common factor is $\beta^{(N_o-N_T)}$ while if $N_T > N_o$, the common factor will be $(1-P_D)^{(N_T-N_o)}$. The same probability of detection (P_D) has been assumed for all tracks, but the extension to track dependent P_D is direct. Finally, the normalized probabilities $P(H_l)$ are computed in the standard manner (where N_H is the total number of hypotheses):

$$P(H_l) = \frac{P'(H_l)}{\sum_{l=1}^{N_H} P'(H_l)}$$

As an example, consider the condition shown in Fig. 10-6, with two-dimensional measurement, in which

$$M = 2, \qquad \sqrt{|S_i|} = \sigma_{\tilde{x}}\,\sigma_{\tilde{y}}$$

and with numerical values

$\sigma_{\tilde{x}} = \sigma_{\tilde{y}} = 1,\ \beta = 0.03,\ P_D = 0.7$
$d_{11}^2 = 1,\ d_{12}^2 = 2,\ d_{13}^2 = 4$
$d_{22}^2 = 2.5,\ d_{23}^2 = 3$

Table 10-4 gives the probabilities associated with the various hypotheses.

To compute the probability p_{ij} that observation j should be assigned to track i, a sum is taken over the probabilities from those hypotheses in which this assignment occurs. For example, for track 1 (noting that $j = 0$ refers to no assignment), the probabilities are

$$p_{10} = P(H_1) + P(H_5) + P(H_8) = 0.011 + 0.041 + 0.032 = 0.084$$
$$p_{11} = P(H_2) + P(H_6) + P(H_9) = 0.086 + 0.306 + 0.239 = 0.631$$
$$p_{12} = P(H_3) + P(H_{10}) = 0.053 + 0.145 = 0.198$$
$$p_{13} = P(H_4) + P(H_7) = 0.019 + 0.068 = 0.087$$

TABLE 10-4
TARGET ORIENTED HYPOTHESIS MATRIX FOR
EXAMPLE OF FIGURE 10-6

Hypothesis Number	Track Number 1	2	Hypothesis Probability $P'(H_l)$	Probability Values for Example*
1	0	0	$(1-P_D)^2\beta^3$	$2.4\times10^{-6}(0.011)$
2	1	0	$g_{11}P_D(1-P_D)\beta^2$	$1.82\times10^{-5}(0.086)$
3	2	0	$g_{12}P_D(1-P_D)\beta^2$	$1.11\times10^{-5}(0.053)$
4	3	0	$g_{13}P_D(1-P_D)\beta^2$	$4.1\times10^{-6}(0.019)$
5	0	2	$g_{22}P_D(1-P_D)\beta^2$	$8.6\times10^{-6}(0.041)$
6	1	2	$g_{11}g_{22}P_D^2\beta$	$6.47\times10^{-5}(0.306)$
7	3	2	$g_{13}g_{22}P_D^2\beta$	$1.44\times10^{-5}(0.068)$
8	0	3	$g_{23}P_D(1-P_D)\beta^2$	$6.7\times10^{-6}(0.032)$
9	1	3	$g_{11}g_{23}P_D^2\beta$	$5.04\times10^{-5}(0.239)$
10	2	3	$g_{12}g_{23}P_D^2\beta$	$3.06\times10^{-5}(0.145)$

*Normalized values, $P(H_l)$, within paretheses.

Similarly, for track 2,

$$p_{20} = P(H_1) + P(H_2) + P(H_3) + P(H_4) = 0.169$$
$$p_{21} = 0$$
$$p_{22} = P(H_5) + P(H_6) + P(H_7) = 0.415$$
$$p_{23} = P(H_8) + P(H_9) + P(H_{10}) = 0.416$$

Thus, as expected, the most heavily weighted events are computed to be the assignment of $O1$ to $T1$ and either $O2$ or $O3$ to $T2$.

If an observation does not fall within the gate of a given track, the associated probability is, of course, taken to be zero ($p_{21} = 0$ for our example). The remaining calculations are then performed using (10.8) through (10.11) to update filter estimates and covariance terms.

10.4 CONCLUDING REMARKS

The MHT and PDA methods originated around the same time [1,5], and development has proceeded in parallel. The PDA and the later JPDA are, however, basically a special case of MHT, and the calculations are similar to those required for MHT. The advantage of the JPDA is that it is a relatively simple recursive method which does not require the storage of past observation data nor multiple hypotheses.

The discussion in this chapter has been weighted towards the MHT approach. This is consistent with the overall emphasis upon airborne radar applications where it is important to maintain the identity of individual tracks and where false target densities are typically moderate. However, Bar-Shalom and others have found extensive application for the JPDA method in sonar and other surveillance systems. These applications are well documented in the literature. In addition to the basic references [5,6,7] cited, the reported applications include observations having random arrival times [9], adaptive thresholding [10], possibly unresolved measurements [11], and maneuver detection and tracking in clutter [12].

An apparent disadvantage associated with the JPDA is the lack of an explicit mechanism for track initiation. As discussed in [7], however, it might be suitable to employ other batch-type algorithms for track initiation and then to use the JPDA for track maintenance. Similarly, there is no well-defined technique for track deletion associated with the JPDA, but as with track initiation, some experimentation should produce acceptable algorithms for specific applications.

A summary of the logic required for MHT has been presented. A more detailed description of a particular application will be given in Chapter 14. A survey of the literature on MHT leads to the conclusion that a variety of approaches has been successfully used (for example, [13–15] as well as [1–4]). The details of implementation are largely up to the ingenuity of the designer and are dependent upon the particular application.

The most important factor in the choice of MHT *versus* JPDA methods is probably the false alarm (or false target) density. For high false target densities, such as in sonar or radar air-to-ground tracking applications, MHT is probably not feasible, so the JPDA is favored. However, MHT becomes feasible for the lower false target densities associated with the radar air-to-air tracking problem.

With reference again to Fig. 1-4 of Chapter 1, the following general guideline to the choice of data association methods is offered. First, for sparse environments, the NN method, with possible provision for limited branching or covariance modification under uncertain correlation conditions, can be used. As the target or false return density increases, application of MHT techniques becomes most appropriate. Ultimately, as the density further increases, the use of heavy pruning is required for MHT, and the JPDA becomes an attractive alternative. Finally, in an extremely dense target environment, such as for tracking convoys of ground targets, the concept of tracking individual targets probably must be abandoned. For a very dense environment, targets should be tracked as groups using the methods discussed in the next chapter.

REFERENCES

1. Singer, R.A., R.G. Sea, and R.B. Housewright, "Derivation and Evaluation of Improved Tracking Filters for Use in Dense Multi-Target Environments," *IEEE Transactions on Information Theory*, IT-20, July 1974, pp. 423–432.

2. Reid, D.B., "An Algorithm for Tracking Multiple Targets," *IEEE Transactions on Automatic Control*, AC-24, Dec. 1979, pp. 843–854.

3. Reid, D.B., "A Multiple Hypothesis Filter for Tracking Multiple Targets in a Cluttered Environment," Lockheed Missiles and Space Company Report, No. LMSC, D-560254, Sept. 1977.

4. Chong, C.Y., *et al.*, "Distributed Hypothesis Formation in Distributed Sensor Networks," Advanced Information and Decision Systems Report No. TR-11015-1, AD-A122618, Dec. 7, 1982.

5. Bar-Shalom, Y., and E. Tse, "Tracking in a Cluttered Environment with Probabilistic Data Association," *Automatica*, Vol. 11, Sept. 1975, pp. 451–460.

6. Fortmann, T.E., Y. Bar-Shalom, and M. Scheffe, "Multi-Target Tracking Using Joint Probabilistic Data Association," *Proceedings of the 1980 IEEE Conference on Decision and Control*, Albuquerque, NM, Dec. 1980, pp. 807–812.

7. Fortmann, T.E., Y. Bar-Shalom, and M. Scheffe, "Sonar Tracking of Multiple Targets Using Joint Probabilistic Data Association," *IEEE Journal of Oceanic Engineering*, OE-8, No. 3, July 1983, pp. 173–184.

8. Pattipati, K.R., and N.R. Sandell, Jr., "A Unified View of State Estimation in Switching Environments," *Proceedings of the 1983 American Control Conference*, Vol. 2, San Francisco, CA, Sept. 1983, pp. 458–462.

9. Bar-Shalom, Y., and G.D. Marcus, "Tracking with Measurements of Uncertain Origin and Random Arrival Times," *IEEE Transactions on Automatic Control*, AC-25, Aug. 1980, pp. 802–807.

10. Fortmann, T.E., *et al.*, "Detection Thresholds for Multi-Target Tracking in Clutter," *Proceedings of the 1981 IEEE Conference on Decision and Control*, San Diego, CA, Dec. 16–18, 1981, pp. 1401–1408.

11. Chang, K.C., and Y. Bar-Shalom, "Joint Probabilistic Data Association for Multi-Target Tracking with Possibly Unresolved Measurements and Maneuvers," *IEEE Transactions on Automatic Control*, AC-29, July 1984, pp. 585–594.

12. Birmiwal, K., and Y. Bar-Shalom, "On Tracking a Maneuvering Target in Clutter," *IEEE Transactions on Aerospace and Electronic Systems*, AES-20, Sept. 1984, pp. 635–644.

13. Nagarajan, V., V. Hanuma Sai, and G.K. Chaturvedi, "A New Approach to Scan-to-Scan Correlation and Its Implementation," *Proceedings of the IEEE International Conference on Acoustic, Speech, and Signal Processing*, April 14–16, 1983, Boston, MA, pp. 711–714.

14. Hughes, R.P., "A Distributed Multiobject Tracking Algorithm for Passive Sensor Networks," M.S. Thesis, Massachusetts Institute of Technology, AD-A086228, June 23, 1980.

15. Washburn, R.B., *et al.*, "Hybrid State Estimation Approach to Multiobject Tracking for Airborne Surveillance Radars," Alphatech, Inc., Burlington, MA, Report TR-180, AD-A148459, Oct. 1984.

Chapter 11

Group Tracking*

11.1 INTRODUCTION

This chapter discusses the intuitively appealing approach of tracking, as a group, such closely spaced targets as aircraft in formation or ground vehicles traveling in a convoy. This general concept — denoted group, formation, or cluster tracking — typically involves the computation of a group centroid and a group velocity. However, a number of other issues, such as incorporating new members into the group and splitting and merging group segments, are involved.

A group can be loosely defined as a set of targets traveling in the same direction and with the distances between group members being much less than the distances between groups. The set of returns from a given group should be sufficiently separated from returns which are not produced by the group so that ambiguity does not occur.

Group tracking has a number of conceptual advantages when compared with standard methods (where individual tracks are maintained on all targets) for tracking closely spaced targets. First, for the typical radar tracking problem discussed by Taenzer [1], a primary advantage is the conservation of radar resources. The group centroid is illuminated rather than each of the individual group members. Thus, fewer radar actions are required. However, it should be noted that targets can generally be tracked as a group, even if they are not all within the beamwidth of the radar. Fewer track files are required for group tracking because a single group track replaces the individual target tracks. This latter point is particularly important for air-to-ground tracking situations where the tracking of convoys containing many vehicles all traveling together may be required. For this and for similar situations it may be neither possible, nor necessary, to track every target individually.

**The author wishes to acknowledge the helpful comments from Mr. E. Taenzer during the preparation of this chapter.

Experience indicates that miscorrelation is inevitable for closely spaced target tracks. Typical performance was shown in Figs. 1-5 and 1-6 with tracks wandering between targets. Also, for certain spacings (the unstable region) the tracks will frequently be extrapolated away for the group, as shown in Fig. 1-5, and later deleted. The use of group tracking is designed to provide stability and additional smoothing for these conditions. Finally, the use of group tracking will tend to ensure that some information is received from each target group, even if the probability of detection for the individual members is low.

11.1.1 Overview of Issues

Some of the issues involved in group tracking system design are the same as those involved in other, more conventional, approaches. First, group track initiation, confirmation and deletion logic must be defined. Second, filtering and prediction methods are required, and the same trade-offs exist between the use of fixed-coefficient filtering *versus* Kalman filtering. For example, Taenzer [1] chooses (as a function of range) between different sets of tracking coefficients while Frazier and Scott [2] use Kalman filtering. Finally, gating methods are also required for group tracking. However, despite the apparent simplicity of the group tracking concept, a number of difficult issues, unique to group tracking, are introduced.

One major difficulty involved in group tracking is recognizing when the group size changes due to splitting or merging of target groups. In particular, an orderly transition to the individual target track condition must be provided for targets that split away from the group, and redundant tracks must be eliminated when target groups merge. A related problem is the usual requirement to estimate the number of targets in the group. Another related problem is maintaining separate tracks on different groups of crossing targets. Finally, for ground targets, problems may arise because of masking or targets stopping.

Group tracking is frequently complicated by missing observations due to non-unity probability of detection or target masking. Also, the number of targets detected can increase as previously unresolvable targets become resolved. These conditions can lead to instability in the estimates of the number of targets in the group, the group position centroid, and the group velocity.

Another major question involves the use of measurement data for group track updating. One approach is to form a centroided group target measurement (as, for example, an average of all the individual measured positions) in order to update the estimated centroid and velocity of the group track.

An alternative approach correlates individual measurements with predicted target positions within the group. Then, the correlating measurements are extrapolated to the next update time according to the estimated group velocity.

A final problem may arise with the use of group tracking if certain individuals within the group have distinct value. For example, in a convoy of many military vehicles, there may only be one or two targets of tactical value, or it may be necessary to track the lead vehicle. Thus, under some conditions, tracking a group while also tracking individual members of the group may be required.

The next two sections outline approaches for addressing the issues involved in group tracking. The first approach, illustrated in Fig. 11-1, tracks the group centroid and the group velocity, but also attempts to estimate the dispersion of the group. This approach will be denoted the centroid group tracking method. Figure 11-1 illustrates the centroid group tracking method for a two-dimensional geometry. An ellipse is formed about the group centroid. The parameters of the ellipse are computed using the dispersion of the observations that were used to form the group, the measurement error statistics, and the target maneuver capability. The centroid position is

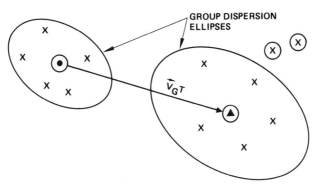

GROUP DISPERSION ELLIPSES

$\bar{V}_G T$

(•) GROUP CENTROID AT SCAN k

(▲) PREDICTED GROUP CENTROID FOR SCAN k + 1

X RADAR OBSERVATIONS INCLUDED WITHIN GROUP GATE ARE USED FOR GROUP UPDATE

(X) RADAR OBSERVATIONS NOT TO BE INCLUDED IN GROUP (MAY START NEW GROUP)

$\bar{V}_G$ = GROUP VELOCITY VECTOR

T = EXTRAPOLATION TIME

FIGURE 11-1. ILLUSTRATION OF CENTROID GROUP TRACKING METHOD

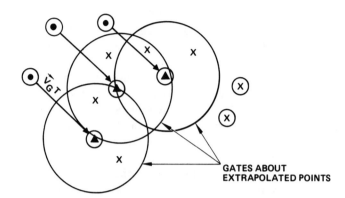

OBSERVATIONS RECEIVED AT SCAN k

EXTRAPOLATION OF OBSERVATIONS TO SCAN k + 1

X   RADAR OBSERVATIONS FALLING WITHIN GATES OF
      GROUP MEMBERS MAY BE INCLUDED IN GROUP

ⓧ   RADAR OBSERVATION NOT TO BE INCLUDED IN
      GROUP (MAY FORM NEW GROUP)

$\bar{V}_G$ = GROUP VELOCITY VECTOR

T = EXTRAPOLATION TIME

**FIGURE 11-2. ILLUSTRATION OF FORMATION
GROUP TRACKING METHOD**

predicted using the estimated group velocity. The size of the dispersion ellipse increases with the extrapolation time. Then, when the next set of observations is received, those observations that fall within a group gate, defined by the dispersion ellipse, are considered for group update.

The second approach, illustrated in Fig. 11-2, also computes a group velocity based upon the motion of the group centroid. However, the individual measurements, as received on each scan, are extrapolated ahead using the group velocity and gates about these observations define the group extent. More detailed discussions of these methods follow.

11.2 CENTROID GROUP TRACKING

Probably the most direct group tracking method is to work exclusively with centroids, both for the track and for the measurements. Using this approach, group track centroids are correlated with, and updated by, measurement centroids. Following [2], implementation of the approach is discussed next. Figure 11-3 presents a flow chart of the logic and Appendix 11A gives a more detailed description of the elements required for implementation.

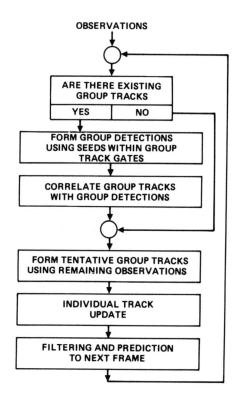

FIGURE 11–3. FLOW CHART OF CENTROID
GROUP TRACKING METHOD

11.2.1 Choice of Tracking Coordinates and State Variables

The standard question again arises between tracking in Cartesian *versus* polar coordinates. References [2,3] use Cartesian coordinates. However, if a measured range rate is available, a coordinate system such as discussed in Chapter 3, that uses as states the range and the angles with respect to an inertial reference frame, is probably preferable.

The standard tracking state variables, such as discussed in Chapter 3, can be used. However, for the ground-moving target case, the use of velocity magnitude and directional angle should be considered [2]. This approach yields a smoother estimate of velocity magnitude using the assumption that speed changes less dynamically than does direction of movement.

11.2.2   Group Track Initiation and Confirmation

Operator assistance may be used for group track initiation [2]. Alternatively, a group track may be initiated automatically using a group observation (formed from a group of closely spaced individual observations) that is not assigned to an existing group track. In the absence of a range rate measurement, a large circular gate is drawn about the original measured centroid. The radius of this circle is the product of the elapsed time between data sets and the maximum expected target velocity, with an added factor included to account for measurement error and group dispersion. If measured range rate is available the target component can be used to extrapolate the centroid position.

A search is performed within the gate for correlating group observations. As with individual target tracking, one or more correlations are required for confirmation and one or two update attempts without correlation lead to deletion of the tentative group track.

11.2.3   Track Update

Assume the existence of one or more group (centroid) tracks and the associated predicted centroid positions. For a given track, the first step is to form a gate about the predicted centroid position. As discussed above, for tentative tracks this gate may just be a circle around the original measured centroid. The other alternatives are rectangular or ellipsoidal gates. These gates should account for target maneuver, for the dispersion of the group and for the measurement noise.

As an example of ellipsoidal gating, Frazier and Scott [2] define a generalized residual covariance matrix as

$$S_G = \hat{S}_D + R_G + HPH^T \tag{11.1}$$

The covariance defined by (11.1) represents an extension to the group tracking problem of the residual covariance matrix used previously throughout the book when referring to the tracking of individual targets. The newly defined matrix $\hat{S}_D$ represents an estimate of the dispersion of the group. The group measurement covariance matrix is R_G. It may differ from the matrices defining individual target measurements (as discussed in Appendix 11A). The matrix HPH^T represents the standard contribution due to target dynamics (or maneuver), and is defined using the one-step prediction covariance matrix $P(k+1|k)$ and the measurement matrix H. Finally, the standard form of gating between the group centroid and the observations, with residuals $\tilde{y}$, is applicable. Thus, an observation is considered to satisfy the centroid gate if

$$d^2 = \tilde{y}^T S_G^{-1} \tilde{y} < d_{max}^2 \tag{11.2}$$

where d_{max}^2 is the maximum allowable normalized distance function. An additional test using the actual (un-normalized) distance from the observation to the centroid position may also be required if the dispersion ellipse is likely to grow too large due to extrapolation [2].

The choices for $\hat{S}_D$ and R_G vary with the application, the particular geometry and the number of targets in the group. Appendix 11A discusses in more detail these issues and the process of updating group track estimates with group observations.

If one or more observations satisfy a gating test, such as (11.2), the closest (smallest normalized distance) observation is used as a seed for the formation of a group observation. The group observation is formed by starting with the original observation and by adding additional members based upon considerations such as

1. Any individual observation that is added to the group observation should satisfy distance criteria with respect to its nearest neighbor or the group centroid;
2. The maximum number of observations in a group may be limited;
3. If range rate is measured all members of the group may be required to satisfy range rate gating criteria.

An additional editing process may also be defined by computing the centroid and dispersion matrix of the newly formed group observation. Then, observations that do not satisfy a normalized distance criterion, using the group observation centroid and dispersion matrix, are dropped from the group observation. This editing process will eliminate outlying observations that are separated from a dense cluster.

The next question involves updating a group track with a single (rather than group) observation. This might occur if the closest observation does not produce a group observation because the requirements for forming a group observation, such as outlined above, are not satisfied. One approach is to require that group tracks be updated only with group observations (the following discussion will assume that this approach is taken). Then, if the closest individual observation does not form a group measurement the next closest observation is tested, *et cetera*, until a measurement group is successfully formed or until there are no more individual observations in the group track gate defined by (11.2). This process is repeated for all existing group tracks.

Next, all detections that have not been used to form group observations are tested for the formation of additional group observations. Once all group observations have been formed, the group centroids are computed and the group observation-to-group track correlation process begins. Correlation conflict situations involving group observations and group tracks may occur in the same manner that they occur for individual target tracks and observations. The most direct approach is to assign group observations to the group tracks that produced the seed observations. Alternatively, the standard means of resolution (such as use of the assignment matrix) can be applied.

Finally, a provision must be made for tracking and updating individual tracks. Here, the question arises concerning the update of individual tracks with group observations. The answer to this question, like many aspects of group tracking, is probably application dependent. For example, certain ground-moving targets are expected to travel in convoys so that isolated targets are unlikely. For such a case, an individual track should readily be converted to a group track if a correlating group observation is found.

Once a group measurement is correlated with a group track, the measured group centroid is combined in the standard manner with the group track predicted position to form the filtered and the new predicted position estimates. As discussed in Appendix 11A, the measurement error is a function of the number of elements in the group measurement and the relative position of the radar antenna with respect to the targets. Thus, Kalman filtering is preferable because of the convenient manner in which it adapts the gain sequence to the centroid measurement error.

11.2.4 Other Implementation Issues

The number of elements in the group should be estimated. This can be done by using smoothing on the number of observations contained in the group detections included in the track. Alternatively, Frazier and Scott [2] use the maximum number that have been detected as the estimate of the total number in the group. This method would be inaccurate in the presence of a high clutter density.

The dispersion matrix, $\hat{S}_D$, for a group is also calculated. For example, for the two-dimensional tracking case (x,y) $\hat{S}_D$ is defined as:

$$\hat{S}_D = \begin{bmatrix} s_x^2 & s_{xy}^2 \\ s_{xy}^2 & s_y^2 \end{bmatrix}$$

where

s_x^2, s_y^2 = estimated variances in x,y positions of the group

s_{xy}^2 = covariance between x and y position

The estimated centroid variances (s_x^2, s_y^2) and means ($\overline{x}$, $\overline{y}$) are computed for a given group measurement in the standard manner. The covariance, s_{xy}^2, is

$$s_{xy}^2 = \frac{1}{N} \sum_{i=1}^{N} (x_i - \overline{x})(y_i - \overline{y})$$

where (x_i, y_i) is the position of the ith target and N is the number of members in the group. Again, smoothing can be applied to the matrices $\hat{S}_D$ of the group observations as they are included in the group track. Alternatively, Reference [2] takes the $\hat{S}_D$ from the most recent group observation included in the group track as the dispersion matrix for the group track. However, this approach may lead to variations in the dispersion matrix.

Another important issue is how to handle the conditions of splitting and merging groups. If the maximum group gate size and the extent of the group measurements are limited, a diverging target (or target group) should automatically set up a new group track. Conversely, as the members of two groups merge, the group observations for each group will include members of the other groups. Then, the group centroids will merge and a redundancy elimination test will be required so that two (or more) group tracks are not maintained on the same set of objects. An alternative, discussed by Binias [3], is to track the outlying (or extreme) values of the position coordinates (x_{min}, x_{max}, *et cetera*). Using this approach, the group track boundaries are determined by a parallelepiped and decision logic is defined to decide when groups split and merge.

A final major issue with the centroid tracking approach is the manner in which the estimates are corrupted by false observations and by missing observations from true targets. For example, the presence of false observations in a group observation may distort the dispersion matrix and also imply a false confidence on the measurement because the number of elements in the group observation can be too large. Finally, as discussed in the next section, missing true target observations, such as would occur when targets are masked (and, thus, systematically drop out of sight), could badly disrupt group velocity estimation. For example, as a group of vehicles enters a masked area, the lead vehicles will drop out of sight and the group velocity will falsely appear to decrease.

11.3   FORMATION GROUP TRACKING

Flad [4] and Taenzer [1,5] have proposed an approach in which an accounting for individual targets is maintained within a group tracking structure. This approach has the following features [1]:

1. Radar and computer resources are conserved;
2. Individual target position estimates are provided;
3. The adverse effects of missing and false measurements are reduced;
4. The same logic is applied to both group and individual target tracking.

The conservation of radar resources occurs because the targets are illuminated as a group, and thus individual illumination is not required for all targets. This feature can also be associated with the centroid tracking method discussed in the previous section. However, the other features represent an improvement over the centroid method.

Although similar in approach, the methods of Flad and Taenzer differ in several respects. Flad maintains individual formation tracks, but does not maintain an estimate of the group centroid. Taenzer maintains a single formation track file with an estimated centroid. This track file also contains the relative positions of the members of the formation with respect to the centroid. Probably the most important difference is that Flad does not consider missed observations while, as discussed below, Taenzer has developed a method for maintaining a stable centroid in the presence of missing observations. The technique discussed below basically follows Taenzer [1].

11.3.1 Outline of Formation Tracking Method

The general approach and the manner in which the formation tracking method can improve upon the centroid method discussed in the previous section are illustrated with an example. Referring to Fig. 11-4, consider a group of four targets that enter a masked area. On the first scan all targets are detected. Then, the two lead targets are masked on the second scan. Finally, the two lead targets leave the masked area and are detected, but the other two targets are masked on the third scan.

In the notation of Fig. 11-4, TIJ refers to the position of target I on scan J. Also, CJ and CJ^* refer to the measured and the true centroids on scan J. Note that $C1$ and $C1^*$ are the same because all four targets are detected on the first scan. Finally, for ease of presentation, it has been assumed that the observations (OIJ) correspond to the true positions. Note that the apparent velocity vector found using the measured centroids is very erratic and a dispersion matrix, such as required for the centroid method discussed in the previous section, would also be very inaccurate. A likely result for centroid tracking in this situation is that the group track would be lost after the lead targets emerged from the masked area. This problem was noted in the discussion of results presented in [2].

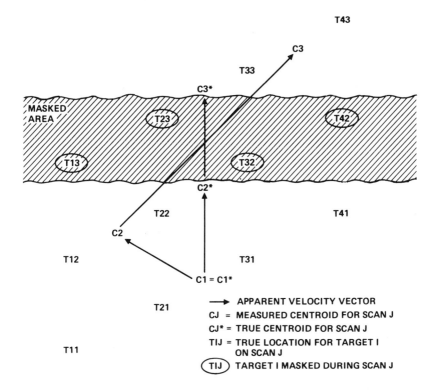

FIGURE 11-4. EXAMPLE OF ERRATIC MEASURED CENTROID BEHAVIOR
DURING TARGET MASK

The formation group tracking method addresses the problems illustrated in Fig. 11-4 by maintaining individual target position estimates. The predicted positions are formed by extrapolating measured observations, that satisfy group conditions, with the estimated group velocity. Then, predicted positions replace missing observations for the group centroid and velocity computations.

Figure 11-5 illustrates the manner in which the formation tracking method will handle the situation shown in Fig. 11-4 for the second scan of data. First, the individual detections received on the first scan are extrapolated forward, using the group velocity, v_G, and the sampling interval, T, and gates are formed about the predicted positions. Then, on the second scan, observations $O12$ and $O22$ are received within the gates of extrapolated points 1 and 2, but, since targets 3 and 4 are masked, there are no correlating observations received for extrapolated points 3 and 4.

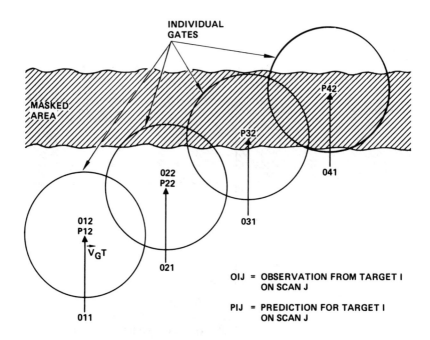

**FIGURE 11-5. ILLUSTRATION OF FORMATION GROUP
TRACK UPDATE METHOD**

The formation tracking method uses the predicted positions $P32$ and $P42$ in place of the observations that were not received. Then, the measured centroid (for use in updating the estimated group velocity) is computed using $O12$, $O22$, $P32$, and $P42$. Thus, a stable centroid is computed and the resultant estimated group velocity will not be as erratic as that computed using centroid tracking. A simple deletion rule is required so that points produced by false alarms or by targets that have left the group are not extrapolated indefinitely. For example, the system described in [1,5] uses two consecutive misses for deletion. Finally, the group velocity calculation remains accurate because deleted members of the group track are removed from both the present and the previous centroids before the group velocity estimate is updated.

The structure of the group is determined by the extrapolated points and the gates around those points. Thus, there is no need to compute a dispersion matrix to determine the shape of the group, nor to determine whether observations that are received are potential candidates for group track update. Gates about the extrapolated position estimates serve to determine what observations are potential candidates for inclusion in the group. This approach has an effect similar to the use of a dispersion matrix because the gates grow with elapsed time since the last update. As targets leave the group or as they approach each other so that observations are merged, the group track should make a smooth transition into an individual target track.

The methods proposed by Flad and Taenzer differ somewhat in the manner in which new observations are included in the group track. Following Flad, new members (observations) are added to the group only if they fall within the gates of existing members. Alternatively, Taenzer includes all observations that fall within range and angle gates of the predicted group track centroid. Figure 11-6 illustrates the difference. Taenzer's gate is defined by the beamwidth in angle and by range intervals, ΔR_G, illustrated in Fig. 11-6, around the nearest (shortest range) and farthest track position. The method of Flad would only accept $O1$, $O2$, and $O3$, while Taenzer would also consider $O4$ (subject to validation tests discussed below). Both would reject $O5$ as not being part of the group.

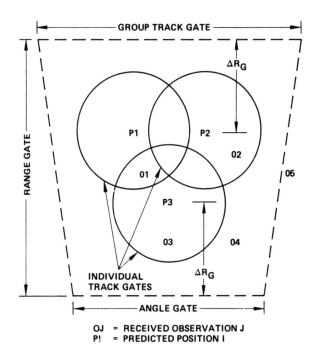

OJ = RECEIVED OBSERVATION J
PI = PREDICTED POSITION I

FIGURE 11-6. FORMATION GROUP TRACK GATING METHODS

Finally, it should again be emphasized that no position smoothing is required although individual target position estimates are maintained. The measurements are used as the best current estimates of the target state and these estimates are extrapolated forward in time using group velocity estimates. Thus, formations are represented by groups of target position estimates, which are computed using the direct, unsmoothed measurements and the group velocity. Next, the logic required to implement formation tracking is described in more detail.

11.3.2 Description of Formation Tracking Logic

Although the formation tracking method is relatively simple in principle, a complex logic is still required to handle the many types of conditions that can occur. Reference [5] gives a detailed description of one such logic. Here, we will summarize the basic principles, beginning with the logic that would be applied to the set of observations shown in Fig. 11-6.

First, the observations are tested for potential inclusion in the group using gating logic such as illustrated in Fig. 11-6. For this example (using Taenzer's method), $O1$, $O2$, $O3$, and $O4$ would be considered for inclusion. Then, a simple nearest-neighbor type correlation procedure can be performed to associate the new observations with the existing members. The result of this logic should be that $O1$, $O2$, $O3$ are correlated with the existing members and that $O4$ is considered an excess member whose true existence is to be validated.

A validation procedure is performed by pointing the antenna beam at the predicted group centroid position and requiring a validation detection of the excess member. If the validating detection is received, a further gating test with other group tracks is performed to ensure that the excess member is not part of another, previously established group that may be crossing the group track under consideration. If this gating test proves positive (that is, the excess member could have been produced by another group track), a further test is performed by comparing group velocities to determine if the group tracks are merging. If the group tracks are determined to be crossing, rather than merging, the excess member is not included in the group track. If the tracks are determined to be merging the excess member will be accepted by the group track and the second, now redundant, group track is dropped.

Returning to the example of Fig. 11-6, assume that $O4$ (in addition to $O1$, $O2$, and $O3$) is to be included in the group. Thus, the best present estimate of the group centroid is found by averaging all four observations. However, for the purposes of updating the group velocity, the centroid of observations $O1$, $O2$, and $O3$ is used in comparison with the centroid of the predicted positions ($P1$, $P2$, and $P3$). The estimated group velocity (and possibly acceleration) is updated using standard fixed-coefficient or Kalman filtering techniques. Finally, the observations ($O1$ through $O4$) are predicted ahead to the next scan time where illumination occurs based upon the predicted centroid of these four group members.

As previously noted, in the case where existing members do not receive correlating observations, the measured centroid is computed by replacing the missing observations with predicted positions. Thus, probably the major feature of this method is the manner in which a more stable centroid is computed for use in estimating the group velocity.

Using Taenzer's method, the potential necessity to merge groups is automatically recognized by the existence of excess members found during a group track illumination. For other systems with conditions of lower detection probability, P_D, it may be that excess members are not found. Then, additional tests may be required to recognize merging target conditions.

Splitting targets (or target groups) are recognized using Taenzer's method by divergence tests, which compare the range estimates of the group members with those of their neighbors and compare the angle estimates with the group angle centroid. Using the method of Flad, the condition where a single observation falls within an individual track gate, such as illustrated in Fig. 11-5, is used to establish that the track may be diverging (or splitting) from the formation. However, an additional test, such as used by Taenzer, would be required using Flad's approach to detect diverging subgroups.

There are several additional points that should influence the design of a formation group tracking algorithm. First, the maneuver potential for formation aircraft may be less than that for individuals (as long as they remain part of the group), and this constraint may be included in the filter and gating design [4]. However, it must be recognized that group members at some point may scramble apart at their maximum individual maneuver capabilities. The process of validating excess members introduced by Taenzer is very important, and it should decrease the problems associated with false alarms that were noted to occur with the centroid method of Scott and Frazier [2]. However, to reduce the time required for validation actions, additional excess members that may be detected during a validation action should probably be ignored as in Taenzer's recommended logic. Finally, the splitting (or separation) of formation tracks may only be allowed under conditions of full information. Thus, Taenzer only allows formation splitting if there are no missing or excess observations.

11.4 SUMMARY AND EXTENSIONS

This chapter has presented an overview of the techniques that have been proposed for group tracking. Although the applications seem apparent, the development or reporting of methods for group tracking has lagged that of other techniques. However, two distinct approaches are available.

The centroid group tracking method is the most direct because only the group centroid is measured and estimated. No provision is required to track individual elements. However, in the cases of nondetected group elements or of false alarms included in the group measurement the measured centroid can be unreliable. The result of inaccurate centroid measurements will be inaccurate group velocity estimates and, as in the results reported in [2], track loss.

The key to successful use of the centroid group tracking method is probably the number of elements in the group. The difficulty reported for certain conditions of the study in [2] may have been related to the relatively small number (four) of targets being tracked. A more stable centroid would be obtained with more targets. Also, the use of cartographic information to aid velocity estimation and to discriminate against false alarms should greatly enhance performance. For example, given a range rate measurement and cartographic information, the target velocity can be estimated. Thus, the centroid group tracking method appears most applicable to tracking ground-moving targets, such as convoys of vehicles, where there are typically many targets moving together and where the use of cartographic information may be applicable.

The formation group tracking approach uses the information contained in the individual measurements. It has many advantages that have been outlined here and which are discussed in more detail in the references. The principal advantage is the more stable computed group centroid and the more stable group velocity estimates which result, but, since individual position estimates are maintained, the resulting computations are more involved. Thus, the formation group tracking method is probably most applicable for airborne targets where the numbers of aircraft in formation are limited and where it is more important to account for individual targets. However, this approach may also be useful for tracking ground-moving targets when potential problems due to masking exist or where recognition of individual targets of particular tactical values is required.

Other approaches are worth investigating. Binias [3] outlines a centroid tracking method where individual tracks are maintained on the coordinates of the targets representing the boundaries of the formation. Ramachandra [6] has presented a method in which individual group targets are tracked, but the state estimates are computed by a single Kalman filter that models the common group dynamics. Finally, as suggested in [2], the effects of missing or false observations in the formation of a group observation may be decreased by using a probabilistic weighting of the elements included. This approach is similar to that of the JPDA method, discussed in Chapter 10, and extension of the JPDA method to group tracking might logically be considered.

REFERENCES

1. Taenzer, E., "Tracking Multiple Targets Simultaneously with a Phased Array Radar," *IEEE Transactions on Aerospace and Electronic Systems*, AES-16, Sept. 1980, pp. 604–614.
2. Frazier, A.P., and J.A. Scott, "ATOMS-1: An Algorithm for Tracking of Moving Sets," System Planning Corporation, Arlington, VA, Report No. ECOM-0510-4, AD-B015080L, Aug. 1976.
3. Binias, G., "The Formation Tracking Procedure for Tracking in Dense Target Environment," *AGARD Conference Proceedings No. 252, Strategies for Automatic Track Initiation*, Monterey, CA, Oct. 1978, pp. 12–1 to 12–11.
4. Flad, E.H., "Tracking of Formation Flying Aircraft," *Proceedings of the IEE 1977 International Radar Conference*, London, Oct. 1977, pp. 160–163.
5. Taenzer, E., "Tracking Multiple Targets Simultaneously with a Phased Array Radar," *Proceedings of EASCON '77*, Washington, DC, Sept. 1977, pp. 10–6A to 10–6R.
6. Ramachandra, K.V., "Multitarget Kalman Tracking Filter," *Electro-Technology* (India), Vol. 23, March 1979, pp. 1–8.

Appendix 11A

Processing for the Centroid Group Tracking Method

This appendix elaborates on the steps involved in implementation of the centroid group tracking method. The exact details of implementation are system dependent and may be defined based upon *ad hoc* rules. Reference [2] describes one implementation while a second operational system, known to the author, followed a similar approach, but differed somewhat in the details. Thus, we will outline the steps, but avoid the specific details, which are probably best determined by experimentation for the particular application. Assume that we start with a group track (or tracks) and consider the steps involved in track update and maintenance.

Formation of Group Observations

After a set of observations has been received, the first step is to consider each group track GT_i and to search for observations that satisfy the group gate defined by (11.2). First, the residual (between a member of the measurement group and the group track centroid) covariance matrix used in the gate calculation is defined

$$S_G = \hat{S}_D + R_G + HPH^T$$

The term HPH^T represents uncertainty in the centroid due to target maneuver and is similar to the corresponding term used for individual target tracking. The term R_G is the measurement error covariance matrix. In general, R_G will be computed using a transformation matrix C from the measurement coordinates (such as the antenna coordinate frame) to the tracking frame. Thus,

$$R_G = C\, R_m\, C^T \tag{11.A.1}$$

where R_m is the covariance matrix in the measurement coordinate frame. Finally, $\hat{S}_D$ is the estimated group track dispersion matrix whose computation is discussed below.

Assuming such an observation exists, the observation that satisfies (11.2) and that has minimum normalized distance (d^2) is chosen as a seed for a group observation GO_j. Then, other observations are tentatively added to GO_j if they satisfy both (11.2) and a nearness criterion (such as being within a dispersion ellipse) with respect to the original seed observation. Finally, an additional editing process may be included to determine which tentative numbers of GO_j are allowed to remain. For example, any observation that is not within some predetermined distance of its nearest neighbor may be eliminated.

The above process is repeated to form other group observations using seeds found for other group tracks. The remaining observations, not thus far used in the formation of a group observation, are tested for formation of additional group observations. Finally, the centroided positions and the dispersion matrices for each of the group observations are computed.

Correlation and Update

Assume a set of group tracks GT_i and a set of group observations GO_j. The most direct correlation approach is to assign each group observation to the group track that produced the seed for that group observation. Alternatively, a correlation algorithm can be defined in which all group tracks and group observations are considered for potential correlation. The solution to this correlation problem would be obtained, using the normalized distances between the group track centroids and the group observation centroids, in the same manner as for individual tracks and observations.

Consider the update of group track GT_i with group observation GO_j and assume that Kalman filtering is used for the group track state estimation update process. The first step is to determine the measurement noise covariance matrix, R_c, used for the Kalman gain computation. Define:

NO_j = number of individual observations in GO_j

$\hat{N}_i$ = estimated number of elements in GT_i

Then,

$$R_c = \frac{R_G}{NO_j} + f(NO_j, \hat{N}_i)\, \hat{S}_{Di} \qquad (11A.2)$$

where

$\hat{S}_{Di}$ = estimated dispersion matrix for group track i

$f(NO_j, \hat{N}_i)$ = weighting factor that is a function of the number of elements in the observation and of the estimated number of members in the group track

The measurement noise covariance matrix given by Equation (11A.2) and defined for group track update is the sum of two matrices. The first, R_G/NO_j, represents the error in measuring the centroid due to radar measurement error and is decreased by the number of elements in the measured centroid. The second term represents the uncertainty in the measured centroid due to the fact that all elements of the group may not have been observed. If the number of group elements were known to be N_i and if there were no false returns (so that $NO_j \leq N_i$), the weighting factor defining the second term would be

$$f(NO_j, N_i) = \frac{(N_i - NO_j)}{(N_i - 1)\, NO_j} \qquad (11A.3)$$

Note that the limits on the function given by Equation (11A.3) are zero when all elements are detected and unity when a single element is detected.

Given R_c from (11A.2), the standard Kalman filtering solution can be applied for state estimation. A convenient means for recursively estimating the number of elements in the group track and the group dispersion matrix is through use of the α-tracker:

$$\hat{N}_i(k) = (1 - \alpha)\,\hat{N}_i(k-1) + \alpha\,NO_j(k)$$
$$\hat{S}_{Di}(k) = (1 - \alpha)\,\hat{S}_{Di}(k-1) + \alpha\,\hat{S}_{DOj}(k) \tag{11A.4}$$

where k is the time index and $\hat{S}_{DOj}$ is the estimated dispersion matrix associated with GO_j. Finally, note that it may be preferable to update $\hat{N}_i$ and $\hat{S}_{Di}$, using (11A.4), before computing R_c from (11A.2).

REFERENCE

1.   Frazier, A.P., and J.A. Scott, "ATOMS-1: An Algorithm for Tracking of Moving Sets," System Planning Corporation, Arlington, VA, Report No. ECOM-0510-4, AD-B015080L, Aug. 1976.

Chapter 12

*Applications of the Radar Electronically Scanned
Antenna to Multiple-Target Tracking**

12.1 INTRODUCTION

This chapter discusses techniques for utilizing the powerful adaptive features of the electronically scanned antenna (ESA, agile beam or phased array radar). The ESA has the capability to perform adaptive sampling by directing the radar beam without inertia in any direction. This property gives the ESA the potential to achieve MTT performance that is significantly improved over that obtainable with the conventional mechanically scanned antenna (MSA). However, efficiently utilizing this capability requires a considerable departure from the previous track-while-scan (TWS) type of system design used with the MSA. The correlation logic becomes more complex and new problems, such as specifying adaptive illumination logic, are introduced.

Because the MSA is mechanically gimballed, it is almost always constrained to a set of predetermined fixed scan patterns. These patterns can be changed periodically, such as to increase elevation coverage at the cost of azimuth. However, the inertia of the moving antenna severely limits the pointing flexibility of the MSA. On the other hand, the ESA can be repositioned within a few microseconds, using electronic phase shifting rather than mechanical gimballing.

The MSA scan constraints naturally lead to the fixed sampling rate TWS system. Using the TWS approach, all targets within the scan volume are illuminated during the scan interval (or frame) and the observations are saved for processing at the end of the scan interval. Thus, for the TWS system, illumination for both search and track update is done simultaneously. Then, at the end of the scan interval, all observations received during the scan are correlated with the existing tracks. This fixed schedule greatly reduces timing and other computational complexities.

By utilizing its agile beam pointing capabilities, the ESA can separate the functions of search and track update illumination. The agile beam can

---

*This chapter was co-authored by Mr. T.J. Broida.

illuminate existing target tracks one at a time and interleave search for new targets among update illuminations of existing tracks. Because the ESA is without inertia, it is convenient to choose track update sampling rate and search illumination volume based upon such considerations as track quality and proximity between existing target tracks. Another important feature is that, at the cost of additional processing and time on target, the probability of detection can be enhanced (for both track update and search).

By removing mechanical limitations, the ESA can conveniently perform operations that are much more difficult to perform with the MSA. Without the constraint of having to change the mechanical scanning rate, it is relatively easy to vary the time spent on target illumination during a given sample. Also, the antenna can be quickly backscanned after repositioning. Thus, even if the antenna has been repositioned, additional looks at the target can be quickly obtained by backscanning. The additional looks may be required if an initial look does not produce a detection. These features allow convenient use of the techniques for enhancing detection performance discussed below. Finally, it may be desirable to adaptively vary the search pattern for new targets to reflect the expected new threat density based on *a priori* information or the density of previously detected targets. However, the required departure from the simple data processing structure of the MSA TWS system leads to increased complexities that must be addressed.

It is desirable to exploit the ESA capability for a fast update rate for selected individual targets, such as those determined to be maneuvering. However, the illumination of individual target tracks, without illumination of neighboring tracks, can lead to correlation problems for closely spaced targets. This means that if nearest-neighbor (NN) sequential correlation techniques are used, care must be taken to illuminate all members of a group before correlation is performed. Also, timing problems become more difficult as tracks are illuminated at different rates and search is intermixed with track update illumination. Thus, although the ESA offers great potential for performance improvement, there are many practical problems involved in the implementation.

We will discuss the theoretical improvements that can be achieved with the ESA and the strategies that have been proposed for obtaining these improvements. First, Section 12.2 outlines techniques for improving radar detection performance with an ESA. Then, the choice of sampling rate is discussed in Section 12.3. Next, the implications of adaptive sampling and enhanced detection for correlation performance in a dense multiple-target environment are presented in Section 12.4. Section 12.5 discusses implementation issues and the relative merits of the use of sequential nearest-neighbor (NN) correlation techniques versus the use of a multiple hypothesis tracking (MHT) approach.

12.2 ENHANCING RADAR DETECTION WITH THE ESA

Tracking and correlation performance in a multiple-target environment is very sensitive to detection performance. If observations can be obtained from all targets, the probability of miscorrelation (and, thus, of degraded tracking performance) can be significantly decreased. Also, Reference [1] and the results of a study summarized in Table 7-3 have shown the payoffs associated with enhanced detection when considering maneuvering target tracking and tracking range performance, respectively. Thus, we outline techniques for achieving enhanced detection with the ESA. Because we are primarily concerned with tracking (rather than detection) performance, only the basic ESA detection principles are discussed with the details (such as the choice of radar waveform) available in the references and in standard radar texts.

There are three main techniques for enhancing detection performance with the ESA. These techniques theoretically could also be used with an MSA, but the agile beam capabilities of the ESA make them much more practical for ESA application. The first method varies the time spent during target illumination at a particular beam position (hereafter referred to as the time on target). This can be achieved by varying the number of integrated pulses used for detection. Reference [1] discusses the manner in which an assumed fixed number of pulses can be allocated for radar detection and tracking between two targets in order to minimize tracking error. Results given there indicate that the allocation of pulses between maneuvering and non-maneuvering targets should be on the order of at least two or three to one. Another way to utilize longer times on target effectively is through sequential methods [2,3]. These methods are readily employed by the ESA because it can conveniently remain on the target (or it can be back-scanned if it has been repositioned) for the time required to perform the sequential detection test.

A second technique for improving the detection performance of a high PRF radar is to transmit two pulse trains with different pulse repetition frequencies (PRFs) at each beam position (known as PRF agility). This strategy can reduce (or essentially eliminate) the eclipsing phenomenon discussed in Chapter 8. Finally, a similar strategy uses several radar frequencies (known as RF frequency agility) in order to use the effects of radar target cross section scintillation to enhance detection performance. Using two or more radar frequencies enhances the probability that the radar cross section variation will be favorable on at least one of the frequencies. The particular is a radar design question that is based upon the expected target signal-to-noise ratio (SNR) and the radar capabilities.

A third processing technique follows an initial detection by a second, confirming update. The same PRF and RF which provided the initial detection are used for the confirming dwell because it can be assumed that these are appropriate choices insofar as they produced the initial detection. Reference [4] provides convenient expressions for determining detection performance using this approach.

Figure 12-1 illustrates the potential for improved detection associated with the use of the ESA. This figure compares the probability of detection that was obtained for a typical ESA system with and without use of the methods discussed above for enhancing detection. The enhanced system (as compared with the nominal) used a combination of longer time on target and RF and PRF agility.

Figure 12-2 shows how the enhanced detection is reflected in the probability of having a track that will not later be deleted. The time on target required during a single dwell for the enhanced system was increased by a factor of over 3.5 as compared to the nominal system. However, from results

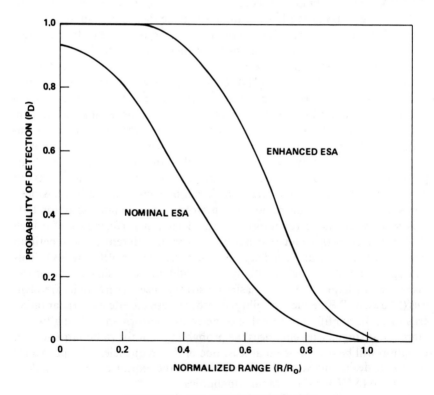

**FIGURE 12-1. ESA ENHANCED DETECTION
PERFORMANCE FOR TRACK UPDATE**

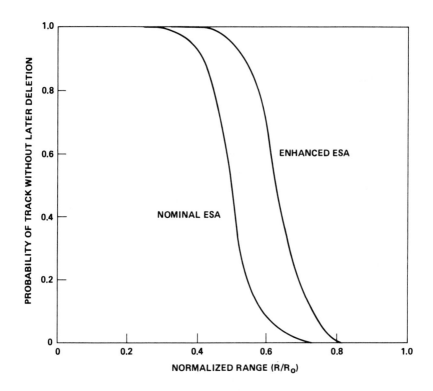

**FIGURE 12-2. INCREASED TRACKING RANGE
RESULTS FROM ENHANCED DETECTION**

derived using the Markov chain method described in Chapter 7, the total illumination time required during the entire run for the enhanced system was only about double that required for the nominal. This is because the enhanced detection scheme is more efficient in the sense that fewer misses occur and thus fewer repeated update attempts are required after unsuccessful looks.

12.3 ADAPTIVE SAMPLING WITH THE ESA

The ability to adaptively vary the update sample rate is probably the most important feature of the agile beam (ESA) radar. It is generally accepted that the sampling rate should be chosen to match target priority, expected target dynamics, and the density of the multiple-target environment. However, there are several approaches to determining the required adaptive sampling logic. These approaches are discussed next.

12.3.1   Use of Several Sampling Rates

One approach is to choose adaptively between three sampling rates [5,6]. First, low priority or non-maneuvering targets are updated at the search scan rate. No special update illumination is required for low priority targets because the search illumination rate is sufficient. Then, two levels of faster sampling are employed for more important or more dynamic targets. The method defined in [5] used a search scan interval of $T_3 = 5.0$ s and adaptively chosen shorter sampling intervals $T_2 = 2.5$ s and $T_1 = 1.25$ s. The adaptive sampling logic was defined by a few simple rules that basically chose T_1 for difficult tracking situations (maneuvering or closely spaced targets), tentative tracks, and tracks with two or more consecutive missed observations. The longest sampling interval ($T_3 = 5.0$ s) was chosen only for the benign condition of a non-maneuvering target for which an observation was received on the last update attempt. The intermediate sampling interval ($T_2 = 2.5$ s) was chosen otherwise. A simple maneuver detector was used to determine sampling rate. It used the range rate residual to determine when a benign (non-maneuvering) target began a maneuver and when a maneuvering target ceased to maneuver. Results were obtained using Monte Carlo simulation in order to compare this method with a method in which a fixed sampling rate was used.

The Monte Carlo simulation considered a single target performing an S-shaped weave intermixed with segments of straight-line flight. Four levels of target maneuver were examined. The first three cases used $5\,g$, $2.5\,g$, and $1\,g$ target accelerations normal to the target velocity vector during the S-turns while the fourth used a randomized maneuver history based on the Singer model discussed in Chapter 2. Comparative results were obtained for the ESA system with adaptive sampling and for a system with fixed (2.5 s) sampling interval. Relative performance was evaluated by examining the number of tracks lost (failed to correlate within at least a maneuver gate) and the average number of updates required for those tracks that were not lost.

The results given in Table 12-1 clearly show better tracking performance with fewer required samples for the adaptive system. The adaptive system required fewer samples because the longest sampling interval was chosen during the periods of target straight-line motion. Finally, note that the effective allocation of update illuminations (demonstrated here) for a given track is important so that the remaining radar resources can be used to update other tracks and to search for new targets.

TABLE 12-1
ADAPTIVE UPDATE RATE IMPROVES TRACK RETENTION
AND EFFICIENCY
(Results Based Upon 100 Monte Carlo Runs)

Geometry	Sampling Method	Number of Tracks Lost	Average Number of Updates
1 g "S"	Fixed	0	40
	Adaptive	0	25
2.5 g "S"	Fixed	59	40
	Adaptive	2	30
5.0 g "S"	Fixed	95	40
	Adaptive	46	33
Randomized	Fixed	21	40
	Adaptive	1	29

12.3.2   Relating Sampling Rate to Tracking Accuracy

The approach previously discussed used a simple predetermined sampling schedule. Next, several more sophisticated methods for choosing a variable sampling rate are discussed. These methods do not, however, consider the multiple-target density and the potential for miscorrelation. The subject of false correlation is discussed in a later section.

Van Keuk [7] presents an empirical expression for relating the sampling interval to the prediction error. First, define the one-step prediction error variance (σ_p^2) in terms of the first diagonal element of the Kalman filter, $p_{11}(k+1|k)$, and the observation variance σ_o^2,

$$\sigma_p^2 = p_{11}(k+1|k) = v_o^2 \sigma_o^2 \qquad (12.1)$$

Then, the relationship between the sampling interval, T, and the resulting prediction error can be expressed in terms of the variance reduction ratio v_o^2 and other system parameters

$$T \cong 0.4 \left(\frac{\sigma_o \sqrt{\tau_m}}{\sigma_m} \right)^{0.4} \frac{v_o^{2.4}}{1+0.5v_o^2} \qquad (12.2)$$

where, following the notation of Chapter 2, τ_m and σ_m are the target maneuver time constant and maneuver standard deviation, respectively. The region of validity for (12.2) includes typical encounter conditions [7].

In order to illustrate its use, we compare results obtained from·(12.2) with those obtained using covariance analysis and shown in Fig. 7-3. Considering a range of 20 nmi and assuming a 1 g target acceleration standard deviation, the target acceleration expressed in angular units (rad/s^2) is

$$\sigma_m = \frac{32.2}{20 \times 6076} = 2.6 \times 10^{-4} \text{ rad/s}^2$$

The assumed observation standard deviation (σ_o) was 0.01 rad = 10 mrad. Thus, the term v_o is given by $\sigma_{\theta p}/10$, with $\sigma_{\theta p}$ as taken from Fig. 7-3 (where results are expressed in mrad).

Table 12-2 compares the sampling interval used for the covariance analysis (defined to be T_c) with the value of T computed from (12.2). However, the covariance analysis used a non-unity probability of detection ($P_D = 0.7$). In the case where the probability of detection (P_D) is non-unity, the expected time between track updates is T/P_D. Equivalently, in order to achieve the prediction accuracy defined by v_o, the sampling interval, T, given by (12.2) should be multiplied by P_D. Thus, the final column of Table 12-2 gives the values of 0.7 T. These values are seen to correspond closely to the values (T_c) used for the covariance analysis study.

Table 12-2 indicates a close correspondence between results obtained using covariance analysis and the prediction formula given by (12.2). Thus, (12.2) provides a convenient tool for choosing the sampling interval adaptively as a function of the system parameters and the required tracking accuracy. However, for non-unity P_D the relationship should be modified by the multiplicative factor P_D giving

$$T = 0.4 \, P_D \left(\frac{\sigma_o \sqrt{\tau_m}}{\sigma_m} \right)^{0.4} \frac{v_o^{2.4}}{1 + 0.5 v_o^2} \tag{12.3}$$

The expressions given above define the relationship between steady-state tracking accuracy and sampling interval. Prior to steady-state, a higher sampling rate is typically required. Then, the sampling interval can be chosen adaptively based upon the covariance matrix. For example, the choice of interval, T_{k+1}, between samples k and $k+1$ can be made so that (12.1) is satisfied, for a desired v_o.

12.3.3   Use of Antenna Beamwidth Considerations in Determining the Sampling Rate

For an ESA MTT system the measurement process is dependent upon the tracking accuracy because the primary source of track update observations

TABLE 12-2
COMPARATIVE SAMPLING INTERVALS FOR THREE VALUES
OF PREDICTION ERROR

Covariance Analysis Sampling Interval T_c (s)	Sampling Interval from Equation (12.2)		
	v_o	T (s)	0.7 T
0.5	0.6	0.68	0.48
1.0	0.85	1.36	0.95
2.0	1.25	2.62	1.84

will usually be individual track illumination. The success of the individual track illumination will be dependent upon the accuracy of the antenna positioning, which in turn depends upon the accuracy in target position estimation. This contrasts with a TWS system, using a mechanically scanned antenna (MSA), for which all observations are received during search. For the MSA TWS system, tracking accuracy has only a secondary effect upon the measurement process through the choice of scan volume.

For the ESA MTT system it is desirable to keep the angular prediction error within a small fraction of the antenna beamwidth so that the probability of detection during a track update illumination will not be degraded. Also, accurate antenna pointing will lead to increased *SNR* so that measurement accuracy will be improved. Thus, we present an approach for including antenna beamwidth considerations in the choice of sampling interval [7].

Define x_1 and x_2 to be the azimuth and elevation angular prediction errors, between where the antenna will be positioned and the true target postion. Assume that x_1 and x_2 are zero-mean Gaussian random variables and that each has standard deviation $v_o\sigma_o$. Thus, the joint distribution for x_1 and x_2 is

$$g(x_1, x_2) = \frac{1}{(v_o\sigma_o)^2 \, 2\pi} \exp\left[-(x_1^2 + x_2^2)/2v_o^2\sigma_o^2\right] \quad (12.4)$$

Assume that the probability of detection decreases with angle off-boresight so that the true probability of detection (P_D) is computed from the ideal (target on boresight such that x_1 and x_2 are zero) value, P_{DO}, through the relationship:

$$P_D = P_{DO} f(x_1, x_2) \quad (12.5)$$

where

$$f(0,0) = 1.0$$

Reference [7] chooses the form

$$f(x_1, x_2) = \exp\left[-c(x_1^2 + x_2^2)/B^2\right] \tag{12.6}$$

where c is a constant taken to be 2.0 and B is the radar beamwidth.

An expression can be defined for choosing a fixed sampling interval T so that the expected number of target illuminations is minimized. This expression is based on the assumption that repeated looks are made until detection occurs. Define n to be the number of looks required before a target detection occurs, so that

$$E(n) = E\left[\frac{1}{P_D}\right] = \frac{1}{P_{DO}} \int_{-\infty}^{\infty} \int_{-\infty}^{\infty} [g(x_1, x_2)/f(x_1, x_2)]\, dx_1 dx_2 \tag{12.7}$$

Evaluating (12.7) with the functions given by (12.4) and (12.6) leads to

$$E(n) = \frac{1}{P_{DO}}\left[1 - 2cv_o^2\sigma_o^2/B^2\right]^{-1} \quad \text{for } v_o < \frac{B}{\sqrt{2c}\sigma_o} \tag{12.8}$$

Next, define the expected number of looks per unit time to be the load (L):

$$L = E(n)/T \tag{12.9}$$

Under the condition that repeated looks are made until detection occurs, the value of T is given by (12.2). Then, combining (12.2), (12.8), and (12.9) gives the proportionality relationship:

$$L \sim \left[1 - 2cv_o^2\sigma_o^2/B^2\right]^{-1} \frac{1 + 0.5\, v_o^2}{v_o^{2.4}} \tag{12.10}$$

The value of v_o that minimizes the expected number of required looks per unit time can be found from (12.10) as a function of the parameter c and the ratio σ_o/B. Both of these quantities will be a function of SNR. For example, given the typical values

$$c = 2.0, \quad \sigma_o/B = 0.2$$

the value of v_o that minimizes L is about 1.6.

A similar analysis can be applied to the condition where a single look occurs, rather than repeated looks until detection occurs as previously considered. For this case we can compute the average probability of detection given the effects of target off-boresight angle. Again using (12.4) and (12.6),

$$E(P_D) = \overline{P_D} = P_{DO} \int_{-\infty}^{\infty} \int_{-\infty}^{\infty} g(x_1, x_2) f(x_1, x_2)\, dx_1 dx_2 \tag{12.11}$$

$$= P_{DO}\left[1 + \frac{2cv_o^2\sigma_o^2}{B^2}\right]^{-1}$$

Thus, the value for $\overline{P}_D$ computed in (12.11) can be used to replace P_D in (12.3) in order to include the antenna beamwidth effects in the computation of the steady-state sampling rate that will result in an average prediction error standard deviation $v_o \sigma_o$.

The expressions derived above should be considered guidelines in the choice of sampling rate. The derivations have not considered the potentially deleterious effects of miscorrelation. Also, the correlation of the antenna pointing error between successive looks has not been considered. A detailed study of the interaction of these effects is most conveniently handled by Monte Carlo simulation.

12.3.4 Allocation of ESA Between Search and Track Update

The previous analysis has only considered requirements for track update illumination. However, there always exists the trade-off between using the ESA for the update of existing tracks or for the search for new targets. Thus, the next question that logically arises is the manner for allocation of the ESA sensor between search for new targets and illumination of existing target tracks.

One approach is to maintain a fixed scan rate, but to allow enough "time slots" so that search can be interrupted regularly for track update, if required. This is, in effect, the approach of Reference [1], where it was assumed that a fixed number of pulses were available to allocate for track update. The allocation between targets was based upon a precomputed allocation schedule that would adapt to the sensed environment. Presumably, this approach could be extended so that the overall number of pulses devoted to track update of confirmed tracks could be precomputed as a function of the environment (number of targets, maneuver level of the targets, *et cetera*).

Methods which assign a fixed number of pulses for track update, or which determine sampling interval in order to maintain certain tracking error requirements, only consider existing track quality. A method which simultaneously compares both the expected benefits from updating existing tracks and the benefits from search is preferable. Utility theory [8,9] provides a convenient structure under which this comparison can be made. Also, a significant difference between the utility theory approach, discussed next, to track update scheduling and the previously discussed approaches is that the former controls the actual prediction error, whereas the latter only controls the average prediction error.

We next outline a utility theory approach for adaptively allocating the radar between the functions of search for new targets and update illumination of existing tracks. For this application, utility can be defined as a measure of the importance of a task (such as track update illumination or search) and how effective the sensor will be in performing that task. This approach assumes a statistical knowledge of the number of undetected targets. Then, the expected gain in utility (defined to be the marginal utility) is found for search and for track update, and the option with the highest marginal utility is chosen. This calculation will depend upon such factors as the probability of detection and the target importance (for example, as based on the hypothesized target type).

A utility theory based allocation method, which will be discussed further in the next chapter, was used to determine when to employ the ESA for search and when to perform track update. We define the utility for search based upon the expected number of undetected targets, and thus it is a function of the time since the particular search segment being considered was last scanned. The utility for track update is based upon the assumed target importance and the ratio of the prediction-error standard deviations (as supplied by the Kalman filter covariance matrix) to the desired (or assumed acceptable) estimation-error standard deviations. Utility calculations are made for the options to update each existing track and to search for new targets. Then, whenever the ESA becomes available for reallocation, the option with the highest expected utility gain (marginal utility) is chosen.

Figure 12-3 shows simulation results illustrating the manner in which, by using this method, antenna resources were allocated between search (S) for new targets and the update ($U1$, $U2$, $U3$) of tracks on targets numbered 1 through 3. For simplicity, it was assumed that a single estimation parameter, the range rate prediction error standard deviation, determined utility for track update. Also, it was assumed that target 1 was both more important and required a greater estimation accuracy.

Allocation events occurred for increments of a basic time interval (ΔT). It was assumed that search of a single bar required 5 ΔT, but track update required a single time interval. Once search was allocated for a single bar, it was continued until completion. However, it was assumed that there were 4 bars to search, and allocation for each bar was a separate event.

The time history shown in Fig. 12-3 starts with the conclusion of a search on bar 2. Updates on tracks 1 and 2 are commanded for the next two intervals. During the next search, target 3 is detected (with track 3 being initiated) and immediate update is called for track 3 after the search is completed. Thereafter, the antenna alternates between search (on bars 1 through 4) and track update. Insofar as target track 1 is given a higher importance weighting and because it is assumed to require greater accuracy, it receives more frequent updates and thus maintains a lower estimation error. The estimation error is presented on the scale at the right of Fig. 12-3 as a normalized ratio of the estimation-error standard deviation (taken from the Kalman filter covariance matrix) to the input measurement-noise standard deviation.

Note that track update can also occur in search, even though the search

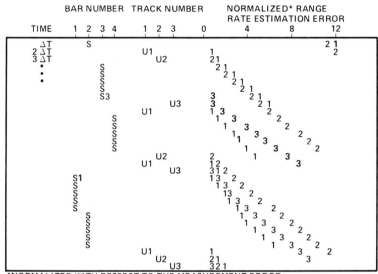

*NORMALIZED WITH RESPECT TO THE MEASUREMENT ERROR
STANDARD DEVIATION

S1 = DETECTION OF TRACK 1 TARGET DURING SEARCH
U1 = UPDATE ILLUMINATION OF TRACK 1

FIGURE 12-3. ALLOCATION OF ESA BETWEEN SEARCH AND TRACK UPDATE

detection threshold setting is generally higher than the setting during track update illumination. After track update occurs through a search detection, the utility for a track update illumination decreases because the tracking error is reduced. For example, referring to Fig. 12-3, track 1 was in the scan volume of bar 1 and received an update during the search of bar 1. Thus, after concluding search bar 1, the search of bar 2 was begun without delay for track update. Otherwise, an update illumination of track 1 would be required after the completion of each search bar.

As radar resources are allocated for track update illumination, there must be some degradation in search performance. For example, this degradation can be measured by the range at which an initial detection is received from a new target entering the scan volume. Results have shown, however, that by efficient allocation it is possible to achieve significant gains in tracking performance (over that achieved with a fixed update rate) with minimal loss in search performance. This is illustrated below with results found by using the utility approach to allocation for another example.

Define R_{90} to be the range at which the cumulative probability of at least one detection of a new target is 0.9. Also, define σ_{xD} to be the desired (or required) tracking error standard deviation for quantity x (such as angle, range or range rate) for an existing target track. Then, Fig. 12-4 shows how

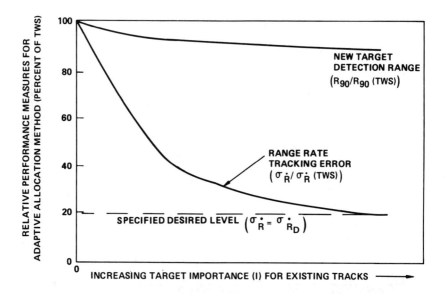

.FIGURE 12-4. COMPARATIVE TRACKING AND SEARCH PERFORMANCE
AS A FUNCTION OF EXISTING TRACK IMPORTANCE

R_{90} decreases and how the range rate tracking error standard deviation approaches the desired value as the assumed target importance increases.

The results shown in Fig. 12-4 were derived using four existing target tracks that were allocated update illuminations using the utility approach according to the target importance (assumed the same for all targets). The nominal ($I=0$) condition corresponds to TWS where no special update illuminations are performed. Results are shown as a percentage of TWS performance. For example, the desired prediction error is twenty percent of the error that would be derived using the TWS operational mode. Eventually, as target importance is increased the desired tracking accuracy is achieved. As more time is spent for track update (so that tracking error is reduced), search performance, as measured by R_{90}, degrades. However, note that when the desired tracking accuracy is achieved, the value of R_{90} is still about ninety percent of the TWS value. Thus, the tracking error decreases much more rapidly with increasing target importance than does R_{90}. This example illustrates that efficient sensor allocation can lead to significant improvements in tracking with only minor decreases in search performance.

12.4 ESA TECHNIQUES FOR IMPROVING NEAREST-NEIGHBOR CORRELATION PERFORMANCE

We next consider how the adaptive update rate and the enhanced probability of detection features of the ESA can be used to improve correlation performance against closely spaced targets. For simplicity, we assume nearest-neighbor correlation techniques. However, the capability of the ESA to improve the information presented to any type of tracker-correlator should lead to comparable improvements for all methods.

We begin by examining correlation results obtained from a simple model. The purpose of this preliminary discussion is to illustrate the complex manner in which correlation performance depends on sampling interval, target separation, and probability of detection. In particular, through use of this simple model we can perform a preliminary study of an important trade-off involved in allocation for track update. This trade-off involves the options of spending more time on target for a given track update illumination *versus* revisiting the track at a greater rate but spending less time on target. In order to perform a valid comparison, both options can be chosen to require the same amount of radar resources. The former approach increases the probability of detection, which, in turn, decreases the probability of false correlation. The latter approach of revisiting the target more frequently decreases the prediction error, which also decreases the probability of false correlation. The interesting question is to determine under what circumstances each of these approaches is most effective.

The simple model to be examined can only give a preliminary indication of expected correlation performance because only a single correlation event is considered. To obtain a more complete picture of how false correlation occurs and how this leads to track degradation, it is necessary to examine an entire encounter history for a group of closely spaced targets. This must be done through Monte Carlo simulation. Thus, correlation performance derived using Monte Carlo simulation will also be presented.

12.4.1   Correlation Results from a Simple Two-Target Model

Assume there are two closely spaced targets with separation (Δx) in the single dimension x. The standard deviation of the prediction error can be defined by

$$\sigma_p = v_o \sigma_o$$

where σ_o is the measurement error standard deviation. Taking P_D to be 0.7, typical values for v_o, given in Table 12-2, were found to be 0.6, 0.85, and 1.25 corresponding to sampling intervals 0.5, 1.0, and 2.0 s, respectively. Define D to be the ratio of the target separation to the observation standard deviation ($D = \Delta x / \sigma_o$). Finally, again for simplicity, assume that the measurement and prediction errors are the same for both target tracks and that there are no false alarms nor new targets detected. Next, we consider correlation performance using this simple model and these parameters.

Even for the simple one-dimensional example described above, the analytical expressions for the probability of false correlation are complex. However, Monte Carlo simultion is very simple for this case. In general,

$$P_{FC} = 2(1-P_D)P_D P_{FC1} + P_D^2 P_{FC2} \qquad (12.12)$$

where P_{FC1} and P_{FC2} are the probabilities of false correlation given the conditions of one and two target detections, respectively. The terms $2(1-P_D)P_D$ and P_D^2 represent the probabilities of one and two target detections, respectively. The evaluation of P_{FC1} and P_{FC2} can be performed using simple Monte Carlo simulation to obtain results as a function of D and v_o. Representative results are given in Table 12-3 with the values for P_{FC2} given in parentheses. The decrease in the probability of false correlation that occurs when both targets are detected is apparent.

Consider the values for v_o of 0.6, 0.85, and 1.25. These values approximately specify prediction error as the sampling interval is successively doubled (starting at 0.5 s) for a typical target-tracking condition (Table 12-2 and Figure 7-3). Using these values of v_o, Figs. 12-5 and 12-6 show the conditional probability of false correlation ($P_{FC/D}$), given that at least one target is detected. The quantity $P_{FC/D}$ is defined

$$P_{FC/D} = P_{FC} / [1-(1-P_D)^2] \qquad (12.13)$$

TABLE 12-3
FALSE CORRELATION PROBABILITIES FOR ONE-DIMENSIONAL TWO-TARGET CASE

Separation $D = \Delta x / \sigma_o$	$v_o = \sigma_p / \sigma_o$		
	0.6	0.85	1.25
2.0	0.098[1]	0.120	0.184
	(0.007)[2]	(0.016)	(0.061)
2.5	0.051	0.066	0.111
	(0.0006)	(0.0021)	(0.023)
3.0	0.026	0.034	0.063
	(~0)	(~0)	(0.008)
3.5	0.011	0.017	0.034
	(~0)	(~0)	(0.002)

Note 1: Values for P_{FC1}.
Note 2: Values for P_{FC2} in parentheses.

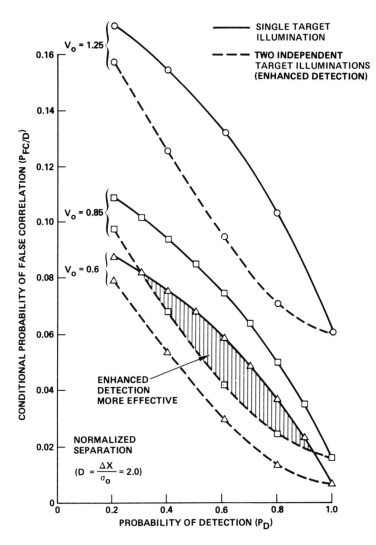

FIGURE 12-5. COMPARATIVE PROBABILITIES OF FALSE CORRELATION
FOR SPACING D = 2.0

It is shown (the unbroken lines) as a function of P_D for D=2.0 and 3.5. The values given in Figs. 12-5 and 12-6 were computed using Eqs. (12.12) and (12.13) and Table 12-3.

The results of Figs. 12-5 and 12-6 clearly indicate that correlation performance improves rapidly with increasing P_D. Next, we consider the relative merits of increasing P_D *versus* decreasing the sampling interval. Increased P_D is modeled by assuming that two independent target illuminations (looks) are obtained and this can be compared with halving the sampling interval. Both methods require the same total amount of resources. The unbroken lines in Figs. 12-5 and 12-6 give comparative results showing the effects of halving the sampling interval. The dashed lines represent the effects of taking two independent looks such that the new effective P_D becomes

$$P_D' = 1-(1-P_D)^2 \qquad\qquad (12.14)$$

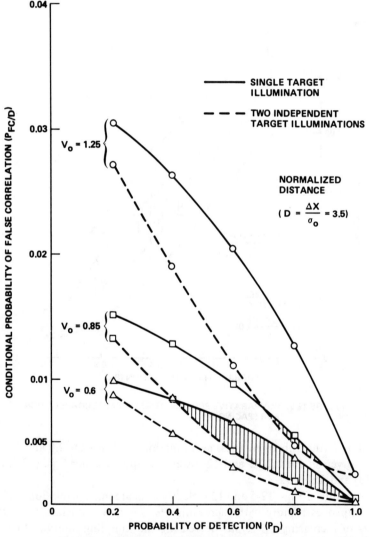

FIGURE 12-6. COMPARATIVE PROBABILITIES OF FALSE CORRELATION
FOR SPACING D = 3.5

The dashed lines were computed from the original curves by shifting the curves according to the relationship of (12.14). For example, for P_D equals 0.4, the value for P_D' is 0.64. Thus, values for the dashed lines at $P_D=0.4$ correspond to the points on the unbroken lines at $P_D=0.64$. This is a conservative approximation to the improvement in correlation performance that would be derived by increased detection probability. The additional improvement that would be derived because v_o would also be decreased as P_D is increased is not included in this approximation.

The results given in Figs. 12-5 and 12-6 compare the performance improvements, given the simple correlation model, associated with increasing P_D through taking two independent looks (as given by (12.14)), and with doubling the sampling rate (leading to decreases in v_o from 1.25 to 0.85 and from 0.85 to 0.6). Both of these approaches basically double the total amount of time required for target illumination.

In order to evaluate the effectiveness of the two methods we compare $P_{FC/D}$ as a function of P_D for the appropriate solid and dashed lines. For example, the dashed line associated with $v_o=1.25$ corresponds to a two second sampling interval with two independent looks per sample. This can be compared with the solid line for $v_o=0.85$ which corresponds to a one second sampling interval but with a single look at the target.

Results show that when the initial value of v_o is 1.25, it is generally more effective to double the sampling rate. The unbroken line for $v_o=0.85$ (corresponding to $T=1.0$ s) is generally lower than the dashed line for $v_o=1.25$ (corresponding to $T=2.0$ s and enhanced detection). The exception is a region about $P_D=0.8$ for $D=3.5$. However, at $v_o=0.85$, it becomes more effective to use enhanced detection. The shaded area indicates the region where this simple model shows enhanced detection to be more effective.

In general there appears to be a complex interrelationship involved in determining the relative merits of sampling more often *versus* spending more time on target to insure detection for a given sample. This conclusion is also apparent from the tracking results of [1] and the Monte Carlo correlation results presented in the next section. Results given here for the two target case favor decreased sampling intervals, while the Monte Carlo results to be presented next, derived using encounter geometries with three and four targets, favor enhanced detection.

12.4.2 Monte Carlo Correlation Performance Evaluation

A Monte Carlo simulation was used to compare correlation performance of tracking systems in a closely spaced target environment. The simulation included a conventional (MSA) system and an ESA system with enhanced detection and adaptive sampling capability. The enhanced detection was again modeled by using two independent looks at the target so that the new probability of detection is given by (12.14). The adaptive sampling logic chose between sampling intervals of 5.0, 2.5, and 1.25 s. The shortest sampling interval was chosen by this logic for closely spaced targets. The MSA system used a fixed sampling interval (T=2.5 s) and the standard single-look probability of detection.

Define D to be the ratio of the target angular separation to the angular measurement-error standard deviation. For spacings in order of D=3.5 or more, the adaptive sampling feature of the ESA was found to significantly improve tracking performance. For example, consider a head-on geometry in which three targets flying with spacing D=4.2 are approaching the tracking radar. Compare performance for a conventional (MSA) system with an ESA system that only utilizes the adaptive sampling feature. Results are summarized in Table 12-4. The first criterion is the probability of false correlation (P_{FC}). A false correlation is defined to occur when the return associated with a particular track is not from the same target that produced the previous correlating return. The second criterion is the number of tracks that became degraded as the result of false correlation, and therefore resulted in deletion. Tracks that were deleted simply as the result of missed observations were not included in this sum. The final criterion is the normalized standard deviation of the estimation error in the component of target velocity normal to the true velocity vector and in the horizontal plane (denoted the target cross velocity). The error is normalized with respect to the value found for the conventional (MSA) system.

Referring to Table 12-4, the proportion of false correlations is small (one percent or less) for both systems. However, the ESA system has significantly fewer deleted tracks. Also, the velocity estimation error is smaller for the ESA system.

The next example considered was the case of three crossing targets as shown in Fig. 12-7. The results are given in Table 12-5 with the performance criteria being the number of track deletions and the number of track switches. Track switches are defined to occur when the track changes from one target to another. Again, the ESA system leads to a significant improvement in tracking performance. Thus, the results shown in Tables 12-4 and 12-5 illustrate the condition where adaptive sampling (decreased sampling interval) significantly improves correlation performance. Use of the shorter sampling interval reduces the unstable tracking region, shown in Fig. 1-4, for these conditions.

For certain combinations of target separations and detection probabilities, it does not appear feasible to eliminate unstable tracking through the use of faster sampling alone. This concept, shown pictorially in Fig. 1-4, is illustrated by the results, derived using a normalized separation D=3.1, shown in Table 12-6. Results are based upon 50 Monte Carlo runs of a four-

TABLE 12-4

SUMMARY STATISTICS FOR THREE TARGETS WITH NORMALIZED SPACING $D=4.2$

Based on 60 Monte Carlo runs
Time Histories for 125 sec
Closing Geometry, 50 nmi to 17 nmi
3 Targets
Single Look at Target

	Probability of False Correlation (P_{FC})	Deletions Resulting from False Correlation (N_{DEL})	Normalized Error in Estimate of Target Cross Velocity $\sigma_{\bar{v}}$
Conventional MSA System, $T=2.5$ s	0.01	25	1.0
ESA, Adaptive Sampling	0.003	5	0.77

TABLE 12-5

ESA SHOWS IMPROVED PERFORMANCE AGAINST CROSSING TARGETS

(3 Crossing Targets, 60 Monte Carlo Runs)

	Deletions	Switches
Conventional MSA System, $T=2.5$ s	12	38
ESA Adaptive Sampling	5	10

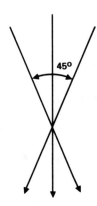

**FIGURE 12-7. THREE TARGET
CROSSING GEOMETRY**

**TABLE 12-6
SUMMARY STATISTICS FOR FOUR
TARGETS WITH NORMALIZED SPACING $D = 3.1$**

	P_{FC}	N_{DEL}	Normalized $\sigma_{\tilde{v}}$
Conventional, $T=2.5$ s	0.06	45	1.0
ESA, Adaptive Sampling	0.04	37	0.80
ESA, Enhanced Detection	0.02	11	0.76
ESA, Enhanced Detection and Adaptive Sampling	0.02	13	0.68

target geometry. Use of adaptive sampling decreases the probability of false correlation, but a large number of tracks are still deleted.

Enhanced detection was again defined to be the application of a second independent detection attempt. This is an approximation of what can be effectively achieved by an ESA system through the use of adaptive RF and PRF selection. Then, upon applying enhanced detection, the number of deletions is significantly reduced even without adaptive sampling. No further correlation improvement is noted when both enhanced detection and adaptive sampling are applied to this case.

Results derived from Monte Carlo simulation of an actual encounter geometry, presented in Table 12-6, lead to somewhat different conclusions than those derived from Figs. 12-5 and 12-6, which were obtained from the simplified correlation example examined in the previous section. The Monte Carlo encounter simulation results favor enhanced detection more than did the results from the simplified correlation example. However, the simplified model only considered two targets and did not include the decrease in prediction error, which would also be associated with increased detection probability. The encounter simulation considered four targets and examined the entire time history of an encounter geometry, including the effects of miscorrelation upon track deletion. Thus, it is more indicative of true expected performance.

A complex relationship is involved. However, both studies lead to the conclusions that a point of diminishing returns is reached with the increased sampling rate approach and that, nonetheless, increasing P_D continues to be effective, even after the decreasing sampling interval is no longer effective.

12.5 IMPLEMENTATION OF MULTIPLE-TARGET TRACKING LOGIC FOR AN ESA SYSTEM

Previous sections have detailed the potential benefits of using the ESA for MTT. These benefits are also well documented in the tracking literature. However, the potential problems associated with using the ESA for MTT are typically not mentioned. Thus, this section discusses various implementation issues (and problems) and outlines approaches for their solution. The choice of techniques remains an open issue and is highly application dependent.

For most applications the sequential nearest-neighbor (NN) correlation approach seems most direct. Figure 12-8 presents a simplified flow chart of an implementation using this approach. However, as indicated in the discussion to follow, the logic required to perform sequential NN correlation, while efficiently using the properties of ESA, can become quite complex.

The problem inherent with the use of sequential NN correlation is the uncertainty associated with making correlation decisions under difficult conditions with insufficient information. Figure 12-9 illustrates this correlation problem for the case of two closely spaced targets. Assume track $T1$ is illuminated and that observation $O1$ is received. Then, if observation $O1$ is closer to $P2$ than to $P1$ the correct assignment will not be made using sequential NN correlation. Thus, it is either necessary to ensure that $T2$ is also illuminated or to hold the correlation decision in abeyance until more data on either $T1$ or $T2$ are received.

As illustrated by the previous example, the multiple hypothesis tracking (MHT) approach discussed in Chapters 10 and 14, in which difficult corre-

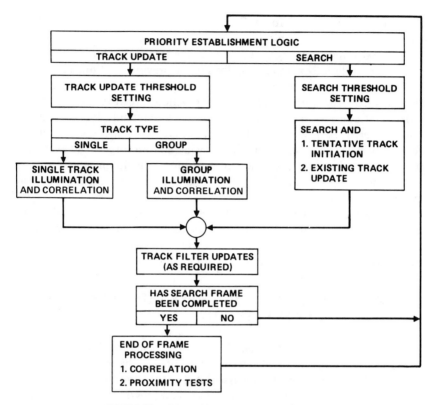

FIGURE 12-8. PROCESSING LOGIC FOR ESA MTT
SYSTEM USING SEQUENTIAL PROCESSING

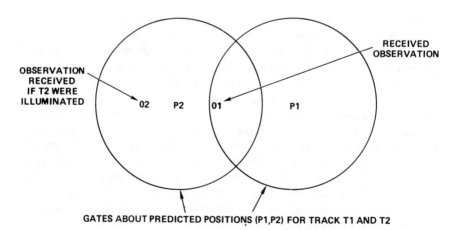

FIGURE 12-9. EXAMPLE OF POTENTIAL MISCORRELATION
DUE TO INCOMPLETE TARGET ILLUMINATION

lation decisions are held in abeyance, is preferable to the sequential NN method. However, the MHT approach represents a significant departure from the more traditional NN methods and the associated combinatoric explosion of the number of possible hypotheses must be limited. Also, the question of sensor allocation becomes less direct when there are a number of different hypotheses and a resultant increase in the number of hypothesized tracks. The issues involved in both the sequential NN and MHT implementation methods are presented next.

12.5.1 Sequential NN Logic for ESA MTT

The flow chart shown in Fig. 12-8 gives an overview of the type of logic required to implement sequential NN correlation for an ESA system. An important feature of the ESA in its application to MTT is that the functions of search and track update can be decoupled. First, priorities are established to determine if the antenna should search for new targets or update existing target tracks. Then, as discussed in Chapter 5, detection threshold settings should be set separately for these two functions.

As the ESA searches for new targets it may also receive returns from targets already in track. Thus, as search observations are received they should be compared, using gating relationships, with the predicted positions of all existing tracks. For this comparison to be accurate, the prediction times must either be variable (performed as observations are received) or all track predictions should be made in several short steps throughout the scan interval. Observations that do not satisfy the gates of any existing tracks can immediately be used to initiate new tracks, which should be updated as soon as possible thereafter. However, those observations that do satisfy gates of existing tracks present other problems.

Except in the most clear-cut situations, there are potential problems associated with assigning search observations to tracks before all search observations are received. As previously discussed, Fig. 12-9 shows a simple example illustrating why all targets should be illuminated before assignments are made. Thus, the immediate assignment of search observations to existing tracks should only be made if the search observations satisfy the gate of a single track.

One solution to conflict resolution with search observations is to save all conflicting observations until the end of the search scan and then to perform correlation using the assignment matrix approach. This solution, in effect, mimics the MSA TWS solution, but can lead to the problem of track update with "stale" search observations. This can occur when a track being considered for update with a search observation is updated with an observation received during track illumination. If the track illumination occurred after the search observation was received, it may be best not to use the search observation for track update.

Next, considering track update illumination, one approach to MTT with an ESA is to treat the problem as a set of independent single-target tracking systems interleaved with the search for new targets. For example, existing tracks could receive update illuminations at a fixed update rate with each track being illuminated individually. However, the difficulties illustrated in Fig. 12-9 will arise if this approach is used for closely spaced targets. Thus, in order to reduce false correlation, it is necessary to identify interacting target tracks and to illuminate these tracks as a group.

Target tracks are defined to be interacting if a return from one target has a significant probability of correlating with a track from another target. This condition can be identified by performing a proximity test (whereby all predicted target positions are compared), or by noting when observations fall within the gates of multiple target tracks. Then, when interacting target tracks are recognized they should be illuminated as a group.

Whenever possible, it is desirable to sample at a sufficiently high rate so that the uncertainty in predicted target position does not lead to the true position being outside the beamwidth of the initial commanded antenna position. However, due to the requirements for search and update of other tracks or due to missed detections, this condition cannot always be satisfied. Thus, a local search may be required even for the update illumination of a single isolated track. Then, because overlapping beams are used, there will again be the necessity for observation redundancy elimination.

Once observations are received, the use of multiple gating tests is appropriate in order to determine subsequent data processing and illumination requirements. For example, using a standard gate (SG) and a maneuver gate (MG) can lead to immediate observation-to-track assignment whenever an observation satisfying the SG is received. However, if only the MG is satisfied, it would be appropriate to attempt immediately to obtain a confirming second observation. Then, if a maneuver is confirmed, it is desirable to increase the filter covariance matrix and to sample at a faster rate as long as the target is determined to be still maneuvering.

12.5.2 Multiple Hypothesis Approach to ESA MTT

Using the measurement-oriented MHT method, the full capability of the ESA theoretically can be achieved. New hypotheses are formed as observations are received and the ultimate correct correlation of observations-to-tracks will be less dependent upon the simultaneous illumination of all target tracks. The methods discussed in Chapters 10 and 14 are directly applicable. However, it is expected that it will be necessary to maintain fewer hypotheses if closely spaced targets can be illuminated as a group.

Sensor allocation is less direct when the MHT approach is used. Specifically, there may be many more tracks contained in the multiple hypotheses than would be formed using the sequential NN method. Thus, the question arises regarding which tracks should be given update illumination. One approach is to illuminate the tracks within the most likely hypothesis. An alternative approach is to illuminate the tracks according to their probability of validity (as computed using all hypotheses).

Finally, it should be noted that efficient use of the ESA ought to make the MHT method more effective. Adaptive sampling can be used to obtain data in order to resolve difficult correlation decisions quickly, and thus reduce the number of required hypotheses. This also leads to the requirement for efficient sensor allocation.

12.6 SUMMARY

This chapter began with an overview of MTT tracking using the ESA and a discussion of how an ESA system can potentially differ from an MSA TWS system. Results have shown that the agile beam capabilities of the ESA can lead to enhanced detection performance, which, in turn, leads to significant increases in target tracking range. By examining a simple analytical model and Monte Carlo simulation performance results, enhanced detection performance is also shown to lead to much improved correlation performance.

The important adaptive sampling features associated with the ESA lead to improvements in correlation performance and in the maintenance of track against maneuvering targets. A simple analytical formula for determining a fixed sampling interval based upon required tracking performance is given by (12.2), and for non-unity P_D by (12.3). However, the more flexible adaptive sampling approaches, also presented above, are preferable whenever computational constraints permit. In particular, the utility theory approach outlined here and in Chapter 13 has shown considerable promise as an efficient means for allocating the ESA between the functions of search for new targets and update illumination of existing tracks.

This chapter closed with a discussion of implementation logic. When considering the logic involved, it becomes apparent that the sequential NN correlation approach is less appealing for the ESA application than it is for the standard MSA TWS application. Thus, unless limited by computational constraints, the multiple hypotheses tracking approach is preferable for the ESA application.

In addition to NN and MHT methods, the JPDA discussed in Chapter 10 and the group tracking methods discussed in Chapter 11 may also be applicable. These methods are most applicable for very closely spaced targets, particularly for aircraft in formation [10]. The ESA offers tremendous potential for improved MTT, but the choice of techniques to utilize this potential remains an area for future research.

REFERENCES

1. Kurniawan, Z., and P.J. McLane, "Parameter Optimization for an Integrated Radar Detection and Tracking Sytem," *IEE Proceedings*, Vol. 132, Part F, No. 1, Feb. 1985, pp. 36–44.

2. Wirth, W.D., "Fast and Efficient Target Search with Phased Array Radars," *Proceedings of the 1975 International Radar Conference*, Arlington, VA, April 21–23, 1975, pp. 198–203.

3. Jackson, M.C., "A Simplified Sequential Detection Scheme," *Proceedings of the 1982 International Radar Conference*, London, Oct. 18–20, 1982, pp. 66–70.

4. Dana, M.A., and D. Moraitis, "Probability of Detecting a Swerling I Target on Two Correlated Observations,"*IEEE Transactions on Aerospace and Electronic Systems*, AES-17, Sept. 1981, pp. 727–730.

5. Blackman, S.S., T.J. Broida, and M.F. Cartier, "Applications of a Phased Array Antenna in a Multiple Maneuvering Target Environment," *Proceedings of the 1981 IEEE Conference on Decision and Control,* San Diego, CA, Dec. 16–18, 1981, pp. 1413–1418.

6. Browne, B.H., L. Ekchian, and L.J. Lawdermilt, "Adaptive Features and Measurement Requirements for Advanced Surveillance Radars," *Proceedings of EASCON '80*, Arlington, VA, Sept. 29 – Oct. 1, 1980, pp. 190–194.

7. Van Keuk, G., "Software Structure and Sampling Strategy for Automatic Target Tracking with a Phased Array Radar," *AGARD Conference Proceedings No. 252, Strategies for Automatic Track Initiation*, Monterey, CA, Oct. 1978, pp. 11–1 to 11–13.

8. Keeney, R.L., and H. Raiffa, *Decisions with Multiple Objectives: Preferences and Value Tradeoffs*, New York: John Wiley and Sons, 1976.

9. Garvey, T.D., and J.D. Lowrance, "Machine Intelligence for Electronic Warfare Applications," SRI, Menlo Park, CA, Report No. AFWAL-TR-83-1168, AD-B080177, Nov. 1983.

10. Taenzer, E., "Tracking Multiple Targets Simultaneously with a Phased Array Radar," *IEEE Transactions on Aerospace and Electronic Systems,* AES-16, Sept. 1980, pp. 604–614.

Chapter 13

The Use of Multiple Sensors for Multiple-Target Tracking

13.1 INTRODUCTION

This chapter presents a survey of techniques for use in extending multiple-target tracking (MTT) theory to systems using multiple sensors. This sensor fusion problem entails the development of methods to control and combine the data from multiple sensors for tracking and identification.

The chapter begins with a discussion of the trade-offs involved in maintaining sensor-level tracks *versus* doing all tracking and correlation in the central computer. Then, an outline is given of a technique for combining sensor-level tracks into a central (or global) track file.

The use of multiple sensors typically requires the fusion of different types of data, including sensor reports containing measured attributes, such as the target type and other target features. Thus, Section 13.4 develops a Bayesian mathematical structure under which observations containing target type and other attribute data (such as vehicle tread type, radar emission characteristics, target shape, *et cetera*) can be combined and used in the data association process.

One approach to the dual tracking and identification problem has been to perform data association based on kinematic quantities and then to compute target ID after the data association occurs using kinematics. This approach is illustrated in Fig. 13-1 where gating and correlation are shown to be done using only kinematic quantities (position, range rate, *et cetera*). Then, once data association is performed using kinematic quantities, attribute estimates (such as target ID) are obtained. However, a potential problem with inconsistent target ID (or other attribute) estimates can occur if correlation is performed using only kinematic data. Thus, before an ID declaration is made using this approach, we must make an assessment of the validity of the data association and the consistency of the attribute information that has been combined.

An alternative approach, shown in Fig. 13-2, where attribute data is used directly in the correlation process is preferable to correlation using only kinematic data. Sections 13.4 and 13.5 present techniques for computing estimates of target ID (and other attributes). Because the preferred overall

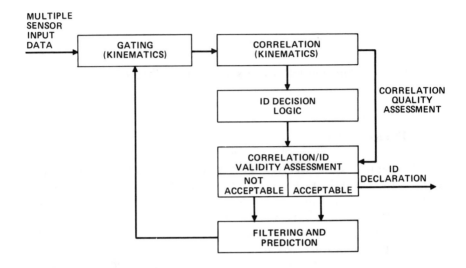

FIGURE 13–1. INDEPENDENT CORRELATION AND ID FUNCTIONS

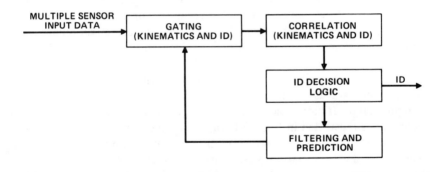

FIGURE 13–2. COMBINED ID AND KINEMATIC CORRELATION

approach uses the attribute estimates in the data association, the appropriate probability terms are defined so that data association can be based upon both kinematic and attribute data. The methods presented in Sections 13.4 and 13.5 for handling attribute data are analogous to the methods given in Chapters 2 and 4 for estimation and correlation using kinematic data.

Section 13.5 outlines the Dempster-Shafer (or evidential reasoning) method that is a generalization of classical Bayesian theory. The application of this technique is particularly convenient for combining multiple sensor data containing attribute information when uncertainty exists because of difficulty in modeling sensor error, unspecified prior distributions, or potential miscorrelation. The Dempster-Shafer method also relaxes the data-base requirements when compared with the Bayesian approach. Again, as with the standard Bayesian approach, a probability term is provided so that data association can be performed using both kinematic and attribute data.

Finally, Section 13.6 briefly discusses the issues involved in sensor allocation (or control) and outlines an approach for sensor allocation. This approach uses utility theory so that sensor allocation is based upon the estimated utility of assignment.

13.2 SENSOR-LEVEL AND CENTRAL-LEVEL MULTIPLE SENSOR FUSION

In a multiple-sensor tracking system the first major conceptual issue is to define the level at which sensor data will first be combined into tracks. The choices are sensor- or central-level tracking, or some combination of both.

The first alternative, illustrated in Fig. 13-3, is to have each sensor maintain its own track file. The tracks in these sensor track files would be established primarily upon measurements received from the individual sensor, but some communication among the sensors and between the sensors and the central track file may be used to update sensor-level track files.

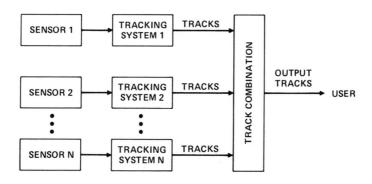

FIGURE 13-3. SENSOR LEVEL TRACKING

However, the sensor-level tracks must eventually be combined into a central track file. Thus, under this (sensor-level) approach each sensor would have separate track files and a central track file would be formed as a composite.

Points cited in favor of sensor-level tracking are reduced data-bus loading, reduced computational loading (in any single processor), and higher survivability due to distributed tracking capabilities. Certain computational advantages may result from the parallel processing that is possible using the sensor-level track approach. Also, if one sensor becomes degraded, its observations will not affect the sensor-level tracks of other sensors. Finally, the use of sensor-level tracking allows for filter design that is specifically tailored to the individual sensors.

If sensor-level tracks are maintained, they must be combined at some point if significant benefit is to be derived from the multisensor fusion approach. The result is central-level tracks that are updated with sensor-level track data, instead of with sensor report data. Several problems arise. First, if a central-level track is updated with a sensor-level track, the usual assumption (valid for the case of raw measurements with uncorrelated measurement error) of error independence from one update period to another is not valid. This can be taken into account in the processing, but it forces additional complexity. Second, less accurate tracking and correlation are to be expected if independent sensor-level tracks are maintained. For example, there will be a higher probability of false correlation in areas affected by clutter because the gate sizes will be larger due to less frequent track updates. Finally, if the multiple hypothesis tracking approach, discussed in Chapter 10, is taken at the central level, when sensor-level tracks are combined, it would also be desirable that this approach be taken at the sensor level as well. However, the maintenance of a single hypothesis tree at a central level is simpler than the maintenance of many hypotheses at each sensor as well as additional hypotheses at the central level to combine the sensor-level tracks.

The alternative to maintaining sensor-level tracks is for all report data to be sent directly to a central processor where a master track file is maintained. This approach, illustrated in Fig. 13-4, also has a number of advantages. First, more accurate tracking should be possible if all data are processed at the same place. A target track that consists of observations from more than one sensor should be more accurate than the tracks which could be established on the partial data received by the individual sensors. Thus, the central processing track approach should lead to fewer miscorrelations. Second, by processing sensor reports directly, the difficulties associated with combining sensor-level tracks are avoided. These difficulties include correlating sensor-level tracks and determining an efficient scheme for combining these tracks.

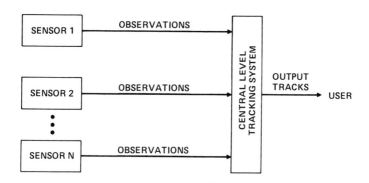

FIGURE 13-4. CENTRAL LEVEL TRACKING

Track confirmation and continuity should also be improved with central-level tracking. The various sensors will, under different circumstances, have varying ability to confirm and sustain a track. Thus, by using detections from all sensors for each track, the probability of confirming and sustaining a track can be improved over that for a single sensor. For example, in a system with radar and an infrared (IR) sensor, IR detections can maintain a track that might otherwise be lost during a fade in the radar return due to radar cross section scintillation. Also, various sensors can be used synergistically, for example, as the radar provides range and range rate while the IR provides more accurate angle measurement. Finally, the approach whereby all data are sent directly to the central processor should, in principle, lead to faster, more efficient computation. The overall time required to develop sensor-level tracks and then to combine these tracks is generally greater than the time required for central-level processing of all data at once.

There can, however, be a major drawback if pure central-level tracking is used. This problem occurs when the data from one sensor can become degraded (and this degradation not immediately sensed), and thus lead to poor central-level tracking. In this case, the possible combination of good data from undegraded sensors with bad data, in effect, will negate the value of the good data. However, if sensor-level tracks are maintained, the good sensor-level tracks will not be corrupted by the bad data. Then, when the sensor with poor data is finally recognized, the central-level tracks can be formed using only sensor-level tracks from undegraded tracks. An example of this is the radar ECM problem where, as discussed in Chapter 5, the radar measurement data may be degraded but knowledge of this degradation may be delayed.

TABLE 13-1
PERFORMANCE MEASURES FOR CENTRAL *VERSUS* SENSOR LEVEL TRACKING

Evaluation Criteria	Type of Tracking System		
	CENTRAL	*SENSOR*	*COMBINED*
Tracking Continuity and Accuracy	Excellent	Fair	Excellent
Survivability	Low	High	High
Invulnerability to Degraded Sensor Data	Low	Moderate	High
Computational Time and Complexity	Moderate	Moderate/High	Very High
Data Transfer Load	High	Moderate	Very High

Finally, it should be noted that there are several other approaches which are intermediary between sensor- and central-level tracking. One technique is to form a central-level track from one of the sensors and then to allow selected measurements from all sensors to update that central track. Another method is to average all observations, for a given time interval, from a given target, and to use the average for update of the central track.

Table 13-1 summarizes the relative measures of performance for central *versus* sensor-level tracking as well as those for a combined system. The combined system would maintain a central-level track file formed using the raw observations in addition to sensor-level tracks as "backup." Consistency checks between the central- and the sensor-level tracks could be performed to detect possible sensor degradation. This technique would optimize performance, but the computational and data transfer requirements would be very high because a great deal of redundant processing and data transfer are required.

In conclusion, the trade-off between distributed sensor-level and central-level processing is basically one between decreased transfer load, the computational advantages of parallel processing, and decreased vulnerability, on the one hand, and the possible introduction of intermediate errors, on the other. The particular application should dictate the best choice of architecture. References [1, 2] discuss different applications where central- and sensor-level tracking were chosen, respectively, while [3] discusses a combined approach. Reference [4] gives a detailed discussion of the issues involved and presents a technique for evaluation between the sensor- and central-level processing options.

Implementation of central-level tracking follows techniques previously discussed (in particular, use of the multiple hypothesis approach discussed in Chapter 10). Next, we discuss implementation of sensor-level tracking.

13.3 IMPLEMENTATION OF SENSOR-LEVEL TRACKING

13.3.1 Track-to-Track Correlation and Combining

Fundamental to the problem of combining sensor-level tracks is determining whether two tracks from different systems (sensors) potentially represent the same target. This problem was first addressed by Kanyuck and Singer [5] and later by the Naval Ocean-Surveillance Correlation Handbook [6] (1978) and by Bar-Shalom [7]. This operation has the function of eliminating unlikely track-to-track pairings, and thus it is effectively a gating operation.

Consider two tracks with, at scan k, state vector estimates and covariance matrices as defined by

track i: $x_i(k)$, $P_i(k)$
track j: $x_j(k)$, $P_j(k)$

In the most general situation the different sensors may maintain different state estimation vectors so that the covariance matrices would also differ. In this case the comparison process, described below, would be performed using the state estimates and corresponding covariance elements, which are common to the two sensors.

Following Wiener [6] and Bar-Shalom [7], a technique is outlined based upon use of the chi-square properties of the difference in the state estimation vectors of x_i and x_j. In general, it would be preferable to consider all points (or, at least, the last few state estimates) contained in the tracks. However, for simplicity and practicality of operation, we will consider only the most recent estimates (at scan k). Finally, note that if the tracks do not receive updates at the same time, their state vectors will be extrapolated to a common time point.

Define d_{ij} to be the difference vector (assumed formed at scan k, but with subscript k omitted) of the common state estimates:

$$d_{ij} = \hat{x}_i - \hat{x}_j \tag{13.1}$$

Then, if the tracks are independent, the covariance matrix (U_{ij}) for $\mathbf{d}_{ij}$ is defined:

$$U_{ij} = P_i + P_j \tag{13.2}$$

Because d_{ij} is conventionally assumed to have the Gaussian distribution, the quantity

$$R^2 = d_{ij}^T U_{ij}^{-1} d_{ij} \tag{13.3}$$

will have the chi-square (χ_n^2) distribution with the number of degrees of freedom (n) equal to the number of elements in the state vectors. A simple test to accept or reject the hypothesis that the two tracks are from the same source can be defined using the similarity threshold T_s:

$R^2 \geq T_s$, tracks are not from the same source
$R^2 < T_s$, tracks are from the same source

The choice of T_s will be based upon the chi-square properties of R^2 with some experimentation probably required for the particular application. The value of T_s would also probably best be chosen as a function of the target density (if known).

Bar-Shalom [7] has pointed out that the covariance defined by (13.2) and the resultant formation of R^2 are not strictly valid because of error correlation between the two sensor estimates. This correlation occurs, even if the measurement errors are independent, because of the common error source due to the target dynamics (that are seen by both sensors). For example, a sudden target maneuver can lead to a bias error for both sensors. Thus, the covariance between the two estimates given by (13.2) should be modified. A technique, derived in [7] and outlined below, to account for this error correlation can be applied to modify the covariance matrix U_{ij}.

Define a cross covariance matrix P_{ij} such that the initial condition is

$$P_{ij}(0|0) = 0$$

Then, later (for $k > 0$) values of $P_{ij}(k|k)$ are computed using the recursive relationship:

$$P_{ij}(k|k) = A_i(k) B(k-1) A_j^T(k) \tag{13.4}$$

where

$$A_i(k) = I - K_i(k) H_i$$
$$A_j(k) = I - K_j(k) H_j$$
$$B(k-1) = \Phi_i P_{ij}(k-1|k-1) \Phi_j^T + Q(k-1)$$

The subscripts i and j refer to sensor systems i and j, while Φ, K, H, and Q are as defined for the Kalman filter in Chapter 2. Finally, the modified covariance, replacing that given by (13.2), becomes [7]:

$$U_{ij} = P_i + P_j - P_{ij} - P_{ij}^T$$

The rest of the test is unaltered.

When tracks are determined to be from the same source, they may be combined. The resulting combined vector, which minimizes the expected error (following the discussion in Appendix 13A), is

$$x_c = x_i + C[x_j - x_i] \tag{13.5}$$

$$C = [P_i - P_{ij}] U_{ij}^{-1}$$

Finally, the covariance matrix associated with the estimate of (13.5) (from Appendix 13A) is

$$P_c = P_i - [P_i - P_{ij}] U_{ij}^{-1} [P_i - P_{ij}]^T \tag{13.6}$$

13.3.2   Formation of Central-Level Tracks from Sensor-Level Tracks

Consider a system in which sensor-level tracks are maintained and where a central (or global) track file is also required. A relatively simple way to form the required central-level track file is to combine periodically (at regular fusion time points) the sensor-level tracks into central-level tracks. Previously formed central-level tracks are replaced by the newly established tracks which have been formed by combining the current sensor-level tracks. These tracks then constitute the new central-level track file. They can be extrapolated forward in time and they are available for use whenever we require an estimate of the environment based on all sensor information. At the next fusion time point, the sensor-level tracks are combined again to re-establish a new set of central-level tracks and the process is repeated. We next outline how the sensor-level tracks are combined to form central-level tracks.

Each time the central-level track file is to be re-established, the current estimates from the sensor-level tracks are compared. This first requires that each sensor-level track be extrapolated to a common fusion time point. Then, the central-level track file is initialized with the track-file from one sensor which is chosen based upon consideration of accuracy, resolution, and detection. Finally, the track-files from the other sensors are correlated, one at a time, with the central-level tracks and new state estimates are formed. Figure 13-5 gives a flow chart of the process.

Correlation of sensor-level to central-level tracks is performed using the same type of logic as is involved in observation-to-track correlation. The preliminary correlation logic discussed in the previous section should be used to eliminate unlikely pairings. Then, for final correlation, the assignment methods discussed in Chapter 4 are applicable. However, the correlation process can be simplified if, as discussed below, previous correlation information is used.

It may be that the correlation of two sensor-level tracks from different sensors has been made repeatedly in the past. Thus, if a track correlation history is maintained, pairings that were previously established using a more complete correlation logic can be re-established if less stringent requirements (such as satisfaction of a simple gating criterion) are satisfied. Similarly, a potential correlation between sensor-level tracks that has been rejected in the past may not need to be reconsidered.

Once a sensor-level track is paired with a central-level track, the track estimates and covariances must be combined. If only two sensors are used and if P_{ij} is computed using (13.4), the estimates given by (13.5) and (13.6) are strictly valid. However, if P_{ij} is not computed, or if tracks from more than two sensors are combined, the correlation due to common target

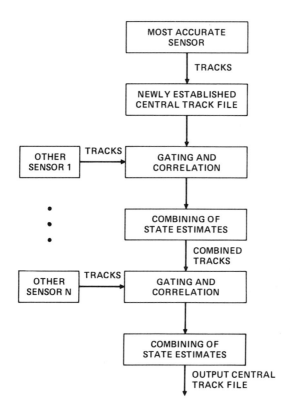

FIGURE 13-5. TECHNIQUE FOR COMBINING SENSOR
INTO CENTRAL-LEVEL TRACK FILES

dynamics cannot be conveniently included. Thus, the solution would be obtained using (13.5) and (13.6), but with the approximation that P_{ij} can be neglected.

The alternative to the technique presented above is to maintain continuous (rather than periodically re-established) central-level tracks, and to use the estimates from the sensor-level tracks to update the central-level tracks. However, due to the time correlation of the errors associated with the sensor-level tracks, they cannot be used to update the central-level tracks in the same manner that raw measurements are used. Because the time correlation associated with the errors in sensor-level tracking would have to be taken into account, the simpler alternative is to re-establish the central-level tracks periodically using sensor-level tracks.

13.4 FUSION AND CORRELATION FOR DATA INCLUDING ATTRIBUTES

This section develops a Bayesian mathematical structure based upon [8,9,10], under which observations containing attribute data as well as kinematics can be combined and updated estimates thereby formed. Attributes are sensed target quantities that are associated with a particular type or class of target. These may include such quantities as wheel (or tread) type for ground targets, engine type for aircraft, type of emitting radar for either ground or aircraft targets, or target image shape. Also, the class or type of target (i.e., truck or tank) may itself be considered an attribute. However, we will consider type separately.

Most previously developed MTT systems have only used kinematic quantities such as position, range rate, *et cetera*. However, with the use of sensors other than radar and with advances in radar signal processing techniques, the efficient use of other types of attribute data now becomes important. In particular, future military MTT systems will use a wide variety of sensors that will measure a number of different attributes. The problem is to correlate these different types of data, to make inferences on the important attributes such as target type, and to assign confidences to these inferences.

The issues addressed here are those generally associated with multiple sensor integration (MSI) or correlation (MSC). However, these issues also arise with a single sensor, such as radar, that can operate in different modes so that different quantities can be measured.

The approach given here follows a standard Bayesian formulation. If the required *a priori* information and the conditional probabilities are available, the Bayesian approach provides the most appropriate structure for representing the relationships among discrete attributes. The next section will present a generalization of Bayesian logic that can operate under a less information-rich environment.

We will consider attributes to be related only through target type. For example, tanks may tend to have certain types of tread (as can be determined by the radar Doppler signature) and certain types of IR signature. Thus, upon detecting a vehicle with the tread likely for a tank (and upon initiating a track on that vehicle), some knowledge of the IR signature expected from the track can be inferred, even though no direct physical relationships between tread type and the IR signature exist. This information can be used in the gating and correlation processes.

In general, it is necessary to maintain separate estimates for the attributes of interest and also for the target type. All attribute information could be incorporated in the target type estimate but this approach can lead to nonoptimal performance. It will be required that target track state vectors include the probabilities associated with the attributes as well as with the target type.

As an example of the necessity to maintain attribute as well as target type estimates, consider the situation where a sensor receives a report indicating that the observed target has emitting radar type 1. Further assume it to be known that radar type 1 can be associated with either target type 1 or type 2. Then, a later report indicates radar type 2 and it is known that radar type 2 can be associated with either target type 2 or 3. Considering radar type, this is an example of conflicting reports that should not be associated. However, if only the target type were considered, the erroneous conclusion that these two reports were consistent and that they both indicated target type 2 would be made.

For certain sensors there may be sensor-level data processors that directly convert measured attributes to estimates of target type while for other sensors the raw attribute measurement data may be conveniently available. Thus, the correlation methods must be able to handle both types of inputs.

The use of *a priori* knowledge will be assumed. First, it is assumed that an estimate of target mix is given so that the *a priori* probabilities associated with the various target types are available. Also, the probabilistic relationships between the attributes and target type are assumed to be known. For example, it might be known that a particular target type has probability 0.7 of having radar type 1 and probability 0.3 of radar type 2. Finally, measurement probabilities are also required.

We next derive a method by which attribute and target type information is included in the overall correlation and target identification process. Each track file will contain estimated probabilities for the appropriate attributes and for the target type. The initial values will be given by the *a priori* probabilities and updates will be computed as outlined below.

13.4.1   General Bayesian Structure for Estimation of Discrete Quantities

First, define A to represent target type with the components a_i representing possible target types and $P(a_i)$ the probability associated with type a_i. Similarly, B and C are defined to be attributes with possible values (or states) b_j, c_l and associated probabilities $P(b_j)$, $P(c_l)$. The process can, of course, be continued for other attributes (D, E, *et cetera*), but use of B and C will illustrate the method.

Consider the problem of estimating attributes B and C from the measured attribute data. This is a problem similar to the use of new kinematic measurement data to obtain estimates of kinematic quantities. The standard solution to the kinematic problem is the use of Kalman filtering. An analogous solution to the estimation of attribute quantities is the application of Bayes' rule. However, as in the Kalman filter, certain assumptions must be made regarding ensemble target statistics and measurement accuracy.

The Kalman filter uses ensemble statistical models to describe target dynamic behavior. Similarly, using the Bayesian technique for attribute estimation, some attributes (such as target amplitude or intensity profile) may be modeled as evolving in time according to a Markov relationship. Reid [8] discusses the Markov model. However, for simplicity in this development, we will only consider the more standard attributes that do not change with time. The extension to a Markov model is direct [8].

The assumed known prior ensemble distribution for target type is used in the same manner that initial conditions are used for the Kalman filter. Then, as attribute measurements are received, the probability vector associated with the attributes is updated using Bayes' rule in the same manner that target kinematic estimates are updated using measured data and the Kalman filtering equations. Finally, the measurement process for the case of attribute estimation update is defined by the relationship:

$P(X_m|X)$ = probability of receiving measurement X_m given that the true quantity is X

Whenever measurement data are received the updated probabilities can be computed using Bayes' rule:

$$P(X|X_m) = \frac{P(X_m|X)\, P(X)}{P(X_m)} \tag{13.7}$$

where

$P(X)$ = prior probability associated with X

$$P(X_m) = \sum_X P(X_m|X)\, P(X)$$

Then, $P(X|X_m)$ becomes the new prior probability for use when further data are received.

To summarize, Bayes' rule, (13.7), is solved recursively as new data are received. This relatively simple relationship provides the estimated probabilities of target type and attribute classes (or states) based directly on the measurements of the involved quantities X_m. However, as discussed next, the estimated probabilities can be improved if known interrelationships between attributes and target type exist.

Measurements of target type a_i can be used to update estimates of attribute state b_j. Similarly, the measurement of attributes can be used to update target type estimates. For example, assume that attribute b_j refers to some type of airborne radar characteristic. Then, clearly there should be a relationship between the aircraft type and the characteristics of its radar. The Boeing 707 jetliner, for example, surely has a different type of radar than the typical combat or reconnaissance aircraft. However, different types of aircraft may still have basically the same radar. Also, the same aircraft may use different types of radar. Thus, although attribute information cannot, in general, be used directly to determine the target type, this information may be used indirectly to improve the estimate of target type, or at least to eliminate certain alternatives.

First, it is necessary to specify relationships between expected attribute and target type using prior information as defined by the matrix $M(B|A)$ with elements:

$$M (B|A)_{ij} = P (b_j | a_i) = \text{conditional probability of attribute } b_j \text{ given target type } a_i$$

Then, our particular problem, shown in Fig. 13-6, is a special case of the general inference net discussed by Pearl [9] and our derivation follows that reference. The parent node A refers to target type with states a_i. The descendents B (with states b_j), C (with states c_l), *et cetera* can be denoted siblings and are only related through the parent so that

$$P (b_j, c_l | a_i) = P (b_j | a_i) P (c_l | a_i)$$

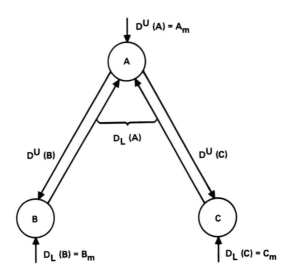

FIGURE 13-6. INFERENCE SYSTEM FOR TARGET TYPE (A)
AND ATTRIBUTES (B, C)

The probability of attribute b_j can be represented by the product of two terms and a normalizing constant (α_B):

$$P(b_j) = \alpha_B \, \lambda\,(b_j)\, q\,(b_j) \tag{13.8}$$

where, for our case,

$$\lambda\,(b_j) = P(B_m|\,b_j)$$

$$q\,(b_j) = P(b_j|\,D^U\,(B))$$

B_m = set of direct measurements on attribute B

$D^U\,(B)$ = data entering the estimate of B from above

Equation (13.8) shows the probability associated with b_j to be the product of a term based upon the direct measurement, B_m, of B (denoted here as λ (b_j)) and another, indirect, term that includes the relationship between attribute and target type. The indirect term uses $D^U(B)$, which in this case includes the data that goes into the estimation of A through prior information on A, through direct measurement on A, and through indirect measurement on A using the attributes (C, D, *et cetera*) other than B.

The indirect term is [9]:

$$q\,(b_j) = \sum_i \left[\frac{P(b_j|\,a_i)\,P(a_i)}{r\,(B \rightarrow a_i)} \right] \tag{13.9}$$

where $r\,(B \rightarrow a_i)$ is the contribution from the estimate of B to the probability of a_i, $P(a_i)$. The division by $r\,(B \rightarrow a_i)$ removes the effect of B upon the estimation of a_i. This term, $r\,(B \rightarrow a_i)$, represents the last message sent from B to A for use in forming the probability vector $P\,(A)$ associated with the estimates of target type. It is given by

$$r\,(B \rightarrow a_i) = \sum_j P(b_j|\,a_i)\,P(B_m|\,b_j) \tag{13.10}$$

In a similar manner, the elements of the probability vector associated with target type a_i are given by

$$P(a_i) = \alpha_A \, \lambda\,(a_i)\, q\,(a_i) \tag{13.11}$$

The term, $q(a_i)$ includes the *a priori* probability, $P_0(a_i)$, of a_i and the contribution from the measurement data set A_m directly related to A. Thus,

$$q\,(a_i) = P(A_m|\,a_i)\,P_0\,(a_i) \tag{13.12}$$

The term $\lambda\,(a_i)$ represents the contribution to the probability $P\,(a_i)$ that is derived from the indirect relationships with the attributes B, C, *et cetera* and the measurement sets (B_m, C_m, *et cetera*) on these attributes. Thus, considering attributes B and C (the extension to more attributes is direct):

$$\lambda\,(a_i) = \left[\sum_j P\,(b_j|\,a_i)\,P\,(B_m|\,b_j)\right]\!\left[\sum_l P\,(c_l|\,a_i)\,P\,(C_m|\,c_l)\right] \qquad (13.13)$$

Finally, a simple technique for including the normalization (and thus effectively to compute α_A) is to compute

$$P'\,(a_i) = \lambda\,(a_i)\,q\,(a_i) \qquad (13.14)$$

and

$$\alpha_A = 1/\sum_i P'\,(a_i)$$

so that

$$P\,(a_i) = \frac{P'\,(a_i)}{\displaystyle\sum_i P'\,(a_i)}$$

A similar relationship can be used for b_j and the other attributes.

13.4.2 An Example Combining Attribute and Type Measurements

Equations (13.8) through (13.14) represent a mathematically consistent technique for using target type and other attribute data. The use of these equations may initially seem complex. Thus, the following relatively simple example is presented in order to clarify the application.

Tables 13-2 and 13-3 define the parameters of the example that will be used for illustration of the methods. Table 13-2 presents the *a priori* probabilities associated with the assumed two target types and the relationships between the attributes and target type. Finally, Table 13-3 defines the measurement statistics for the example.

TABLE 13-2
EXAMPLE TYPE, ATTRIBUTE *A PRIORI* STATISTICS

A Priori *Target* *Type Mix (A)*	*Attribute Conditional Probabilities*	
	B	*C*
$P_0\,(a_1) = 0.6$	$P\,(b_1|\,a_1) = 0.8$	$P\,(c_1|\,a_1) = 0.3$
	$P\,(b_2|\,a_1) = 0.2$	$P\,(c_2|\,a_1) = 0.7$
$P_0\,(a_2) = 0.4$	$P\,(b_1|\,a_2) = 0.4$	$P\,(c_1|\,a_2) = 0.7$
	$P\,(b_2|\,a_2) = 0.6$	$P\,(c_2|\,a_2) = 0.3$

TABLE 13-3
EXAMPLE MEASUREMENT STATISTICS

A	B	C
$P(a_{1m}\|a_1) = 0.8$	$P(b_{1m}\|b_1) = 0.8$	$P(c_{1m}\|c_1) = 0.9$
$P(a_{2m}\|a_1) = 0.2$	$P(b_{2m}\|b_1) = 0.2$	$P(c_{2m}\|c_1) = 0.1$
$P(a_{1m}\|a_2) = 0.3$	$P(b_{1m}\|b_2) = 0.3$	$P(c_{1m}\|c_2) = 0.4$
$P(a_{2m}\|a_2) = 0.7$	$P(b_{2m}\|b_2) = 0.7$	$P(c_{2m}\|c_2) = 0.6$

Continuing with the example, assume that the first measurement indicates target type 1 ($A_m = a_{1m}$) and the second and third attribute measurements give b_{1m} and c_{1m}. First, given the target type measurement and using (13.12), we have

$$q(a_1) = P(a_{1m}|a_1) P_0(a_1) = 0.8(0.6) = 0.48$$

$$q(a_2) = P(a_{1m}|a_2) P_0(a_2) = 0.3(0.4) = 0.12$$

Also, since there are no attribute measurements yet,

$$\lambda(a_1) = \lambda(a_2) = 1$$

Thus, using (13.14),

$$P'(a_1) = 0.48, \qquad P'(a_2) = 0.12$$

$$P(a_1) = 0.48/0.60 = 0.8, \qquad P(a_2) = 0.2$$

The measured target type (a_{1m}) is used to compute attribute estimates through (13.8) and (13.9). First, since there have been no measurements of B or C, the terms $\lambda(b_j)$, $\lambda(c_l)$, $r(B \rightarrow a_i)$, and $r(C \rightarrow a_i)$ are all unity. Thus, using the relationships in Table 13-2 and the $P(a_i)$ computed above:

$$P(b_1) = q(b_1) = 0.8(0.8) + 0.4(0.2) = 0.72$$

$$P(b_2) = q(b_2) = 0.2(0.8) + 0.6(0.2) = 0.28$$

and a similar computation can be used to determine $P(c_1)$ and $P(c_2)$.

Next, consider inclusion of the measured attribute b_{1m}. The updated probabilities, $P(b_1|b_{1m})$ and $P(b_2|b_{1m})$ can be computed directly, using Bayes' rule, Eq. (13.7), to be

$$P(b_{1m}) = 0.8(0.72) + 0.3(0.28) = 0.66$$

$$P(b_1) = \frac{0.8(0.72)}{0.66} = 0.873, \qquad P(b_2) = 0.127$$

Alternatively, continuing with the general approach, we can identify

$$\lambda\ (b_1) = P(b_{1m}|\ b_1) = 0.8, \quad \lambda\ (b_2) = P(b_{1m}|\ b_2) = 0.3$$
$$q\ (b_1) = 0.72, \quad q\ (b_2) = 0.28$$

and use (13.8) to get the same result.

To update the target type probabilities, reflecting the attribute measurement (b_{1m}), we first compute, using (13.13) and Tables 13-2 and 13-3,

$$\lambda(a_1) = 0.8\ (0.8) + 0.2\ (0.3) = 0.70$$
$$\lambda\ (a_2) = 0.4\ (0.8) + 0.6\ (0.3) = 0.50$$

$$(13.15)$$

Note, for later use, that

$$r\ (B \to a_1) = \lambda\ (a_1) = 0.7, \quad r\ (B \to a_2) = \lambda\ (a_2) = 0.5$$

Then, as computed above, we have

$$q\ (a_1) = 0.48, \quad q\ (a_2) = 0.12$$

so that

$$P'(a_1) = 0.7(0.48) = 0.336, \quad P'(a_2) = 0.5(0.12) = 0.06$$
$$P(a_1) = 0.336/0.396 = 0.848, \quad P(a_2) = 0.152$$

Finally, consider the effect of the measured attribute c_{1m} on the estimates of A and B. Considering A, first we find, from (13.13) and (13.15), the new values for $\lambda(a_i)$ to be

$$\lambda(a_1) = 0.7\ [0.3(.09) + 0.7(0.4)] = 0.7(0.55) = 0.385$$
$$\lambda(a_2) = 0.5\ [0.7(0.9) + 0.3(0.4)] = 0.5(0.75) = 0.375$$

Thus, using (13.11) and the previously computed values of $q(a_i)$,

$$P'(a_1) = 0.385(0.48) = 0.185, \quad P'(a_2) = 0.375(0.12) = 0.045$$
$$P(a_1) = 0.185/0.23 = 0.804, \quad P(a_2) = 0.196$$

In order to compute the updated estimates on B, first note the values, from above,

$$r(B \to a_1) = 0.7, \quad r(B \to a_2) = 0.5$$
$$\lambda(b_1) = 0.8, \quad \lambda(b_2) = 0.3$$

Then, using (13.9), we write

$$q(b_1) = \frac{0.8\ (0.804)}{0.7} + \frac{0.4\ (0.196)}{0.5} = 1.076$$

$$q(b_2) = \frac{0.2\ (0.804)}{0.7} + \frac{0.6\ (0.196)}{0.5} = 0.465$$

Thus,

$$P'(b_1) = 0.8(1.076) = 0.861, \quad P'(b_2) = 0.3(0.465) = 0.14$$
$$P(b_1) = 0.86, \quad P(b_2) = (0.14)$$

The method extends directly to handle more measurements. For example, if a second (and, in fact, conflicting), independent measurement of the state of attribute B is b_{2m}, we have

$$B_m = (b_{1m}, b_{2m})$$

and

$$\lambda(b_1) = P(B_m | b_1) = P(b_{1m} | b_1) P(b_{2m} | b_1) = 0.8 (0.2) = 0.16$$
$$\lambda(b_2) = P(B_m | b_2) = P(b_{1m} | b_2) P(b_{2m} | b_2) = 0.3 (0.7) = 0.21$$

Thus, since the values $q(b_1)$ and $q(b_2)$ are unchanged, we have

$$P'(b_1) = 0.16(1.076) = 0.172, \quad P'(b_2) = 0.21(0.465) = 0.098$$
$$P(b_1) = 0.637, \quad P(b_2) = 0.363$$

Continuing with A, from (13.13), and using the previously computed contribution from C,

$$\lambda(a_1) = [0.8(0.16) + 0.2(0.21)] (0.55) = 0.093$$
$$\lambda(a_2) = [0.4(0.16) + 0.6(0.21)] (0.75) = 0.142$$

Thus, since the $q(a_i)$ are also unchanged, we have

$$P'(a_1) = 0.093 (0.48) = 0.045, \quad P'(a_2) = 0.142 (0.12) = 0.017$$
$$P(a_1) = 0.045/0.062 = 0.726, \quad P(a_2) = 0.274$$

Table 13-4 summarizes results for A and B. Also, included is the initial condition on B, which can be obtained, using (13.9), from the initial condition on A. The computations directly associated with attribute C would be performed in a completely analogous manner. Also, the final probabilities are the same if the order in which the measurements are received is changed. Similarly, the methods can be readily extended to more target types (greater than two) and more attribute types.

13.4.3   Data Association Using Combined Attribute and Kinematic Data

The previous section discussed how probabilistic attribute estimates could be updated given the measured data. However, the major problem in a multiple target environment is the assignment of observations to tracks so that track estimates can be updated. Thus, generalizing [10], this section outlines a method for using type and attribute data for data association.

TABLE 13-4
SUMMARY OF EXAMPLE CALCULATION RESULTS

	Type Estimates		*Attribute Estimates*	
Measurement	$P(a_1)$	$P(a_2)$	$P(b_1)$	$P(b_2)$
Initial Condition	0.6	0.4	0.64	0.36
a_{1m}	0.80	0.20	0.72	0.28
b_{1m}	0.848	0.152	0.873	0.127
c_{1m}	0.804	0.196	0.86	0.14
b_{2m}	0.726	0.274	0.637	0.363

First, we compute the probability term associated with the potential assignment of an attribute (or type) measurement to a given track. Assume that an estimate of attribute (or type) has been formed from previous measurements assigned to the track in question. Then, given the present measurement Z_m and the set of previous measurements D_p associated with the track, the probability of the track in question producing this measurement is given by

$$P(Z_m|D_p) = \sum_Z P(Z_m|Z) P(Z|D_p)$$

where Z represents the set of parameter values that may be assumed by the measured attribute or type.

To illustrate this computation we continue with the example discussed above, in which the previous data set was $D_p = \{a_{1m}, b_{1m}, c_{1m}\}$. The probabilities associated with attribute B, as computed just after receipt of the measurements, from Table 13-4, are

$$P(b_1) = 0.86, \quad P(b_2) = 0.14$$

Now, given an observation containing attribute measurement b_{2m}, the probability associated with this measured attribute value, using the values from Table 13-3, is

$$P(b_{2m}|D_p) = 0.2(0.86) + 0.7(0.14) = 0.27$$

The probability (0.27) that the track will produce observation b_{2m} may be compared with the probability that a new source (NS) will produce b_{2m}.

Using the initial condition (or prior) values for $P(B)$ from Table 13-4, we write

$$P(b_{2m}|NS) = 0.2(0.64) + 0.7(0.36) = 0.38$$

Thus, based upon the measured attribute value alone the new source hypothesis is more likely. Next, consider how attribute and kinematic quantities are combined.

In general, kinematic measurement data (position, range rate, *et cetera*) will be received in addition to attribute data. Then, given both kinematic and attribute data it will be necessary to correlate observations with existing tracks or to start new tentative tracks. As discussed in the previous Chapters 4 and 9 the *a posteriori* probability of the measured kinematic data is

$$f(\tilde{y}) = \frac{e^{-\frac{d^2}{2}}}{(2\pi)^{M/2}\sqrt{|S|}}$$

where

$$d^2 = \tilde{y}^T S^{-1} \tilde{y}$$

$\tilde{y}$ = residual vector (difference between predicted and measured quantities)

S = residual covariance matrix

$|S|$ = determinant of S

M = measurement dimension

Thus, the generalized *a posteriori* probability associated with both kinematic ($\tilde{y}$) and attribute (Z_m) measured data becomes

$$f(\tilde{y}, Z_m) = \frac{e^{-\frac{d^2}{2}}}{(2\pi)^{M/2}\sqrt{|S|}} P(Z_m|D_p) \tag{13.16}$$

The factor $P(Z_m|D_p)$, or its logarithm if the score function is used, can be used in the multiple hypothesis tree formulation to aid in the choice of the proper hypothesis. Finally, taking the logarithm of (13.16), note that a modified (to account for the attribute measurement) normalized distance function can be defined by adding $-2\ln[P(Z_m|D_p)]$ to the normalized distance previously defined by (4.12).

As an example of the use of combined attribute and kinematic data in correlation, consider potential observation-to-track correlation for a two-dimensional ($M = 2$) case with parameter values

β = new source density = 10^{-4}

P_D = probability of detection = 0.69

Also, assume that the Cartesian position (x,y) is measured and that the residual standard deviations are

$$\sigma_{\tilde{x}} = \sigma_{\tilde{y}} = 10$$

Further, assume the residual errors, $(\tilde{x}, \tilde{y})$ to be uncorrelated so that

$$|S| = \sigma_{\tilde{x}}\, \sigma_{\tilde{y}} = 100$$

Finally, assume the measured attribute (b_{2m}) and associated probabilities computed for the example above.

Define H_1 to be the hypothesis that the target track produced no detection so that the received observation was from a new source. Using the methods discussed in this chapter and in Chapters 9 and 10, the unnormalized probability of H_1 is

$$P(H_1) = (1-P_D)\, P(b_{2m}|NS)\, \beta = 1.18 \times 10^{-5}$$

Similarly, if H_2 is the hypothesis that the observation-to-track pairing is valid, we obtain

$$P(H_2) = \frac{P_D\, e^{-\frac{d^2}{2}}}{2\pi\, \sigma_{\tilde{x}}\, \sigma_{\tilde{y}}}\, P(b_{2m}|D_p) = (2.97 \times 10^{-4})\, e^{-\frac{d^2}{2}}$$

The observation-to-track correlation is more likely than the new source hypothesis if $P(H_2) > P(H_1)$. This is the standard gating criterion. Then, the normalized distances (d^2) for which this correlation condition is satisfied are defined by the relationship:

$$e^{-\frac{d^2}{2}} > 0.0397$$

$$d^2 < 6.45 \tag{13.17}$$

Equation (13.17) defines a standard gating condition for the kinematic quantities given that the measured attribute was b_{2m}. If, on the other hand, the measured attribute had been b_{1m}, with probability

$$P(b_{1m}|D_p) = 0.8(0.86) + 0.3(0.14) = 0.73$$

then the gating condition, computed in the same manner, would be

$$d^2 < 8.44$$

Thus, receipt of the less likely measured attribute has led to a more severe requirement for the measured kinematics in order that the standard gating criterion be satisfied.

13.5 THE DEMPSTER-SHAFER (EVIDENTIAL REASONING) METHOD

Dempster [11] and Shafer [12] have developed a method that generalizes Bayesian inference and which has been denoted the Dempster-Shafer or evidential reasoning method. By using the evidential reasoning approach for representing and combining data in the multiple sensor fusion application, each sensor is allowed to contribute information at its own level of detail. The evidential reasoning structure is general enough to utilize fully each sensor's information — regardless of its form.

The implementation of evidential reasoning can be illustrated using an example where target type is to be determined. Suppose one sensor contributes information in the following form:

"I know that the target is one of three possible target types:

a_1, a_2, or a_3."

This information is then stored as it stands, as a single information string. Another sensor then might contribute a second report of the form:

"I think that the target is target type a_1. However, the certainty of this statement is only 90%."

where this information is also stored in the computer as it stands. Only relevant information is considered by the computer: e.g., because there is no evidence yet to suspect that the target is of type a_4, this type is ignored in all subsequent processing. Thus, computational requirements are held to a minimum. Only relevant operations are performed, and only revelant target types are considered.

The process of data fusion consists of finding the intersection of two sensor statements. For instance, we know that the intersection of (a_1 or a_2 or a_3) and (a_1) is equal to (a_1). However, only a probability of 0.9 can be realistically assigned to this product, owing to the 90% confidence on the second sensor report. The remaining probability (0.1) must be assigned to the disjunction or union (a_1 or a_2 or a_3). These statements are stored directly in the computer in the form of assigned target sets and associated probabilities.

Next, assume that a_1 is a hostile target type, while a_2 and a_3 are friendly. Then, we cannot define an exact probability that the target is hostile. However, it can be stated that the probability is at least 0.9 that the target is hostile. Thus, the full extent of each sensor's information is accurately included in the fusion process and in the resulting inferences.

The evidential reasoning method can be readily extended to systems in which inference is performed using both sensor measurements and rules (such as for a rule-based artificial intelligence system). As an example of a rule that can be applied for certain situations, a particular type of target behavior (ship is not within the shipping lanes) can be used to infer the target type (not a cargo ship). This type of information can, in turn, be used to aid in data association. Thus, we will use the more general term knowledge source to denote sensor input measurements as well as inputs from other sources such as the application of rules. References [13, 14, 15] discuss applications to systems that combine information from multiple sensors and rule-based information.

The evidential reasoning approach is more general than the Bayesian. Also, its development has been based upon several perceived weaknesses in the standard Bayesian formulation. A weakness of the Bayesian approach is the lack of a convenient representation for ignorance or uncertainty. For example, a question arises concerning the representation of an uncertain prior distribution with the standard Bayesian approach. The evidential reasoning method handles this situation quite simply by allowing the assignment of a probability mass value directly to uncertainty.

The evidential reasoning method also handles the problem of incomplete or uncertain sensor measurements. First, sensor error can be conveniently represented by a probability mass assignment directly to uncertainty. Also, the use of evidential reasoning allows a more convenient and accurate representation of the information from certain sensors.

As another example, an IFF (identification friend or foe) sensor may declare the target to be friendly or hostile but give no more target type information. A standard Bayesian approach will then, in effect, assign equal probability masses to all target types within the friendly or hostile categories. However, using evidential reasoning a separate proposition is defined for the friendly and hostile target classes and the IFF sensor measurement is assigned directly to the appropriate (hostile or friendly target class) proposition. Then, when further data are received indicating the target to be a type within the previously established class, the mass associated with the class can be shifted directly to the appropriate type. After defining the elements of the method in more detail, an illustrative example will be presented.

13.5.1   Implementation of Evidential Reasoning

Assume that we have a set of n mutually exclusive and exhaustive propositions, such as that the target is type a_1, a_2. ..., a_n. The method of evidential reasoning can assign a probability mass (denoted $m(a_i)$) to any of the original n propositions or to disjunctions of the propositions. For example, a disjunction is the proposition that the target is of type a_1 or a_2 (denoted $a_1 v a_2$) and the mass assignment is denoted $m(a_1 v a_2)$. There are $2^n - 1$ such general propositions (including all the possible disjunctions) that may be assigned mass, and the masses summed over all of these propositions must equal unity. Note that this more general form of representation differs from the standard Bayesian approach in which probabilities are assigned only to the original n propositions — disjunctions are not considered.

The representation of uncertainty is a mass assignment to the disjunction of all the original propositions and is denoted

$$m(\theta) = m(a_1 v a_2 v \ldots v a_n)$$

Finally, mass can be assigned to the negation of a proposition. For example, the mass assigned to the negation of a_1 (the target is not type a_1) is denoted

$$m(\tilde{a}_1) = m(a_2 v a_3 v \ldots v a_n)$$

To summarize, probability masses may be assigned to individual propositions $m(a_1)$, to disjunctions $m(a_1 v a_2)$, to uncertainty $m(\theta)$, or to the negation of a given proposition, $m(\tilde{a}_1)$. The sum of these masses must equal unity.

The method can be extended, as in [15], to represent more complex propositions that include combinations of nonexclusive propositions (such as a_1 and b_1). However, we will only consider the simpler propositions here.

Another interesting feature associated with the Dempster-Shafer method is the concept of support and plausibility for propositions. The support for a given proposition is the sum of all the masses assigned directly to that proposition. To illustrate, again considering the target type example, the support $(spt(a_1))$ for the basic proposition that the target type is a_1 is just the mass associated with a_1 $(spt(a_1) = m(a_1))$. For a more complex proposition such as that the target is either type a_1, a_2, or a_3, we have

$$spt(a_1 v a_2 v a_3) = m(a_1) + m(a_2) + m(a_3) + m(a_1 v a_2) + m(a_1 v a_3) + m(a_2 v a_3) \\ + m(a_1 v a_2 v a_3)$$

The plausibility of a given proposition is the sum of all mass not assigned to its negation. Thus,

$$pls(a_i) = 1 - spt(\tilde{a}_i)$$

Alternatively, $pls(a_i)$ can be computed by summing all masses associated with a_i and all disjunctions, including θ, that contain a_i. For example,

$$pls(a_1) = m(a_1) + m(a_1va_2) + \ldots + m(\theta)$$

The plausibility of a_i defines the mass that is free to move to the support of a_i. The interval $[spt(a_i), pls(a_i)]$ represent the uncertainty interval with $[0,1]$ representing total ignorance and $[0.6, 0.6]$ representing a certain probability of 0.6.

The manner in which data are combined from multiple sensors (or knowledge sources) is through Dempster's rule of combination. This rule is an extension of Bayes' rule and its application is explained through the following example.

13.5.2 An Example Using Evidential Reasoning

Consider an example where there are four target aircraft types as defined:

a_1 = friendly interceptor (fighter aircraft)
a_2 = friendly bomber
a_3 = hostile interceptor
a_4 = hostile bomber

Assume we start the target type identification problem by noting that the aircraft behavior appears to be that of the class of interceptor (frequent acceleration, not in expected bomber flight paths, *et cetera*). However, this information is not certain so that the following mass assignment vector is defined:

$$\mathbf{m}_1 = \begin{bmatrix} m_1(\theta) = 0.4 \\ m_1(a_1va_3) = 0.6 \end{bmatrix}$$

The assignment of 0.4 to $m_1(\theta)$ represents the uncertainty associated with the rules used to determine that the behavior is that of the interceptor aircraft class.

Next, assume that the target does not respond to an IFF interrogation. We would expect a response from a friendly aircraft so this indicates that the target is probably hostile, but again this is not certain. Thus, we assign to this knowledge source the following mass values:

$$\mathbf{m}_2 = \begin{bmatrix} m_2(\theta) = 0.3 \\ m_2(a_3va_4) = 0.7 \end{bmatrix}$$

$m_1(\theta) = 0.4$	$m(a_3va_4) = 0.28$	$m(\theta) = 0.12$
$m_1(a_1va_3) = 0.6$	$m(a_3) = 0.42$	$m(a_1va_3) = 0.18$
	$m_2(a_3va_4) = 0.7$	$m_2(\theta) = 0.3$

FIGURE 13-7. APPLICATION OF DEMPSTER'S RULE

Dempster's rule can be used to combine m_1 and m_2 as illustrated in Fig. 13-7. The resulting mass vector is

$$\mathbf{m} = \begin{bmatrix} m(\theta) = 0.12 \\ m(a_1va_3) = 0.18 \\ m(a_3) = 0.42 \\ m(a_3va_4) = 0.28 \end{bmatrix} \tag{13.18}$$

Referring to Fig. 13-7, Dempster's rule is implemented by forming a matrix with the probability mass assignments that are to be combined given along the first column and last row. Then, the computed elements (for a given row and column) of the matrix are the product of the probability mass values in the same row of the first column and the same column of the last row. For example, for the (2,2) element of the matrix shown in Fig. 13-7,

$$m(a_3) = m_1(a_1va_3)m_2(a_3va_4) = 0.6\,(0.7) = 0.42$$

The assignment of these elements to the resulting mass vector is according to the following principles:

1. The product of mass assignments to two propositions that are consistent leads to an assignment to another proposition contained within the two original propositions. For example,

   $$m_1(a_i)\,m_2(a_i) = m(a_i)$$

   $$m_1(a_1va_3)\,m_2(a_3va_4) = m(a_3)$$

2. Multiplying the mass assignments to uncertainty by the mass assignment to any other proposition leads to a contribution to that proposition,

   $$m_1(\theta)\,m_2(a_3va_4) = m(a_3va_4)$$

3. Multiplying uncertainty by uncertainty leads to a new assignment to uncertainty,

$$m_1(\theta) \, m_2(\theta) = m(\theta)$$

The above example illustrated Dempster's rule for the condition where there was no inconsistency (or assignment to a null hypothesis) between the knowledge sources. Inconsistency occurs, for example, when one knowledge source assigns mass to a_2 ($m_1(a_2)$) while a second assigns mass to a_1 ($m_2(a_1)$). The product of these mass values is assigned to a measure of inconsistency, denoted k, of the form

$$m_1(a_2) \, m_2(a_1) = k$$

The manner in which inconsistency is handled is illustrated by introducing another hypothetical knowledge source.

Next, assume that another sensor gives the following target type declaration:

$$\mathbf{m}_3 = \begin{bmatrix} m_3(\theta) = 0.2 \\ m_3(a_1) = 0.1 \\ m_3(a_2) = 0.2 \\ m_3(a_3) = 0.3 \\ m_3^{\cdot}(a_4) = 0.2 \end{bmatrix}$$

Figure 13-8 shows how Dempster's rule is used to combine the previous mass vector, **m** from (13.18), with the sensor declaration $\mathbf{m}_3$. Referring to Fig. 13-8,

$m_3(\theta) = 0.2$	m $(a_3 v a_4) = 0.056$	m $(a_3) = 0.084$	m $(a_1 v a_3) = 0.036$	m $(\theta) = 0.024$
$m_3(a_1) = 0.1$	k = 0.028	k = 0.042	m $(a_1) = 0.018$	m $(a_1) = 0.012$
$m_3(a_2) = 0.2$	k = 0.056	k = 0.084	k = 0.036	m $(a_2) = 0.024$
$m_3(a_3) = 0.3$	m $(a_3) = 0.084$	m $(a_3) = 0.126$	m $(a_3) \, 0.054$	m $(a_3) = 0.036$
$m_3(a_4) = 0.2$	m $(a_4) = 0.056$	k = 0.084	k = 0.036	m $(a_4) = 0.024$
	m $(a_3 v a_4) = 0.28$	m $(a_3) = 0.42$	m $(a_1 v a_3) = 0.18$	m $(\theta) = 0.12$

FIGURE 13-8. A SECOND APPLICATION OF DEMPSTER'S RULE

in order to compute the new mass vector, we first sum all the assignments to k, which for this example leads to the value $k = 0.366$. Then, the new mass vector is computed by summing the appropriate entries in the matrix and dividing by the normalization factor $(1 - k = 0.634)$. Thus, the new values are

$m(\theta) = 0.024/0.634 = 0.038$

$m(a_1) = (0.018 + 0.012)/0.634 = 0.047$

$m(a_2) = 0.024/0.634 = 0.038$

$m(a_3) = (0.084 + 0.084 + 0.126 + 0.054 + 0.036)/0.634 = 0.606$

$m(a_4) = (0.056 + 0.024)/0.634 = 0.126$

$m(a_1 v a_3) = 0.036/0.634 = 0.057$

$m(a_3 v a_4) = 0.056/0.634 = 0.088$

Table 13-5 shows the values of support and plausibility for selected propositions of interest. Note that the evidence in favor of a hostile aircraft now becomes

$spt(a_3 v a_4) = m(a_3) + m(a_4) + m(a_3 v a_4) = 0.82$

TABLE 13-5
SUPPORT AND PLAUSIBILITY FOR
SELECTED PROPOSITIONS

Proposition	Support	Plausibility
a_1	0.047	0.142
a_2	0.038	0.076
$a_1 v a_2$	0.085	0.18
a_3	0.606	0.789
a_4	0.126	0.252
$a_3 v a_4$	0.82	0.915

Finally, as examples of the manner in which plausibility is computed:

$pls(a_3) = m(a_3) + m(a_3 v a_4) + m(a_1 v a_3) + m(\theta)$

$\qquad = 1 - m(a_1) - m(a_2) - m(a_4) = 0.789$

$pls(a_3 v a_4) = 1 - spt(a_1 v a_2) = 0.915$

13.5.3 Extensions and Application to Data Association

The evidential reasoning approach can be extended to apply to data association in the same manner as the Bayesian method given in the previous section. First, attributes other than target type can be used in a completely analogous manner if the conditional probability matrix $M(B|A)$ is defined. However, consistent with the evidential reasoning approach, in addition to the terms

$$M(B|A)_{ij} = P(b_j|a_i)$$

the following terms must be defined:

$M(\theta|A)_{ij} = m(\theta|a_i)$ = mass assigned to uncertainty with regard to attribute B given type a_i. For example, uncertainty with regard to the emitting radar for a given aircraft type.

Consider an existing target track, with prior evidential mass vector, and the potential assignment of an observation to that track. Then, the factor k (found using Dempster's combination method) is a measure of disagreement between the track mass vector and the mass vector of the observation. The factor $1 - k$ represents the consistency of the data association hypothesis and is the evidential reasoning equivalent to the term $P(Z_m|D_p)$, in (13.16), used for the Bayesian formulation. Thus, the evidential reasoning approach also produces a term to be used for computing the probabilities of validity for data association hypotheses.

13.6 SENSOR ALLOCATION

Chapter 12 discussed the allocation problem for an agile beam radar when considering the options for the illumination of existing targets and search for new targets. A similar, but generally more complex, situation occurs when considering the allocation of multiple sensors for the surveillance of multiple targets. Following Garvey and Fischler [16], we outline a utility theory approach to sensor allocation in the multiple target environment. For this application, utility will be defined as a measure of value, ranging from zero to one, associated with information about a given target track.

The basic principle is to allocate sensor resources in a way that maximizes the overall utility. The first step in this process is to compute a target track weighting term based upon the probabilities that the target is of various types, the inherent lethality (or threat value) of these types, and the geometry (such as the time required before reaching the lethal radius of the target). Then, the expected gain in utility (the marginal utility) of allocating a sensor to a given track is found by comparing the utility of the expected state of knowledge before and after sensor allocation.

The increased utility associated with improved kinematic estimates is straightforward to compute. The kinematic estimation accuracy before and after sensor application can be conveniently determined using standard filtering theory and the results compared with the values required for successful system operation. For example, the track accuracy (as determined by the Kalman covariance matrix) might be compared with that required for missile launch and a utility defined based upon present and required accuracy.

Figure 13-9 illustrates the manner in which the result of a sensor allocation can be expressed using utility theory. Consider a kinematic quantity x (such as range, range rate, or angle). Then, the utility is shown as a function of the ratio of the true estimation-error standard deviation ($\sigma_{\tilde{x}}$) to the desired (or acceptable) estimation-error standard deviation (σ_{xD}). Thus, the utility is expressed as $U(Q)$ where $Q = \sigma_{\tilde{x}} / \sigma_{xD}$.

The shape of the utility curve is based on the designer's evaluation of the relative utility of different levels of tracking accuracy. The utility function ranges from zero to unity with the utility of no estimation error $U(0)$ being unity. The present utility is computed using the Kalman filter prediction covariance matrix quantities and the expected utility (upon sensor allocation) is computed using quantities from the filtered Kalman covariance matrix. The filtered Kalman covariance matrix will reflect the proposed inclusion of the measurement to be provided by the sensor.

Referring to Fig. 13-9, assume values of Q to be Q_{NU} if no track update occurs and Q_U if update occurs (with resulting decrease in $\sigma_{\tilde{x}}$). Thus, the marginal utility, shown in Fig. 13-9, for track update with the particular sensor is given by $U(Q_U) - U(Q_{NU})$. However, if a detection is not certain this value for the marginal utility should be weighted by the probability of detection, P_D.

Next, consider the problem of sensor allocation to determine target presence (or type). Assume that the probability of target presence has been determined (by *a priori* or other sensor information) to be P_T. Then, define:

$U_D \triangleq$ utility associated with declaring target presence when the target is truly present

$U_{ND} \triangleq$ utility associated with correctly declaring the target not to be present

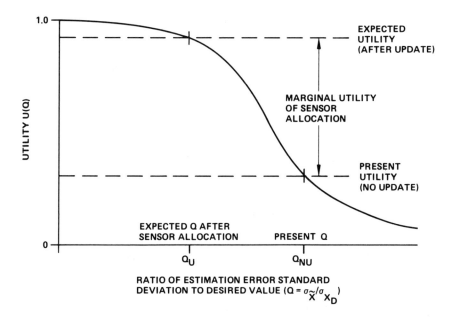

FIGURE 13-9. ILLUSTRATION OF UTILITY COMPUTATION FOR SENSOR ALLOCATION

The utility values U_D and U_{ND} would be based upon the potential target types (and resultant lethality), the geometry, and other tactical considerations. The utility values associated with incorrect decisions are defined to be zero. Alternatively, the problem could be formulated in terms of the costs of wrong decisions [16].

The approach is to compute the marginal utility. This is the difference between the expected utility after sensor application and the expected present utility (without sensor allocation). First, the present expected utility of declaring target presence is the product of the probability (P_T) that the target is present times U_D. Similarly, $(1 - P_T) U_{ND}$ is the expected present utility associated with declaring the target not present. Assume a decision rule that chooses the alternative giving the higher expected utility. Thus, without further sensor allocation, the present expected utility is

$$U_0 = MAX [P_T U_D, (1 - P_T) U_{ND}] \tag{13.19}$$

We will compute the expected utility after sensor application. Once the sensor is applied it will either report the target to be present or not present. This information will be combined with previous information so that a new system declaration (target present or not present) can be made. This declaration may not coincide with the sensor report if the sensor report conflicts with previous information. Thus, it is important to distinguish between what the sensor reports and what the system declares based upon the sensor report and prior information.

In order to compute the expected utility after sensor application we first define:

$P(T|R)$ = probability of target presence given a potential sensor report of target presence

$P(T|\tilde{R})$ = probability of target presence given a potential sensor report that the target is not present

$P(R|T)$ = conditional probability that the sensor will report target presence given that it is present

$P(R|\tilde{T})$ = conditional probability that the sensor will report the target present when it is not

Similar definitions hold for the terms $P(\tilde{R}|T)$, $P(\tilde{R}|\tilde{T})$, $P(\tilde{T}|R)$, and $P(\tilde{T}|\tilde{R})$.

The probability that the sensor will report the target to be present is

$$P(R) = P(R|T)\,P_T + P(R|\tilde{T})\,(1 - P_T) \qquad (13.20)$$

and

$$P(\tilde{R}) = 1 - P(R)$$

Then, the *a posteriori* probabilities of target presence conditioned upon the events that the sensor reports the target to be present (R) or not present ($\tilde{R}$) are

$$P(T|R) = \frac{P(R|T)\,P_T}{P(R)}, \quad P(T|\tilde{R}) = \frac{P(\tilde{R}|T)\,P_T}{P(\tilde{R})} \qquad (13.21)$$

In order to compute the expected utility after sensor allocation, we must average over the events that the sensor reports target presence (R) and absence ($\tilde{R}$). Define U_{SR} and $U_{S\tilde{R}}$ to be the expected utilities after sensor application for these two events, respectively. In analogy to (13.19), we have

$$U_{SR} = MAX\,[\,P(T|R)\,U_D,\ P(\tilde{T}|R)\,U_{ND}\,]$$
$$U_{S\tilde{R}} = MAX\,[\,P(T|\tilde{R})\,U_D,\ P(\tilde{T}|\tilde{R})\,U_{ND}\,] \qquad (13.22)$$

Averaging over the sensor events, the expected utility after sensor allocation is

$$U_S = P(R)\,U_{SR} + P(\tilde{R})\,U_{S\tilde{R}} \qquad (13.23)$$

The marginal utiilty is then defined to be $U_S - U_0$.

To illustrate, consider an example with the following parameters:

$$P(R|T) = 0.8, \quad P(\tilde{R}|T) = 0.2$$
$$P(R|\tilde{T}) = 0.1, \quad P(\tilde{R}|\tilde{T}) = 0.9$$
$$P_T = 0.6$$

Also, assume utility values that are weighted in favor of target declaration,

$$U_D = 0.9, \quad U_{ND} = 0.4$$

Finally, directly applying (13.19) through (13.23), we obtain

$$U_0 = MAX\,[0.6(0.9), 0.4(0.4)] = 0.54$$
$$P(R) = 0.8(0.6) + 0.1(0.4) = 0.52, \quad P(\tilde{R}) = 0.48$$

$$P(T|R) = \frac{0.8(0.6)}{0.52} = 0.923, \quad P(\tilde{T}|R) = 0.077$$

$$P(T|\tilde{R}) = \frac{0.2(0.6)}{0.48} = 0.25, \quad P(\tilde{T}|\tilde{R}) = 0.75$$

so that

$$U_{SR} = MAX\,[0.923(0.9), 0.077(0.4)] = 0.831$$
$$U_{S\tilde{R}} = MAX\,[0.25(0.9), 0.75(0.4)] = 0.3$$

and

$$U_S = 0.52(0.831) + 0.48(0.3) = 0.576$$

Thus, the marginal utility for the potential sensor application discussed in the above example is the difference between U_S and U_0, which is 0.036.

Assume that there are multiple potential targets and multiple sensors that may be applied to verify the existence or the presumed type of these targets. Then, the marginal utilities that are computed for all potential sensor-to-target pairings are placed in an assignment matrix. The problem is thus reduced to the solution of the assignment matrix for the maximum overall marginal utility. Solution of the assignment matrix is discussed in the next chapter.

The final questions involve choice of utility values and the combining of utilities for different measures of system performance (for example, utilities for kinematics and target type). These types of issues are discussed in detail in Keeney and Raiffa [17] and other texts on utility theory.

13.7 SUMMARY

This chapter has outlined some of the important issues involved in multiple sensor fusion for the MTT problem. First, a discussion was given of the relative merits of central- *versus* sensor-level tracking. Central-level tracking is probably best implemented by a direct application of the data association methods discussed elsewhere in this book. In particular, the multiple hypothesis tracking methods discussed in Chapter 10 are most applicable due to potential uncertain correlations when combining data from disparate sensors.

A technique for track-to-track correlation and other issues involved in implementing a sensor-level tracking system have been discussed. However, due to the difficulties involved in combining sensor-level tracks, the central-level tracking approach appears to be preferable if the system can provide adequate data transfer.

A standard Bayesian approach and the more general evidential reasoning approach have been presented for application to the formation of estimates for attribute quantities. An important feature is that both of these techniques provide a measure of the validity of a given data association based upon the attribute quantities. Thus, it is desirable that correlation (data association) be done using both kinematic quantities and, when available, attributes.

Finally, the problem of assigning multiple sensors to multiple target tracks was briefly addressed. The approach discussed uses utility theory and assigns sensors to collect data based upon the estimated utility of the overall assignment.

The field of multiple sensor-multiple target tracking is very broad. Thus, there are several important issues involving multiple sensor tracking and identification that are not discussed here. First, the problems (and outlined solutions) associated with multiple sensor misalignment are discussed in References [1, 2, 18]. The question of determining when the declaration of target ID can be made is discussed in References [19, 20]. Reference [21] discusses how multiple sensor performance requirements can be determined based upon overall system requirements. Finally, Reference [22], in addition to giving an overview of multiple sensor fusion, discusses computational issues.

Sensor fusion applications can be divided into two broad categories. The category that has primarily been discussed here, local sensor fusion, may be defined as the integration of data from sensors on board a single platform. For this application the data from each sensor can conveniently be transmitted to a single central computer and all sensors essentially look at the targets from the same aspect.

A second type of sensor fusion occurs with sensors that are widely distributed. For this case additional problems, such as the allocation of resources between performing local computations and communicating with other sensors, are introduced. References [23, 24] discuss some of the issues involved in this, the distributed sensor fusion or distributed sensor network problem.

REFERENCES

1. Polly, D.W., "Integrated Tracking", *Military Electronics*, Vol. 9, No. 3, 1983, pp. 274–278.
2. Bowman, C.L., "Multisensor Integration for Defensive Fire Control Surveillance", *Proceedings of NAECON 1979*, Dayton, OH, May 15–17, 1979, pp. 176–184.
3. Cantrell, B.H., and A. Grindlay, "Multiple Site Radar Tracking System," *Proceedings of the IEEE 1980 International Radar Conference*, Arlington, VA, April 28–30, 1980, pp. 348–354.
4. Farina, A., and G. Pardini, "Introduction to Multiradar Tracking Systems," *Rivista Technica Selenia*, Vol. 8, No. 1, 1981, pp. 14–26.
5. Kanyuck, A.J., and R.A. Singer, "Correlation of Multiple Site Track Data", *IEEE Transactions on Aerospace and Electronic Systems*, AES-6, March 1970, pp. 180–187.
6. Wiener, H.L. *et al.*, "Naval Ocean-Surveillance Correlation Handbook, 1978", NRL Report 8340, Naval Research Laboratory, Washington, DC, Oct. 31, 1979.
7. Bar-Shalom, Y., "On the Track-to-Track Correlation Problem," *IEEE Transactions on Automatic Control*, AC-26, April 1981, pp. 571–572.
8. Reid, D.B., "The Application of Multiple Target Theory to Ocean Surveillance," *Proceedings of the 1979 IEEE Conference on Decision and Control*, Fort Lauderdale, FL, Dec. 12–14, 1979, pp. 1046–1051.
9. Pearl, J. "Reverend Bayes on Inference Engines: A Distributed Hierarchical Approach," *Proceedings of the Second Annual Conference on Artificial Intelligence*, Pittsburgh, PA, Aug. 1982, pp. 133–136.
10. Atkinson, D.A., "A Bayesian Analysis of Surveillance Attribute Data," *Proceedings of the 1980 IEEE Conference on Decision and Control*, Albuquerque, NM, Dec. 10–12, 1980, pp. 826–828.
11. Dempster, A.P., "A Generalization of Bayesian Inference," *Journal of the Royal Statistical Society*, Series B, Vol. 30, 1968, pp. 205–247.

12. Shafer, G., *A Mathematical Theory of Evidence*, Princeton, NJ: Princeton University Press, 1976.

13. Garvey, T.D., J.D. Lowrance, and M.A. Fischler, "An Inference Technique for Integrating Knowledge from Disparate Sources," *Proceedings of the 7th International Conference on Artificial Intelligence*, Aug. 1981, pp. 319–324.

14. Dillard, R.A., "Computing Confidences in Tactical Rule-Based Systems by Using Dempster-Shafer Theory," Technical Document 649, Naval Ocean Systems Center, San Diego, CA, AD-A137274, Sept. 14, 1983.

15. Garvey, T.D., and J.D. Lowrance, "Machine Intelligence for Electronic Warfare Applications," SRI, Menlo Park, CA, Report No. AFWAL-TR-83-1168, AD-B080177, Nov. 1983.

16. Garvey, T.D., and M.A. Fischler, "Machine-Intelligence-Based Multisensor ESM System," SRI, Menlo Park, CA, Report No. AFWAL-TR-79-1162, AD-B045790, Oct. 1979.

17. Keeney, R.L., and H. Raiffa, *Decisions with Multiple Objectives: Preferences and Value Tradeoffs*, New York: John Wiley and Sons, 1976.

18. Bath, W.G., "Association of Multisite Radar Data in the Presence of Large Navigation and Sensor Alignment Errors," *Proceedings of the 1982 IEE International Radar Conference*, London, Oct. 18–20, 1982, pp. 169–173.

19. Nahin, P.J., and J.L. Pokoski, "NCTR Plus Sensor Fusion Equals IFFN or Can Two Plus Two Equal Five?," *IEEE Transactions on Aerospace and Electronic Systems*, AES-16, May 1980, pp. 320–337.

20. Blackman, S.S., T.A. DuPuis, and A.J. Mendez, "Applications of Multi-Sensor Correlation Techniques to the Target Validation Problem," *Proceedings of the First U.S. DoD Tri-Service Conference on Total Target Identification Technology*, Fort Monmouth, NJ, Oct. 27–29, 1981, pp. 699–713.

21. Dana, M.P., "Establishment of Air Defense Sensor Requirements for Automatic Aircraft Tracking," *AGARD Conference Proceedings No. 252, Strategies for Automatic Track Initiation*, Monterey, CA, Oct. 1978, pp. 19–1 to 19–20.

22. Waltz, E.L., "Computational Consideration for Fusion in Target Identification Systems," *Proceedings of NAECON 1981*, Dayton, OH, May 19–21, 1981, pp. 492–497.

23. Deley, G.W., "A Netting Approach to Automatic Radar Track Initiation, Association and Tracking in Air Surveillance Systems", *AGARD Conference Proceedings No. 252, Strategies for Automatic Track Initiation*, Monterey, CA, Oct. 1978, pp. 7–1 to 7–10.

24.   Tong, R.M., R.P. Wishner, and E. Tse, "Distributed Hypothesis Formation in Sensor Fusion Systems", *Proceedings of the 1981 Conference on Decision and Control*, San Diego, CA, Dec. 1981, pp. 1421–1424.

Appendix 13A

Track Fusion Relationships

We begin by considering the fusion relationships for a scalar such that a composite estimate, using estimates x_1 and x_2, is

$$x_c = x_1 + c (x_2 - x_1) \tag{13A.1}$$

where c is a weighting factor that will be chosen so that the expected mean-squared error (MSE) on x_c is minimized. The error in x_c is defined as

$$\delta x_c \triangleq \delta x_1 + c (\delta x_2 - \delta x_1)$$

Then, the error variance on δx_c is defined

$$\epsilon^2 \triangleq E[\delta x_c^2] = \sigma_1^2 + 2cE[\delta x_1 \, \delta x_2] - 2c\sigma_1^2 + c^2\sigma_\delta^2 \tag{13A.2}$$

where

$$\sigma_1^2 = E[\delta x_1^2], \quad \sigma_2^2 = E[\delta x_2^2], \quad \sigma_\delta^2 = E[(\delta x_2 - \delta x_1)^2] = \sigma_1^2 + \sigma_2^2 - 2E[\delta x_1 \, \delta x_2]$$

The correlation between errors is defined:

$$E[\delta x_1 \, \delta x_2] = R_{12}$$

Equation (13A.2) becomes

$$\epsilon^2 = (1 - 2c + c^2) \, \sigma_1^2 + c^2 \, \sigma_2^2 + 2(c - c^2) \, R_{12} \tag{13A.3}$$

In order to form the minimum MSE estimates, we have

$$\frac{\partial \epsilon^2}{\partial c} = -2(1 - c) \, \sigma_1^2 + 2c \, \sigma_2^2 + 2(1 - 2c) R_{12} = 0 \tag{13A.4}$$

Solving (13A.4) for c gives

$$c = \frac{\sigma_1^2 - R_{12}}{\sigma_1^2 + \sigma_2^2 - 2 R_{12}} \tag{13A.5}$$

In the special case of no correlation ($R_{12} = 0$), we have

$$x_c = x_1 + \frac{\sigma_1^2}{\sigma_1^2 + \sigma_2^2} (x_2 - x_1) = \frac{\sigma_2^2 x_1 + \sigma_1^2 x_2}{\sigma_1^2 + \sigma_2^2}$$

In the case of combining state estimation vectors (x_1, x_2) the same general relationships given by (13A.1) and (13A.5) are used, except that the variances become covariances:

$$\sigma_1^2 \rightarrow P_1, \quad \sigma_2^2 \rightarrow P_2, \quad 2R_{12} \rightarrow P_{12} + P_{12}^T \tag{13A.6}$$

and c becomes a weighting matrix:

$$C = [P_1 - P_{12}][P_1 + P_2 - P_{12} - P_{12}^T]^{-1}$$

Finally, using (13A.3) and (13A.5), the resulting error variances (or covariances) are

$$\sigma_{x_c}^2 = \sigma_1^2 - \frac{(\sigma_1^2 - R_{12})^2}{\sigma_1^2 + \sigma_2^2 - 2R_{12}}$$

In the special case of no correlation ($R_{12} = 0$), we have

$$\sigma_{x_c}^2 = \frac{\sigma_1^2 \sigma_2^2}{\sigma_1^2 + \sigma_2^2}$$

The state vector extension becomes

$$P_c = P_1 - [P_1 - P_{12}][P_1 + P_2 - P_{12} - P_{12}^T]^{-1}[P_1 - P_{12}]^T$$

Chapter 14

Special Topics

14.1 INTRODUCTION

This chapter discusses four special topics. First, we give a solution to the assignment problem, which is useful for solving the observation-to-track association problem and also for sensor allocation.

The second topic is an outline of a particular implementation of the multiple hypothesis tracking method discussed in Chapter 10. This presentation elaborates on some of the issues involved in developing a multiple hypothesis tracking algorithm. Next, two approaches are presented for MTT system implementation in the presence of a large number of input observations. Finally, an overall system architecture incorporating all the elements of MTT is presented which indicates how the elements of classical MTT, artificial intelligence (AI), and sensor allocation interact for a total system concept.

14.2 A SOLUTION FOR THE OPTIMAL ASSIGNMENT PROBLEM*

The algorithm presented below is directly applicable to the assignment matrix method (discussed in Chapters 4 and 9) for assigning observations to tracks in a sequential nearest-neighbor correlation system. The algorithm will be used to solve the observation-to-track assignment problem. However, the algorithm can also be applied to the problem (discussed in Chapter 13) of assigning sensors to tracks in a multiple sensor-multiple target tracking problem. For the latter application, the goal is to assign sensors to tracks so as to maximize the total utility of all assignments. Because utility values range from zero to one, a cost can be defined as one minus utility. Then, the solution with minimum cost is found and is equivalent to the maximum utility solution.

An assignment matrix is typically formed for observation-to-track assignment using the sequential nearest-neighbor correlation method. The elements of this matrix are equal to the normalized distance functions associated with

---

*This section was contributed by Ms. Elana Dror of Hughes Aircraft Company.

the assignment of each of the N_o observations to each of the N_T tracks. If the gating relationship is not satisfied, the observation-to-track pairing can be given a very large distance in order to penalize this assignment. Then, if, in the attempt to maximize the number of assignments, the algorithm still chooses a pairing that does not satisfy the gate, the assignment is later removed.

The objective of the assignment matrix method is to assign n observations to n different tracks ($n = min\,(N_o, N_T)$), such that the sum of the n normalized distance functions is minimized. The most straightforward solution is to list all the possible $m!/(m-n)!$ assignments, where $m = max\,(N_o, N_T)$, and compute the total distance for each.

Because the computational cost of the most straightforward method can be prohibitive, other methods are sought. Candidate methods include Munkres' algorithm [1], the Ford-Fulkerson method [2], and the Hungarian method [3]. The number of operations required by these algorithms can be less than the factorial requirements of the straightforward solution. For example, the requirements for Munkres' algorithm are on the order of n^2m. Preliminary study by the author has indicated the computational requirements for the three methods to be comparable when considering matrices of up to order 12.

The Munkres optimal assignment algorithm, modified by Burgeois and Lassalle [1], is summarized below. An advantage of this method is that the matrix of observation-to-track correlation distances need not be square. Also, this method is probably the easiest to understand and to program. An example illustrating application of the rules will follow.

Preliminaries

The rows and columns of the matrix may be marked and refrerred to as covered. The zeros may be marked by being starred (*) or primed ('). To begin:

   a. Initially, no lines are covered and no zeros are starred or primed.
   b. Let $k = min$ (number of rows, number of columns).
   c. If the number of rows is greater than the number of columns, go to the last step (f) of the preliminaries.
   d. For each row in the matrix, subtract the smallest element of the row from each element in the row.
   e. If the number of columns is greater than the number of rows, go to Step 1.
   f. For each column in the matrix, subtract the smallest element of the column from each entry in the column.

Step 1

    a. Find a zero, Z, of the matrix.
    b. If there is no starred zero in its row or its column, star the zero (Z^*).
    c. Repeat Step 1(b) for all zeros of the matrix.
    d. Go to Step 2.

Step 2

    a. Cover every column containing a starred zero (Z^*).
    b. If k columns are covered, the locations of the Z^* form the row-column associations (observation-track pairs). The algorithm is now *finished.*
    c. Otherwise, go to Step 3.

Step 3

    a. Choose an uncovered zero and prime it to (Z').
    b. If there is no starred zero in the row of Z', go to Step 4.
    c. If there is a starred zero (Z^*) in the row of Z', cover this row and uncover the column of Z^*.
    d. Repeat Step 3 until all zeros are covered.
    e. Go to Step 5.

Step 4

    a. The sequence of alternating starred and primed zeros is as follows:
       1. Let Z_0 denote the uncovered Z'. If there is no Z^* in the column of Z_0, go to Step 4 (a-6).
       2. Let Z_1 denote the Z^* in the column of Z_0.
       3. Let Z_2 denote the Z' in the row of Z_1.
       4. Continue performing steps 4 (a-2) and 4 (a-3) (where in Step 4 (a-2) look in the column of Z_2 instead of Z_0) until a Z_2 which has no Z^* in its column is found.
       5. Unstar each starred zero of the sequence.
       6. Star each primed zero of the sequence.
    b. Erase all primes from primed zeros and uncover every line.
    c. Go to Step 2.

Step 5

    a. Find the smallest uncovered element in the matrix and call it h; h will be positive.

    b. Add h to each covered row.

    c. Subtract h from each uncovered column.

    d. Return to Step 3 without altering stars, primes, or covered lines.

14.2.1   Example of Optimal Assignment Algorithm

As an example, consider the assignment matrix:

$$A = \begin{bmatrix} 10 & 5 & 8 & 9 \\ 7 & X & 20 & X \\ X & 20 & X & X \\ X & 15 & 17 & X \\ X & X & 16 & 20 \end{bmatrix} = a_{ij}$$

The matrix given above has more rows (5) than columns (4), so that $k = 4$. This corresponds to a condition with five tracks and four observations and the entries X represent unacceptable assignments (observation is outside of the track gate). Since these entries are unacceptable, no modifications will be indicated. The numbers represent hypothetical normalized distance functions. Referring to Fig. 14-1, we will now follow the steps outlined previously to show how the solution is found using the optimal assignment algorithm.

The preliminary step (f) subtracts the minimum value in each column $(7, 5, 8, 9)$ from all elements in that column. Next, Steps 1 and 2 are used to identify two Z^* values and to cover the columns (first and second) containing them. However, because the third and fourth columns are still uncovered, we proceed to Step 3, where the zero value for a_{13} is primed. Then, because a_{12} is a Z^* in the row of a_{13}, the second column is uncovered and the first row is covered. Because all zeros are covered, we now proceed to Step 5.

In Step 5 we identify the value of 8 (for a_{53}) as the smallest uncovered element (h). After adding 8 to each covered row and subtracting 8 from each uncovered column, we return to Step 3 where the zero in element a_{53} is primed. Because there is no Z^* in the fifth row, we proceed without further modification to Step 4, where a_{53} is denoted Z_0. Because there is no Z^* in the third column, the zero in a_{53} is starred. All primes are removed and all

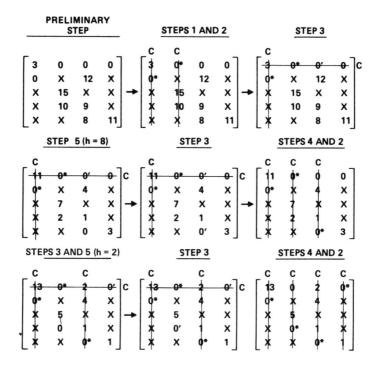

FIGURE 14-1. EXAMPLE OF SOLUTION USING OPTIMAL ASSIGNMENT ALGORITHM

lines are uncovered. After returning to Step 2, the first three columns are covered. However, because the fourth column is uncovered, we must return to Step 3.

Step 3 primes the zero in a_{14}, uncovers the second column, and covers the first row. Then, at Step 5, the value of 2 (in a_{42}) is identified as h and the appropriate modifications are made. The return is made to Step 3, where the uncovered zero in a_{42} is primed. Finally, because there is no Z^* in the fourth row we return again to Step 4.

Step 4 completes the process by identifying the primed zero in a_{42} as Z_0. Then, the Z^* in element a_{12} is Z_1, and is unstarred. The primed zero in a_{14}, Z_2, has no Z^* in its column. Thus, the two primed zeros, a_{42} and a_{14}, are now starred. All lines are uncovered and we return to Step 2. At Step 2 we note that all columns can now be covered and that the starred elements $(a_{21}, a_{42}, a_{53}, a_{14})$ comprise the solution. Referring back to the original matrix the minimum distance solution is

$$D = 7 + 15 + 16 + 9 = 47$$

14.3   AN IMPLEMENTATION METHOD FOR MULTIPLE
HYPOTHESIS TRACKING*

In a dense target environment, studies have shown that the simple nearest-neighbor correlation algorithms lead to frequent miscorrelations and resulting track instability. The multiple hypothesis tracking (MHT) approach reduces the amount of miscorrelation and, significantly, the more serious the consequences, the more likely it is that the MHT algorithm will resolve the correlation conflict as the error develops. For example, consider the incorrect correlation of a false alarm with a track. If the false alarm is far from the true target position, the resulting track prediction will be in error more than if the false alarm were close to the true position. However, using the MHT method, the former error will be more readily detected later when true target observations are received.

In order to review the general MHT approach presented in Chapter 10, Fig. 14-2 gives an overview of a typical MHT logic. Clusters of hypotheses that interact only with each other are formed. As observations are received, they will be assigned to the appropriate clusters for further hypothesis formation. If observations satisfy gates of tracks within more than one cluster, the clusters will be merged.

New hypotheses are generated as observations are received. The number of hypotheses is limited through the use of combining and pruning methods. Using the approach to be discussed below, similar tracks are combined and then equivalent hypotheses are defined to be hypotheses with the same tracks. Finally, after all observations for a given scan are processed, track deletion and prediction for the next scan occur. Also, an attempt may be made to split clusters.

The details of a particular implementation of MHT will be presented. However, the discussion will be limited primarily to the operations to be performed within a single cluster.

The main features of the implementation are the use of a score function for multiple hypothesis evaluation and the use of dynamic data structures for execution. The development of an MHT program is, by necessity, quite complex, but experience has indicated that the use of the methods described below can lead to an efficient implementation. In the following sections, various hypothesis operators are first described (scoring, combining, pruning), and the general MHT structure is presented. Finally, an example will be presented to illustrate operation of the methods.

*The author acknowledges the assistance of Dr. P.L. Bogler, Dr. I.P. Bottlik, and Mr. T.J. Broida of Hughes Aircraft Company during the preparation of this section. Dr. Bogler co-authored the section and Dr. Bottlik was instrumental in the implementation of the methods described.

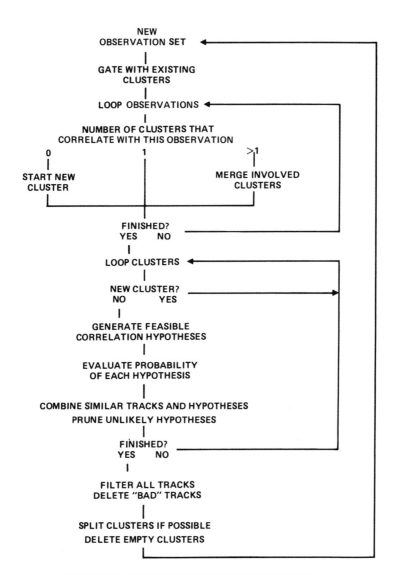

FIGURE 14–2. HIGH LEVEL FLOW CHART OF MULTIPLE
HYPOTHESIS TRACKING ALGORITHM

14.3.1   Track Scoring and Track Deletion

Regardless of the method of implementation, it is necessary to define a technique for evaluating hypotheses and tracks. For the implementation presented here, this evaluation is based on the use of the score function derived in Chapter 9. A score is computed for each track. This track score is the logarithm of the probability that the track is valid. Then, the hypothesis score is the sum of the scores of the individual tracks within that hypothesis. As in Chapter 9, a track may also be deleted whenever its score falls below a certain threshold (thereby considered a lost track).

The following discussion is based on Chapter 9, particularly the track life stages presented in Table 9-1. However, a slight notation change is introduced: it is convenient to eliminate the distinction between a single-point hypothesis representing a new true target and a single-point hypothesis representing a false target (i.e., a false alarm). At the cost of some additional notation, the elimination of this distinction reduces the number of hypotheses required.

Next, we show how the score function is computed for the four stages of track life defined in Table 9-1. These operations are preliminary to the multiple hypothesis logic developed in the later sections. The development in this chapter begins with Eq. (9.8).

Potential Track

A potential track consists of a single observation. Thus, there is just the original point and some number (N_m) of unsuccessful track update opportunities. The score function for this type of track is:

$$L = \ln \left[1 + \frac{\beta_{NT}}{\beta_{FT}} (1 - P_D)^{N_m} \right] \tag{14.1}$$

where

$\beta_{NT} \triangleq$ new target density
$\beta_{FT} \triangleq$ false target density
$P_D \triangleq$ probability of detection

The score function given by (14.1) results from a derivation in which a single point that appeared N_m scans in the past is hypothesized to be either a new target (β_{NT}) or a false target (β_{FT}). The probability of the combined hypotheses is just the sum of the probabilities from the individual hypotheses.

Based on (9.8), the individual probabilities are given by

$$P_{FT} = \beta_{FT}, \quad P_{NT} = \beta_{NT} (1 - P_D)^{N_m}$$

Equation (14.1) results after summing the two probabilities, normalizing by β_{FT} and taking the logarithm of the sum. The exponential track life factor has been approximated by unity in this derivation.

Tentative Track

A tentative track is a collection of two or more observations that have not yet satisfied the confirmation criterion. However, with the addition of the second observation, the false target option has been eliminated by that hypothesis. Thus, the form of the equation follows directly from Eq. (9.11):

$$L_i = \ln \left(\frac{\beta_{NT}}{\beta_{FT}}\right) + N_m \ln (1 - P_D) + \sum_{l=2}^{NU_i}$$

$$\left\{ \ln \left[\frac{P_D}{\beta_{FT}(2\pi)^{M/2} \sqrt{|S_{il}|}} \right] - \frac{d_{il}^2}{2} \right\}$$

(14.2)

where

NU_i = number of target detections beyond the original for track i
N_m = number of target misses
S_{il}, d_{il}^2 = residual covariance, normalized distance function associated with the lth point of the ith track

Confirmed Track

Given $L_{i,k}$ (for $L_{i,k}$ the score of track i at scan k) the criterion for track confirmation, from Eq. (9.12) is,

$$L_{i,k} > \ln D_E$$

(14.3)

for D_E, the *a priori* expected track length. The score for a confirmed track is also given by (14.2).

The only difference between a confirmed track and a tentative track is in the deletion logic used, and the resulting score after deletion. Once (14.3) is satisfied, the likelihood of the observations forming a track is always greater than the likelihood that the observations correspond to unconnected false alarms. Therefore, when a confirmed track is deleted, it must be treated as a good track that has become lost or moved out of the scan volume. Otherwise, if the track confirmation criterion is not satisfied, the collection of observations must be treated as a series of false alarms. This is discussed in more detail next.

Deleted Track

A deleted track is defined as a track that is no longer active and, thus, is no longer a candidate for further updating. Track deletion is discussed for the cases of potential, confirmed, and tentative tracks, respectively.

The simplest application of track deletion occurs for the case of a potential (one-point) track. From (14.1), the score of a potential track slowly decays to zero as the number of misses, N_m, increases. Therefore, at some point, it is advisable to assume that the track was a false alarm and to delete it from further processing, thereby conserving computational resources. Deletion occurs whenever the score falls below a threshold:

$$L_{i,k} < T_{UC}$$

Upon deletion, the score associated with the potential track is set to zero.

The score for a confirmed track will also be compared with a threshold. In the case of a confirmed track, however, the score will rise to a maximum and then, if the track is lost, the score will start to decay. Therefore, the amount of decay relative to the maximum score, $L_{i,MAX}$, is of greater interest to track deletion. Track deletion for a confirmed track is thereby defined by the condition:

$$L_{i,k} < L_{i,MAX} - \ln D_E - \Delta L_L$$

where ΔL_L is a premature deletion cost term discussed in Chapter 9. Since the track was once valid, the previously achieved track score, $L_{i,MAX} - \ln D_E$, is still associated with the hypotheses containing the track even after the track is itself deleted. This, in effect, ensures that track deletion does not penalize the hypothesis score because that hypothesis is being ranked among all the competing hypotheses.

Theoretically, the problem of deleting tentative tracks should not occur because, if a tentative track is not valid, the hypothesis containing that track will be pruned. In other words, if a hypothesis contains a tentative track that becomes insupportable then, theoretically, it will be pruned in favor of that hypothesis which states that the observations were all false alarms. However, in practice, provision must be made for the system to recover from any mistakes that may occur due to premature pruning of hypotheses. Thus, deletion of tentative tracks may be required, and this logic is similar to that for potential tracks; again the score is reset to zero upon deletion.

14.3.2 Track and Hypothesis Combining

To combine similar tracks, the N-scan criterion has been chosen because of its ease of implementation. Using this criterion, two tracks are defined as "equivalent" if the N most recent observations contained in the tracks are the same. Then, the track with the highest score (among those that are equivalent) is chosen to replace the others in each of the hypotheses. This operation conserves computational and storage resources.

The hypothesis score must remain unchanged after track combining because this combining procedure is essentially only a bookkeeping operation designed to limit the number of tracks to be stored. This constraint is maintained through the use of a residual hypothesis score (SCRES). Whenever a track is replaced, SCRES is incremented by the difference in score between the former track and the track that is replacing it. Thus, after combining tracks, the hypothesis score is the sum of the scores of all the tracks contained in the hypothesis plus SCRES.

After combining equivalent tracks the next step is to combine equivalent hypotheses (i.e., hypotheses containing the same set of tracks). In the simplest implementation, combining two hypotheses merely means dropping that hypothesis with the lower score. However, as shown next, the score L_C associated with the combined hypothesis is computed using the scores (L_1, L_2) of the hypotheses being combined via the relationship:

$$L_C = L_1 + \ln(1 + e^{-\Delta L}) \tag{14.4}$$

where, assuming $L_1 > L_2$,

$$\Delta L = L_1 - L_2$$

The relationship given in (14.4) is derived upon noting that the hypothesis probabilities are proportional to the exponential of the score function. Then, defining P_C, P_1, and P_2 to be the exponential quantities that are proportional to the probabilities of the combined hypothesis and the first and second hypotheses, respectively,

$$P_C = P_1 + P_2 = e^{L_1} + e^{L_2} = \exp(L_1) \cdot (1 + e^{-\Delta L})$$

so that

$$L_C = \ln(P_C) = L_1 + \ln(1 + e^{-\Delta L})$$

Thus, when two hypotheses are combined, the residual score (SCRES) of the remaining hypothesis is incremented by $\ln(1 + e^{-\Delta L})$.

14.3.3 Hypothesis Pruning

As discussed in Chapter 10, there are several approaches to limiting the number of hypotheses through deletion. The simplest approach to pruning is probably just to limit the number of hypotheses to the M most likely. This method was chosen for the implementation discussed here.

To limit the growth of hypotheses, the pruning operation is implemented once per frame, and also after each observation is received within the frame. The value of M taken in the two cases was

$$
M = \begin{cases} M_1, & \text{after processing each observation} \\[2mm] M_2, & \text{after processing each frame (or set) of observations and} \\ & \text{combining equivalent hypotheses} \end{cases}
$$

where M_1 should exceed M_2. Typical values for conditions with up to four interacting targets were 32 and 16 for M_1 and M_2, respectively.

A slightly more complex pruning technique is presented next. It adapts to the number of hypotheses being evaluated and their relative probabilities. For this technique the hypotheses are first ranked. Then, the hypothesis with rank $N + 1$ will be deleted if

$$
\sum_{i=1}^{N} L_i - N \cdot L_{N+1} > T_S
$$

where

$$
L_i \triangleq \text{score function for hypothesis ranked number } i
$$
$$
T_S \triangleq \text{threshold}
$$

Note that this test is equivalent to comparing the product of the ratio of hypothesis probabilities to a threshold. The equivalent representation of the test is

$$
\prod_{i=1}^{N} \left(\frac{P_i}{P_{N+1}} \right) > e^{T_S}
$$

where

$$
P_i = \text{probability for hypothesis ranked number } i
$$

Values for T_S of about 7 have been found to give good results, but T_S could be chosen as a function of the number of clusters and the available computer resources.

Next, dynamic data structures and their application to MHT logic are discussed. Only a brief description will be given. Standard reference books (such as [4]) give a more detailed discussion of these structures.

14.3.4 Definition of Dynamic Data Structures

In any static data structure, such as those associated with FORTRAN programs, it is always necessary first to declare the data structure (e.g., by using a declarative DIMENSION statement, which declares the data structure of a single array). In other words, in a static data structure the values of the data may be changed (such as when an array element is changed), but the structure of the data itself is fixed for the entire program.

Dynamic data structures, on the other hand, may be changed during the operation of the program. No statement is required to declare the underlying structure of the data itself. A construct, called a pointer, is used instead to build a wide variety of possible structures. In particular, pointers are used to connect blocks of stored data such as integers, numbers, arrays, characters, and records, thereby building a data structure. The advantage of a dynamic data structure is that a complex notation is not required in order to access and store data of changing format.

Figure 14-3 is a simple example of this concept, where the arrows represent pointers and the boxes represent stored data. One way to change a dynamic data structure is to insert an additional data set. Referring to this figure, note that the insertion of an additional data set is accomplished simply by replacing one pointer (arrow) with two others, leading to and from the inserted data set.

Records are a more general type of data set or array. They are useful when it is desired to store data of many different types at a single locale, for example, storing an array and a pointer together. Records will be used exclusively herein to store data, and so the boxes in the figures will always represent records.

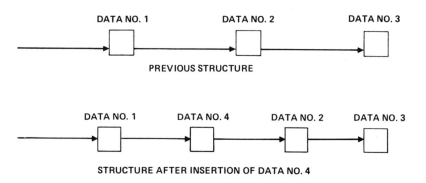

DATA NO. 1   DATA NO. 2   DATA NO. 3

PREVIOUS STRUCTURE

DATA NO. 1   DATA NO. 4   DATA NO. 2   DATA NO. 3

STRUCTURE AFTER INSERTION OF DATA NO. 4

FIGURE 14-3. EXAMPLE OF A DYNAMIC DATA STRUCTURE

It is important to emphasize that records, like arrays, have a fixed data structure. Pointers are used to change the data structure.

The only way to move around in this structure is to follow the pointers. To move to a particular record, the pointers are followed until the particular record of interest is encountered. Moving in this fashion is called traversing the list, where a list denotes any sequence of data elements. A structure connected in this manner is referred to as a linked list.

Typically, it is desired to perform a similar operation in turn on each consecutive record in the list. This is accomplished by traversing the list, performing that operation in turn until the end of the list is encountered (which then signals termination).

The pointers may be changed any time during the execution of the program, enabling a dynamic data structure. A change in the structure is accomplished by traversing the list until the pointer that is to be changed is encountered. Changing a pointer amounts to erasing the pointer arrow and redrawing it so that it points elsewhere. For example, a new record is inserted anywhere, as in Fig. 14-3, simply by erasing and redrawing arrows to accommodate the new record. Thus, a dynamic data structure is made possible via the use of pointers.

14.3.5   Application to Multiple Hypothesis Tracking

Next, we show how the concepts of dynamic data structures apply to implementation of the multiple hypothesis tracking method. An overview of this implementation is as follows. The multiple hypothesis data structure contains a linked list of clusters. Clusters contain linked lists of hypotheses whose tracks interact (or could interact) with each other. Hypotheses are represented by parameters and a linked list of pointers to the tracks that comprise the hypotheses. Finally, tracks are represented by parameters and a linked list of observation identifiers, so that the N-scan combining rule can be implemented.

The lowest level element in the data structure is the track record, containing information pertaining to a single track. This record contains a fixed amount of information, including the current Kalman filter estimates of the kinematic state, individual track score, and the track life stage (i.e., is it potential, tentative, or a confirmed track).

A hypothesis is simply a collection of track records, linked by pointers, that together form an estimate of the state of all the targets. This can be represented as shown in Fig. 14-4. Each hypothesis record contains various items; primary among these being a pointer to the first track record in a linked list of attendant tracks. Also contained in the hypothesis record is an integer

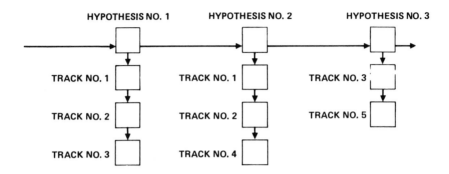

FIGURE 14-4. HYPOTHESIS AND TRACK DATA STRUCTURE

indicating the total number of tracks contained in that hypothesis, and the total score (i.e., sum of the scores of all the tracks). Finally, the set of all hypotheses is also joined together in a list, linked by pointers, as shown in Fig. 14-4.

New hypotheses are generated as observations are received. The insertion of these new hypotheses into the data structure is easily accommodated. When a new hypothesis is generated, it is, in effect, stored immediately behind the old hypothesis that originated it. A single old hypothesis is then continually expanded in this manner until all reasonable (as determined by gating relationships) track associations have been considered. The last hypothesis to be so generated will always be the hypothesis indicating that the current observation corresponds to a new target or to a false alarm; this hypothesis replaces the old hypothesis in the line (thus, ensuring that the list contains only current records). Then, the next hypothesis in the list is considered for expansion, and is finally replaced as a new target hypothesis, and so on. The end result is that the linked list of hypotheses is expanded in such a manner that it now contains many new possible hypotheses, with the old outdated hypotheses replaced by new target hypotheses.

In order for an observation-to-track association to be considered, two important criteria need to be satisfied. First, the observation must lie within the validation region (or gate region) of the track. Second, no prior observations must have been previously assigned to that track within the current frame time. Assigned tracks are so labeled in order to permit this second exclusion.

If these two conditions are satisfied, a new hypothesis is then generated from that single data association. Hypothesis generation then proceeds as outlined above. At the end of the frame time, all tracks are Kalman filtered, scoring takes place, and the labels given to tracks assigned observations are reset. This then completes a single processing cycle.

The processing described above permits an easy generalization to an ESA design. In an ESA design, the above would differ only in that the labels are reset every fraction of a frame time rather than once per frame time (thereby allowing multiple track updates per frame).

If hypothesis generation were to proceed unchecked, storage space and processing time would quickly become exhausted. Thus, after each expansion phase, pruning of the least likely hypotheses occurs. Also, as will be discussed next, common track records are shared as much as possible in order to reduce redundant storage. Furthermore, processing is performed in a manner such that a track need be processed only once per observation, even though it may be contained within multiple hypotheses.

In order to economize on the required computational space, tracks are shared among multiple hypotheses. Track sharing is maintained through the use of track lists, as illustrated in Fig. 14-5. Each hypothesis has associated with it a distinct track list. A track list is a linked list of pointers, with one pointer designating a single track-file, and the other pointer allowing the track list to be traversed. In conclusion, a track list is a way of reducing the repetitive nature of the hypothesis data structure (to repetition only in the track lists, and not in the tracks themselves).

Track sharing unavoidably produces some additional complications which require mentioning. In the process of pruning (deleting) hypotheses, it is not always possible to delete automatically the attendant tracks (because a single track may be shared among several hypotheses). Thus, a mechanism is required in order to help decide whether or not a track may be deleted whenever a hypothesis is deleted, and thus reclaim unused track space. This mechanism is provided through the use of reference counts. Each track will have associated with it a count number indicating how many hypotheses reference that particular track. As a hypothesis is being deleted, this number

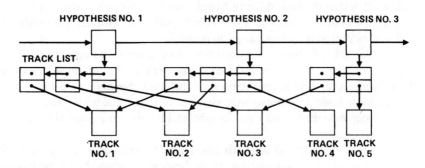

FIGURE 14-5. HYPOTHESES CAN SHARE TRACKS
EFFICIENTLY USING TRACK LISTS

is checked. Only if this number equals one (for the hypotheses being deleted) will track deletion concurrently take place with hypothesis deletion.

The phenomenon of track sharing also implies that there may exist many more hypotheses than tracks. In certain operations (such as gating), it is convenient to access the tracks directly, and thus bypass the hypotheses entirely. In other words, for any operation involving the tracks as a group it is convenient to have a method of quickly accessing the tracks by themselves without having to go through the numerous hypotheses. To permit this, a different track list, called a master track list, is maintained by linking up all the tracks. This is shown in Fig. 14-6.

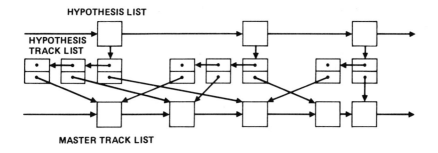

HYPOTHESIS LIST

HYPOTHESIS TRACK LIST

MASTER TRACK LIST

FIGURE 14-6. DATA STRUCTURE INCLUDING MASTER TRACK LIST

Furthermore, the phenomenon of track sharing implies that a given observation may encounter the same track many times as it traverses the hypothesis list. This is redundant since the same processing is being performed many times per observation-track pair. Thus, a mechanism is required in order to ensure that a given track is processed no more than once per observation update. This mechanism is provided through the use of a flag. If an observation-track pair has been previously processed, then that track will be flagged and the updated version is placed at the address next in line in the master track list. This flag is checked before any processing occurs in each subsequent hypothesis. The flags are reset to zero after every observation is processed.

One other operation needs to be mentioned. The constraint that a track cannot be updated more than once per scan must be maintained. This requires a means of identifying or labeling tracks that have already been updated with an observation on the current scan. This can be achieved by always placing the updated tracks at the head of the track list. In particular, when a track is updated, it is always put at the head of its own track list. Then, when a new observation is received, only the subset of tracks past a certain point in the track list need be considered. An additional pointer marks the start of this subset of tracks.

More saving space is possible if the entire set of hypotheses can be divided up into sets of independent clusters. A cluster is by definition a set of hypotheses that are found to be physically close and interacting. On the cluster level, the data assignment should be relatively straightforward. Only within the cluster will be observation assignment be ambiguous. Validating to which cluster an observation belongs is achieved while traversing the master track list and, in turn, testing each track in that cluster for proximity to that observation. Having validated that an observation belongs to a certain cluster, hypothesis generation then proceeds only internally to that cluster. However, if more than a single cluster satisfies this validation test, then the clusters must be merged to form a supercluster, and hypothesis generation proceeds internally to that supercluster.

Traversing between clusters is accomplished via a doubly linked list of joined clusters. This is configured as shown in Fig. 14-7.

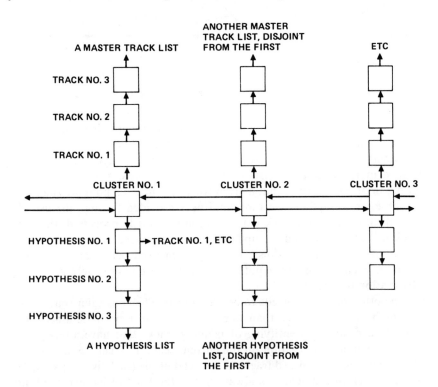

FIGURE 14-7. DATA STRUCTURE WITH LINKED CLUSTERS

14.3.6 An Example of Multiple Hypothesis Tracking

Consider tracking two targets moving in parallel as shown in Fig. 14-8. This example was chosen as a simple one-dimensional test of the MHT logic. The figure shows the position measurements as a function of scan number. Following the notation of Chapter 10, $y_j(k)$ is defined to be the *j*th observation received on scan k.

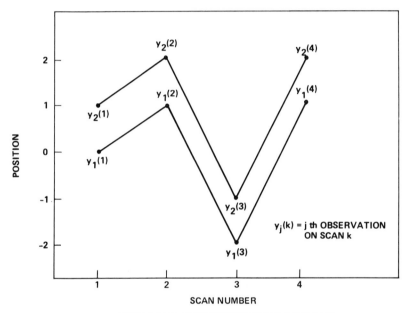

FIGURE 14-8. TEST GEOMETRY FOR MHT LOGIC

A simple Kalman filtering model was assumed. Using this filter model the target motion was described by a random walk, so that

$$x(k) = x(k-1) + \sigma_x r(k)$$

with $r(k)$ a zero-mean unit standard deviation Gaussian and σ_x chosen to be 10. The measurement noise standard deviation used in the filter model was chosen to be 1.0, but the actual observations input to the system were as shown in Fig. 14-8. Finally, P_D was modeled (for the purposes of score function computation) as 0.9. This high assumed value of P_D has the effect of greatly reducing the probabilities associated with hypotheses containing tracks with missing observations. Thus, the more likely hypotheses turned out to be those that contained only tracks with no missing observations.

The system used pruning to 16 hypotheses after each observation and to four hypotheses after each scan ($M_1 = 16$, $M_2 = 4$) and two-scan combining of tracks. Tables 14-1 through 14-5 summarize the hypotheses that were 'formed and give the associated probabilities. The probabilities, $P(H_i)$, associated with the M hypotheses that remained after pruning were computed in a direct manner from the associated score functions L_i using the relationship:

$$P'(H_i) = e^{L_i}, \quad P(H_i) = \frac{P'(H_i)}{\sum_{l=1}^{M} P'(H_l)}$$

After the first scan there is the single hypothesis that y_1 (1) and y_2 (1) are new sources. Table 14-1 shows the seven hypotheses that were formed after the second scan of data and their associated tracks and probabilities. However, only four hypotheses were maintained (after pruning). Table 14-1 also shows the normalized probabilities associated with those four hypotheses that remained after pruning. This table uses brackets to denote tracks, so that [y_1 (2), y_1 (1)] represents a track consisting of observations y_1 (2) and y_1 (1).

The correct hypothesis is that y_1 (2) and y_1 (1) form one track and that y_2 (2) and y_2 (1) form a second track. This hypothesis is given probability 0.30 of being correct (after pruning), but the other three surviving hypotheses have comparable probabilities. For example, the hypothesis that y_1 (2) and y_2 (1) form one track, and that y_2 (2) and y_1 (1) are independent observations from different sources has probability 0.21. Also, note that the hypotheses which were pruned, although incorrect, had fairly large probabilities. Finally, there can be no combining after two scans.

Track combining first occurs after the first observation is received on the third scan. At this time the first step is to combine the tracks $T1$ and $T1'$, where

$$T = [y_1 (3), y_1 (2), y_2 (1)], \quad T1' = [y_1 (3), y_1 (2), y_1 (1)]$$

The result was that $T1$ had a slightly larger score than $T1'$, so $T1$ replaced $T1'$ in those hypotheses previously containing $T1'$. Similarly, the tracks $T2$, $T2'$, and $T2''$ were combined, where

$$T2 = [y_1 (3), y_2 (2), y_2 (1)], \quad T2' = [y_1 (3), y_2 (2), y_1 (1)]$$
$$T2'' = [y_1 (3), y_2 (2)]$$

Hence, since $T2$ had the largest score it replaced $T2'$ and $T2''$ wherever these tracks previously appeared.

A total of 14 hypotheses were formed, but none could be combined. Table 14-2 shows only the eight most likely hypotheses and their associated

TABLE 14-1
HYPOTHESES AFTER SECOND SCAN

Hypothesis Number	Hypothesis Tracks	Probabilities Before Pruning	After Pruning
1	$[y_1(2), y_1(1)]$ $[y_2(2), y_2(1)]$	0.20	0.30
2	$[y_1(2), y_2(1)]$ $[y_2(2), y_1(1)]$	0.19	0.29
3	$[y_1(2), y_2(1)]$ $y_2(2)$ $y_1(1)$	0.14	0.21
4	$[y_1(2), y_1(1)]$ $y_2(2)$ $y_2(1)$	0.13	0.20
5	$[y_2(2), y_2(1)]$ $y_1(2)$ $y_1(1)$	0.13	Deleted
6	$[y_2(2), y_1(1)]$ $y_1(2)$ $y_2(1)$	0.12	Deleted
7	$y_2(2)$ $y_1(2)$ $y_2(1)$ $y_1(1)$	0.09	Deleted

probabilities. However, since M_1 was 16, all 14 hypotheses were carried to the next stage where the second observation was processed.

Referring to Table 14-2, note that hypotheses 1, 4, and 6 are inconsistent because each has the point $y_2(1)$ in two tracks. This is because of the track combining (or replacements) discussed above (Track $T1$ replaced $T1'$ in hypotheses 1 and 6, and $T2$ replaced $T2'$ in hypothesis 4). This inconsistency illustrates that inherent in the choice of an N-scan combining approach is the assumption that assignment of points beyond the last N scans is not of consequence. Thus, inconsistencies are to be expected for assignment beyond the last N scans.

Because tracks $T1$ and $T2$ had slightly higher scores than did the equivalent tracks $T1'$, $T2'$, and $T2''$, they replaced these tracks. For the hypotheses in which these replacements occurred, the values for the SCRES terms were set to the negative of the score differences. For example, since hypothesis 1 now contains $T1$ (rather than $T1'$), the value of SCRES for this hypothesis was computed, so that

$$\text{SCRES} = - [\text{SCORE}(T1) - \text{SCORE}(T1')]$$

Thus, the score, $\text{SCORE}(T1')$, associated with the original track $T1'$, was effectively maintained with the hypothesis even though track $T1$ replaced $T1'$.

TABLE 14-2
THE EIGHT MOST LIKELY HYPOTHESES AFTER
THE FIRST OBSERVATION OF SCAN THREE

Hypothesis Number	Hypothesis Tracks	Probability
1	$[y_1(3), y_1(2), y_2(1)]$ $[y_2(2), y_2(1)]$	0.15
2	$[y_1(3), y_1(2), y_2(1)]$ $[y_2(2), y_1(1)]$	0.14
3	$[y_1(3), y_2(2), y_2(1)]$ $[y_1(2), y_1(1)]$	0.11
4	$[y_1(3), y_2(2), y_2(1)]$ $[y_1(2), y_2(1)]$	0.11
5	$[y_1(3), y_1(2), y_2(1)]$ $y_2(2)$ $y_1(1)$	0.10
6	$[y_1(3), y_1(2), y_2(1)]$ $y_2(2)$ $y_2(1)$	0.10
7	$[y_1(2), y_1(1)]$ $[y_2(2), y_2(1)]$ $y_1(3)$	0.06
8	$[y_1(2), y_2(1)]$ $[y_2(2), y_1(1)]$ $y_1(3),$	0.06
All Others		0.17

Table 14-3 shows the six most likely hypotheses that were formed after the second observation was received on scan three. The first four hypotheses of Table 14-3 represent the addition of the new observation, $y_2(3)$, to the second tracks contained in the first four hypotheses shown in Table 14-2. Also, the addition of the new observation to hypotheses 7 and 8, shown in Table 14-2, moves the ranking of these hypotheses up to 5 and 6, respectively, in Table 14-3.

Extensive combining occurs after the second observation, $y_2(3)$, is received on scan three. Beginning again with track combining, we see, from Table 14-3, that tracks $T3$ and $T3'$ can be combined, as can $T4$ and $T4'$. Track $T3$ had a higher score than $T3'$, so it replaces $T3'$ in hypothesis 2. The result is that hypotheses 1 and 2 are now equivalent and can be combined. Similarly, $T4$ replaces $T4'$ in hypotheses 3 and 5 with the result that hypotheses 3 and 4 can also be combined. However, hypotheses 5 and 6 remain distinct.

TABLE 14-3
SIX MOST LIKELY HYPOTHESES
BEFORE COMBINING ON SCAN THREE

Hypothesis Number	Hypothesis Tracks	Probability
1	$[y_1(3), y_1(2), y_2(1)] = T1$ $[y_2(3), y_2(2), y_2(1)] = T3$	0.123
2	$[y_1(3), y_1(2), y_2(1)] = T1$ $[y_2(3), y_2(2), y_1(1)] = T3'$	0.113
3	$[y_1(3), y_2(2), y_2(1)] = T2$ $[y_2(3), y_1(2), y_1(1)] = T4'$	0.113
4	$[y_1(3), y_2(2), y_2(1)] = T2$ $[y_2(3), y_1(2), y_2(1)] = T4$	0.105
5	$[y_2(3), y_1(2), y_1(1)] = T4'$ $[y_2(2), y_2(1)]$ $y_1(3)$	0.062
6	$[y_2(3), y_1(2), y_2(1)] = T4$ $[y_2(2), y_1(1)]$ $y_1(3)$	0.056
All Others		0.428

Table 14-4 shows the four hypotheses that remained after combining and pruning occurred. Hypotheses 1 and 2 were combined into a new hypothesis 1. Similarly, the combined hypotheses 3 and 4 became new hypothesis 2, and the previous hypotheses 5 and 6 become hypotheses 3 and 4. Since the pruning algorithms used $M_2 = 4$, only these four hypotheses remain. The probability of hypothesis 1 is the sum of the combined hypotheses renormalized, so that

$$P(H_1) = \frac{0.236}{0.572} = 0.412$$

with similar computations for the other hypothesis probabilities.

TABLE 14-4
REMAINING HYPOTHESES AFTER THIRD SCAN COMBINING
AND PRUNING

Hypothesis Number	Hypothesis Tracks	Probability (After Normalization)
1	$[y_1(3), y_1(2), y_2(1)]$ $[y_2(3), y_2(2), y_2(1)]$	0.41
2	$[y_1(3), y_2(2), y_2(1)]$ $[y_2(3), y_1(2), y_2(1)]$	0.38
3	$[y_2(3), y_1(2), y_2(1)]$ $[y_2(2), y_2(1)]$ $y_1(3)$	0.11
4	$[y_2(3), y_1(2), y_2(1)]$ $[y_2(2), y_1(1)]$ $y_1(3)$	0.10

Due to the erratic measurement pattern, the probabilities were distributed over many hypotheses and the resultant pruning led to the loss of hypotheses containing combined probability 0.43. Pruning to four hypotheses after each scan was used here for simplicity of representation. Experience indicates that more hypotheses must be maintained for difficult conditions. However, for this example, the correct hypothesis was maintained throughout.

Table 14-5 summarizes the results of processing data from the fourth scan. The test input trajectories of Fig. 14-8 also make large jumps on the fourth scan. The result is that, at the end of scan 4, the sum of the probabilities of pruned hypotheses is again quite large (0.37). However, as shown in Table 14-5, the correct hypothesis is still computed to be the most likely.

TABLE 14-5
REMAINING HYPOTHESES AFTER FOURTH SCAN COMBINING AND PRUNING

Hypothesis Number	Hypothesis Tracks	Probability (After Normalization)
1	$[y_1(4), y_1(3), y_1(2), y_2(1)]$ $[y_2(4), y_2(3), y_1(2), y_2(1)]$	0.42
2	$[y_1(4), y_2(3), y_1(2), y_2(1)]$ $[y_2(4), y_1(3), y_1(2), y_2(1)]$	0.39
3	$[y_1(4), y_2(3), y_1(2), y_2(1)]$ $[y_1(3), y_1(2), y_2(1)]$ $y_2(4)$	0.10
4	$[y_1(4), y_2(3), y_1(2), y_2(1)]$ $[y_1(3), y_2(2), y_2(1)]$ $y_2(4)$	0.09

14.4 MTT IMPLEMENTATION IN DENSE TARGET ENVIRONMENTS*

14.4.1 Data Rate Adaptive MTT

In a dense target environment the number of observations can overwhelm both computational and storage capacity. For example, this is quite likely to occur for an air-to-ground MTT system that must track many vehicles in a high false target environment. If the MTT system is not designed to deal with data inundation, whole frames of observations can be lost, or the processing may become so far behind that the track file information will be of decreased value.

Consider the first case, in which MTT processing starts anew (with *redundancy elimination*) at the beginning of each frame. If the processing in a certain frame does not finish before the allotted time, it will most likely be interrupted during *data association*, since that is the function which is most time consuming. If this happens, the track files will not be updated, and the whole frame of data is effectively lost.

In the second case, the processing in any frame starts up where it left off in the previous frame. This prevents loss of the current frame of data, but the system can become further and further behind until the track file

*This section was contributed by Mr. R.T. Marloth of Hughes Aircraft Company.

information is not relevant to the current situation. The data buffers will fill up and finally overflow.

It is possible to monitor the number of observations and to cull them, so that, at least on the average, the processing keeps up with the flow of data. The number of observations accepted for processing is a function of both the amount of time that the processing is in arrears and the number of frames of data in the buffer.

Consider an MTT system for which observation data are entered in batches into an *input buffer*, which holds up to five batches. The time allocated to processing for the MTT system is defined to be T_p. This time may, in general, be less than the frame time if the radar system has other modes in addition to MTT.

A block diagram of a system with an adaptive multiple-target tracker (MTT) is shown in Fig. 14-9. The MTT system is enclosed by dashed lines. It consists of the usual three blocks (with *gating* and *correlation* combined into *data association*) plus the one of particular interest here, the *culler*.

If the multiple-target tracker cannot keep up with the flow of observations, the buffer will overflow and data will be lost. In order to discard data in an orderly way, the culler has been inserted. It computes an allowable number of observations, (N_A), that should be processed from the current batch. N_A is based upon the queue length in the buffer, (N_B), the amount of computer time available, (T_p), and the time, (T_c), taken for the previous batch of data. The culler then selects the observations to be processed and those to be discarded. An empirically developed function for N_A is

$$N_A(k) = min \left\{ \left(\frac{T_p}{T_c}\right)^d \left[1 - \left(\frac{N_B - b}{c}\right) \right] N_A(k-1), N_M \right\}$$

$$N_A(1) = min \left\{ \frac{N_M}{2}\left(\frac{T_p}{T_o}\right), N_M \right\}$$

where

T_p = frame time allocated to processing
T_c = time to process batch $k-1$
T_o = initial value used before T_c is available
N_A = allowable number of observations
N_B = number of batches in queue

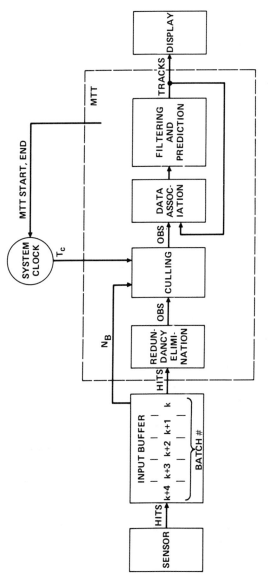

FIGURE 14-9. DATA RATE ADAPTIVE MTT SYSTEM

N_M = maximum number of observations that are to be allowed for processing

b = nominal queue length

c = queue length attenuator

d = computation time attenuator

The function $N_A(k)$ is computed recursively; besides depending upon $N_A(k-1)$, it also depends upon the time used on the previous cycle, the time available, and the number of batches in the queue. The objective is to take as many observations as can be processed in the available time up to a maximum of N_M, while maintaining a nominal queue length. When T_p is relatively large, it is expected that N_A will stay near N_M and the queue length will remain between 1 and 0. Only for short frame times is the adaptivity expected to be important. The factor

$$\left(\frac{T_p}{T_c} \right)^d$$

increases N_A from the previous frame if the previous frame requires less than the nominal allocated time ($T_c < T_p$) and decreases N_A if the previous frame took longer than expected. The attenuating exponent $d(d < 1)$ keeps this factor from inducing wide fluctuations in N_A. The factor

$$\left[1 - \left(\frac{N_B - b}{c} \right) \right]$$

increases N_A from the previous frame if the queue is short ($N_B < b$) and *vice versa*. The factor c is an attenuator analogous to d. Note that when $N_B = b$, the nominal queue length, this factor is equal to unity.

The initial value of N_A was purposely chosen small to keep the system from falling behind early. If things go well, it only takes a few cycles for N_A to reach N_M.

Qualitatively, the effect of the culler will be to maintain an equilibrium value of N_B. If the input buffer contains more than b batches, N_A will be reduced, which allows the system to catch up with the data stream, thus shortening the buffer queue. On the other hand, if N_B is less than b, N_A will be increased to allow more observations to be processed.

Numerical Example

The method for computing $N_A(k)$ was tested in a simple simulation. The time required to process a batch of N_o observations was assumed to be given by the function

$$T_c(N_o) = 0.1 + 0.002\,N_o + 0.00005\,N_o^2$$

The constant term represents overhead, the linear term tracking and redundancy elimination time, and the square term data association time. For this choice of parameters, we have

$$T_c(200) = 2.5 \text{ s}$$

The processing time (T_p) was assumed to be 1.4 s. System constants were chosen to be

$$b = 2, \quad c = 10.0, \quad d = 0.3, \quad N_M = 256$$

The value 2 was chosen for b to ensure that the system would not unnecessarily delete observations. The values for c and d were chosen empirically, but similar performance was achieved using the values 20.0 and 0.2, respectively.

Figures 14-10 through 14-12 illustrate results. Three inputs were used: a constant 200 observations; a constant 100 with a triangular surge of 100; and a constant 150 with the same surge. The number of inputs, number allowed, and the queue length are all shown. Note that the equilibrium value for N_A is 143, since

$$\dot{T_c}(143) = 1.4 \text{ s} = T_p$$

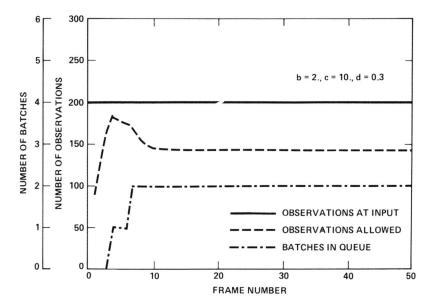

FIGURE 14-10. CULLER RESPONSE FOR CONSTANT INPUT

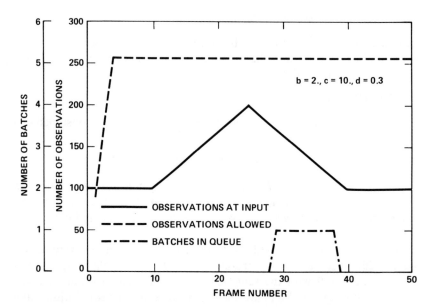

FIGURE 14-11. CULLER RESPONSE FOR FIRST TIME-VARYING INPUT

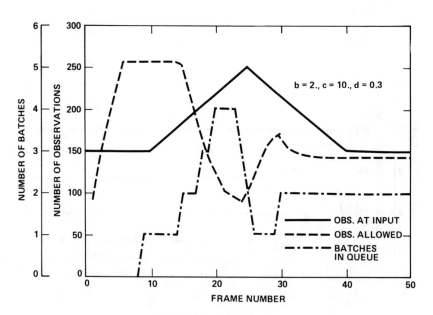

FIGURE 14-12. CULLER RESPONSE FOR SECOND TIME-VARYING INPUT

As shown in Fig. 14-10 this number is reached in steady state when the number of input observations exceeds 143, which in this case is 200.

Figures 14-11 and 14-12 show culler response for the triangular input sequences. For the case shown in Fig. 14-11, no observations were lost because the system continues to allow up to 256 observations. In contrast, a nonadaptive system that allows input of no more than 143 observations per frame would lose about 500 observations.

For the case shown in Fig. 14-12, the response is more dynamic as the number of input observations during the surge greatly exceeds capacity. In this case, the system using the culler lost about 50 fewer observations than did the nonadaptive system.

Assessment

The culler has been shown to maintain stability in the number of observations processed for constant and time-varying input functions. An important question is that of which observations to cull. Retaining observations close to existing tracks would prolong average track life, but implementation itself would be time consuming, thus reducing the number of allowed observations. In one system, it has proved useful to keep observations with greater amplitude because these are less likely to be either false alarms or targets so small that they will produce very short tracks.

The processing delay introduced by a non-zero equilibrium value for queue length could be troublesome in tactical systems. However, in reconnaissance-type systems, which are normally designed to process hundreds of observations, this delay is less of a problem.

14.4.2 Implementation of MTT Logic on a Sector Basis

Again consider an environment producing many observations. Assume a scanning sensor (such as for a TWS system). Then, it may be inefficient to collect an entire scan's data before processing. A more efficient approach is to process input data, as received, by sectors. Thus, data collection and processing are done in parallel so that memory requirements and processing delays are minimized.

Following Nagarajan [5] and Trunk [6], Fig. 14-13 presents a timing diagram showing how operations are performed on a sector basis. When the sensor is in sector n, gating is performed for tracks in sector $n-2$. These predicted track positions are compared with observations received during the sensor scan of sectors $n-3$ through $n-1$.

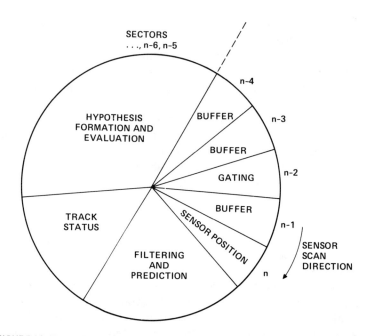

FIGURE 14-13. TIMING DIAGRAM FOR PERFORMING OPERATIONS ON SECTOR BASIS

There will be one or two sectors as a buffer between those tracks (in sector $n-2$) for which gating is being performed and those tracks for which data association hypotheses are formed. As shown in the diagram, while the sensor is scanning sector n, hypothesis formation will be occurring for tracks in sectors $n-5$ and beyond (sectors $n-6$, $n-7$, *et cetera*).

For a sequential correlation method (such as sequential NN) the hypothesis formation and evaluation logic would be replaced by an assignment algorithm, such as solution of the assignment matrix discussed in Section 14.1. Again, only tracks in sectors $n-5$ and beyond would be considered for assignment of observations. However, a problem could arise due to conflict situations with tracks in the buffer (sector $n-4$). This problem could be handled be deferring solution of the assignment matrix until such time (that value of n) as there were no conflict situations involving tracks in sectors $n-4$ and $n-5$. Finally, after hypothesis formation (or correlation) logic is performed, track status is updated, and filtering and prediction occurs in preparation for more observation data.

14.5 A TOTAL ARCHITECTURE INCLUDING MULTIPLE-TARGET TRACKING

In future developments, the multiple-target tracking (MTT) functions will typically be included as part of a larger system architecture. This section briefly discusses one such architecture in which MTT, artificial intelligence (AI), and sensor allocation are integrated. By integrating MTT and AI techniques, the functions of both can be enhanced.

14.5.1 System Overview

Figure 14-14 gives a high-level flow chart of a system that integrates MTT, sensor allocation, and two AI functions. The MTT function processes the input data from multiple sensors to form track files using the techniques presented throughout this book. The first AI function is called *object analysis*. It uses the correlation hypotheses generated by the MTT function to infer additional information about single objects (targets) or small groups of targets traveling together.

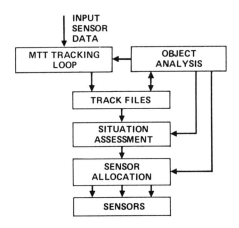

FIGURE 14-14. HIGH LEVEL INTEGRATED
SYSTEM FLOW CHART

A second AI function, *situation assessment*, draws more global inferences about the behavior of all the tracks based upon the track file information and upon the output of *object analysis*. The information from situation assessment is used for sensor allocation, and may, in general, be used for other higher-order decisions such as tactics (should a maneuver be performed in order to evade hostile threats, *et cetera*). Finally, sensor allocation (as discussed previously in Chapter 13) determines the manner in which sensor resources are used to collect further data. Note that there may also be other allocation functions, such as for computational resources or electronic countermeasures (ECM). We next discuss the AI functions (object analysis and situation assessment) in more detail.

14.5.2   Object Analysis

Pope [7] presents the development of an object analysis (OA) function for an avionics system. Our discussion is based upon that reference. The OA function takes the correlation hypotheses (and corresponding track file data) and infers additional information, such as target intent and the existence of likely but undetected target threats. It does so using a predetermined data base of target information and expert rules. Thus, as discussed in [7], the OA function will be an *expert system*.

Utilization of the OA function is illustrated with an avionics example. It is well known that aircraft fly in formation and that faster moving fighter aircraft typically escort bombers. When the formation is cruising far from the planned target, fighters weave and execute "S-turns" so that they do not overtake their partners. Thus, upon noting a single track with frequent "S-turns," we could logically infer the existence of other members of a formation, even if these other members were as yet undetected. Furthermore, using the position knowledge of our own bases and the expected "firepower" necessary to attack these friendly bases, we might also infer the expected number of targets in the formation and their expected future heading. This information could be used to aid the MTT process and to determine sensor allocation so that, for example, postulated, but as yet undetected, threats could be searched for and ascertained.

The OA function will also aid sensor allocation by identifying what information will be the most useful for completing such required tasks as determining target identification or intent. For example, given a high velocity target, it may be very desirable to allocate a radar sensor in order to measure target cross section, and thus help to determine if the target is a missile. Such information as threat behavior and likely intent will comprise the input for the situation assessment function discussed immediately below.

14.5.3 Situation Assessment

The situation assessment function specifies the way in which the system integrates all the track file information and the knowledge gained from OA into an overall view of the sensed environment. For military applications, this will primarily mean the determination of which targets are the most relevant. For example, the characteristics (position, velocity, estimated intent, *et cetera*) of target tracks can be compared with data-base information to determine sensor allocation priorities. Other tactical decisions such as when to perform evasive maneuvers, when to launch missiles, and how to allocate countermeasures can also be determined using information from situation assessment.

The situation assessment function might involve development of a rule-based AI expert system. It may also include the process of aggregation [8, 9], in which elements are linked together to infer information concerning the entire engagement. Again, the purpose of situation assessment is to develop a global picture of the overall situation in order to set priorities for gathering more information and (for an avionics system) to aid the pilot in determining crucial tactical decisions.

14.5.4 Future Integration of MTT and AI Techniques

This section has briefly outlined how MTT and AI functions can be integrated into a total system. In future military systems, the MTT design will be part of an overall system development in which tracking, target identification, resource allocation, and tactics determination are integrated. The two main elements of this overall system development will be MTT techniques, such as discussed in this book, and AI techniques, such as expert system development discussed in [7, 8].

The success of using AI techniques for tactical applications depends upon the quality of the target track file information that is used as input for the AI system. Given that this input information is adequate, AI techniques can provide additional information beyond that typically provided by a classical MTT system. This information (such as inferred knowledge about previously undetected targets, expected target intent, *et cetera*), in turn can be used to aid the MTT functions of correlation and track prediction. Thus, it is expected that future system design will more fully utilize the complementary nature of MTT and AI techniques.

REFERENCES

1. Burgeois, F., and J.-C. Lassalle, "An Extension of the Munkres Algorithm for the Assignment Problem to Rectangular Matrices," *Communications of the ACM*, Vol. 14, Dec. 1971, pp. 802–806.
2. Ford, L.R., and D.R. Fulkerson, *Flows in Networks*, Princeton, NJ: Princeton University Press, 1962.
3. Kuhn, H.W., "The Hungarian Method for the Assignment Problem," *Naval Research Logistics Quarterly*, No. 2, 1955, pp. 83–97.
4. Aho, A., J.E. Hopcroft, and J.D. Ullman, *Data Structures and Algorithms*, Reading, MA: Addison-Wesley, 1983.
5. Nagarajan, V., V. Hanuma Sai, and G.K. Chaturvedi, "A New Approach to Scan-to-Scan Correlation and Its Implementation," *Proceedings of IEEE International Conference on Acoustics, Speech, and Signal Processing*, April 14–16, 1983, Boston, MA, pp. 711–714.
6. Trunk, G.V., "Survey of Radar ADT," *Microwave Journal*, July 1983, pp. 77–88.
7. Pope, D.E., "An Expert System for Airborne Object Analysis," *M.S. Thesis*, Massachusetts Institute of Technology, Jan. 1985.
8. Spain, D.S., "Application of Artificial Intelligence to Tactical Situation Assessment," *Proceedings of EASCON '83*, Oct. 1983, pp. 457–464.
9. Wright, F.L., and S. Gdowski, "The Art of Multisensor Fusion and Correlation in a Tactical Environment," *Proceedings of IEEE Region 5 Conference and Exposition: Emerging Technology — A Bridge to the 21st Century*, Colorado Springs, CO, May 3–8, 1982, pp. 90–93.

Glossary

The principal symbols and the mathematical notation used in this book are defined below. Some symbols represent more than one quantity; the different meanings are clarified in the text. The following list is meant as a guide to the more important usages.

A. ENGLISH LETTER SYMBOLS

Symbol	Meaning
a	Acceleration
a_i	Target type
A	System matrix of linear state equation
A_m	Target type measurement set
b_j	Attribute
B_m	Attribute measurement set
C^2	Target multiplicity detection statistic
C_M	Volume constant for M-dimensional ellipsoid
c	Speed of light
d_e	Eclipsing factor
d_{ij}^2	Normalized distance of observation j from track i
d_T, d_R, d_D	Antenna transmitting, receiving, and dead cycle times
D	Down direction; difference signal; data set; track length set; used as subscript to indicate declared quantity (as in declared target type); also used as subscript to indicate desired accuracy (for sensor allocation algorithm)
D_E	Expected track length
D_i	Length of track i
E	East direction
E_r	Antenna off-boresight attenuation factor
f	Used as subscript to indicate quantity used by filter (Chapter 7)
f	Deterministic input state vector

$F_{n,m}$	F distributed random variable with n,m degrees of freedom
g_{ij}	Gaussian likelihood function associated with the assignment of observation j to track i
G	Elliptical gate size; antenna gain; used as subscript to indicate group track quantity; system matrix for random forcing function in the linear state equation
H	Kalman filter measurement matrix; used as subscript to indicate horizontal plane quantity
H_l	Hypothesis l
i	Subscript used primarily for track number
$\mathbf{i}$	Unit vector
I	Identity matrix; used as subscript to indicate own-ship quantity; also used as subscript to indicate imaginary
j	Subscript used primarily for observation; imaginary number $\sqrt{-1}$
k	Scan index; measure of inconsistency resulting from combination by Dempster's rule (evidential reasoning)
K	Kalman gain; scan index for last scan of data
K_G	Rectangular gating constant
K_x, K_v, K_a	Position, velocity, acceleration variance reduction ratios
l	Index used to denote the observation number assigned to a given track; hypothesis number
L	Likelihood ratio; score function; system matrix for deterministic input in linear state equation
m	Meter; used as subscript to indicate maneuver
$\mathbf{m}$	Evidential reasoning probability mass vector
M	Measurement dimension; mean passage time matrix (Chapter 7)
n_{TF}	Expected number of false returns within rectangular volume elements (Chapter 4)
N	North direction
N_D	Number of consecutive misses required for a simple track deletion rule
N_{DEL}	Number of deleted tracks
N_{FC}	Number of false correlations
N_o	Number of observations; noise spectral density
o	Subscript to indicate observed quantity; also used to indicate initial condition

OJ	Observation J
p	Subscript to indicate predicted quantity
P_i	Probability of state i, as computed using Markov chain technique
p_{ij}	The i,j element of the Kalman filter covariance matrix
$\mathbf{P}$	Markov chain state probability vector
P	Kalman filter covariance matrix
P_A	True target hypothesis acceptance threshold
P_{CC}	Probability of correct correlation
P_{CD}	Probability of correct decision
P_D	Probability of detection
P_{FA}	Probability of false alarm
P_{FC}	Probability of false correlation
P_G	Probability of valid observation satisfying the gating condition
PI	Predicted position for track I
P_{NE}	Probability that no false (extraneous) observations will satisfy the gating condition
q	Process noise state vector
q_{ij}	The i,j element of the process noise covariance matrix
Q	Process noise covariance matrix; normalized ratio used for sensor allocation utility calculation
r	Zero-mean, unit standard-deviation Gaussian random variable; used as subscript to indicate residual quantity; total number of received observations (Chapter 9)
R	Range; used as subscript to indicate radial direction; subscript to indicate real; subscript to indicate reported quantity (as in sensor reported target type)
R_c	Kalman filter measurement noise covariance matrix
R_o	Range where input signal power equals input noise power; observed range
R_p	Predicted range
R_x	Range at which there is X percent probability of receiving at least one target detection
s	Scintillation variable; used as subscript to indicate smoothed quantity for fixed-gain filters
s_x^2	Estimated variance of quantity x
S	Residual covariance matrix; sum signal
S_D	Group track dispersion matrix
SF	Score function used in Chapter 6
$S_x(\omega)$	Spectral density of process x

t	Variable from the Student's t distribution
T	Sampling interval; used as subscript to indicate target quantity; used as subscript to indicate true quantity
TI	Track I
T_X	Range at which there is at least X percent probability of track without later deletion
$T_1, T_2, \ldots$	Transformation matrices
u	Variable from uniform random distribution
U	Utility; cross coupling term between horizontal and vertical filters (Chapter 3)
U_{ij}	Covariance matrix for difference state vector from track i to track j
v_o	Ratio of prediction-error standard deviation to measurement-error standard deviation
v	Velocity
v_R	Radical velocity (range rate)
$\mathbf{v}$	State measurement noise vector
v_G	Group track velocity
V	Voltage; used as subscript to indicate vertical direction; volume element
V_G	Gate volume
V_S	Scan volume
$\mathbf{x}$	State vector
$\mathbf{y}$	Measurement state vector
$\tilde{\mathbf{y}}$	Residual error vector
$y_j(k)$	The jth observation received on scan k

B. GREEK LETTER SYMBOLS

Symbol	Meaning
α	Fixed-gain filter coefficient; probability of falsely accepting true target hypothesis
β	Fixed-gain filter coefficient; inverse of correlation time constant $(1/\tau)$; total new source density $(\beta = \beta_{NT} + \beta_{FT})$; probability of falsely rejecting true target hypothesis
β_{FT}	False target density
β_{NT}	New (true) target density
χ_M^2	Chi-square random variable with M degrees of freedom
ϵ	Elevation angle
ϵ^2	Expected square estimation error

η	Azimuth angle
γ	Fixed-gain filter coefficient
Λ	Direction cosine; tracking index (Chapter 2)
λ_M	Optimal detection threshold setting
λ_C^2	Target multiplicity detection threshold
μ	Mean; target multiplicity detection parameter (Chapter 5)
ϕ	Aircraft roll angle
Φ	State transition matrix; Markov chain transition matrix
ψ	Aircraft heading angle; signal phase angle
ρ	Correlation coefficient; perpendicular distance of a line to the origin (Chapter 6)
σ	Standard deviation; radar cross section (Chapter 8)
σ_m	Target maneuver standard deviation
τ	Correlation time constant
θ	Aircraft pitch angle; measure of uncertainty used in evidential reasoning (Chapter 13); general use as an angular quantity
ω	Line-of-sight rate; angular frequency

C. SELECTED ABBREVIATIONS

Abbreviation	Meaning
CFAR	Constant false alarm rate
dB	Decibel
ECM	Electronic countermeasures
ESA	Electronically scanned antenna
IR	Infrared
JEM	Jet engine modulation
JPDA	Joint probabilistic data association (all-neighbors correlation method)
ln	Natural logarithm
MG	Maneuver gate
MHT	Multiple hypothesis tracking
mrad	Milliradian
MSA	Mechanically scanned antenna
MSC	Multiple-sensor correlation
MTT	Multiple-target tracking
NED	North-East-Down tracking coordinate system
nmi	Nautical mile

NN	Nearest-neighbor (correlation method)
PDA	Probabilistic data association (all-neighbors correlation method)
PRF	Pulse repetition frequency
rad	Radian
RAM	Raid assessment mode
RHV	Tracking coordinate system using radial, horizontal and vertical direction axes
s, sec	Seconds
SG	Standard gate
SNR	Signal-to-noise ratio
SIR	Signal-to-interference ratio (generalization of SNR)
SPRT	Sequential probability ratio test
TOT	Time on target
TWS	Track-while-scan

D. MATHEMATICAL NOTATION

Notation	**Meaning**
$|x|$	Absolute value of quantity x
$|S|$	Determinant of matrix S
S^T	Transpose of matrix S
x	State vector x
$\mathbf{x}$	Vector quantity $\mathbf{x}$
$\mathbf{a} \times \mathbf{b}$	Cross product of $\mathbf{a}$ and $\mathbf{b}$
$\mathbf{i}_N$	Unit vector in north direction
$\hat{x}$	Estimate of x
$\tilde{x}$	Error in estimate of x
$\tilde{y}$	Residual (innovation) vector
δx	Change (or error) in quantity x
$f(x)$	Probability density of quantity x
$p(n)$	Discrete probability of n
$r \sim N(0,1)$	r has the Gaussian (normal) probability density with zero-mean and unit standard deviation
$E[x]$	Expected value of x
$\Pr(A > B)$	Probability that A is greater than B
$P(A|B)$	Probability of A given B
$\hat{x}(k+1|k)$	Estimate of x at scan $k+1$ given data through scan k
$a \sim b$	a is proportional to b
$a \cong b$	a is approximately equal to b
$a \equiv b$	a is identically equal to b

$a \triangleq b$	a is defined to be b
$a \lor b$	Disjunction (union) of a and b
$\tilde{a}$	Negation of a (used in Chapter 13 with evidential reasoning)
$\Gamma(M)$	Gamma function with argument M

E. FIGURE NOTATION

Notation	Meaning
$\underline{x}$	State vector x
$\vec{x}$	Vector quantity x

Index